An Introduction to Human Disease

A Student Workbook

Seventh Edition

Leonard V. Crowley, MD

Professor
Biology Department
Century College
Honorary Medical Staff Physician
University of Minnesota Medical Center, Minneapolis

JONES AND BARTLETT PUBLISHERS

Sudbury, Massachusetts

BOSTON   TORONTO   LONDON   SINGAPORE

World Headquarters
Jones and Bartlett Publishers
40 Tall Pine Drive
Sudbury, MA 01776
978-443-5000
info@jbpub.com
www.jbpub.com

Jones and Bartlett
Publishers Canada
6339 Ormindale Way
Mississauga, ON L5V 1J2
CANADA

Jones and Bartlett
Publishers International
Barb House, Barb Mews
London W6 7PA
UK

Jones and Bartlett's books and products are available through most bookstores and online booksellers. To contact Jones and Bartlett Publishers directly, call 800-832-0034, fax 978-443-8000, or visit our website www.jbpub.com.

Substantial discounts on bulk quantities of Jones and Bartlett's publications are available to corporations, professional associations, and other qualified organizations. For details and specific discount information, contact the special sales department at Jones and Bartlett via the above contact information or send an email to special-sales@jbpub.com.

Production Credits
Chief Executive Officer: Clayton Jones
Chief Operating Officer: Don W. Jones, Jr.
President, Higher Education and Professional Publishing: Robert W. Holland, Jr.
V.P., Sales and Marketing: William J. Kane
V.P., Design and Production: Anne Spencer
V.P., Manufacturing and Inventory Control: Therese Connell
Acquisitions Editor: Jacqueline Mark-Geraci
Special Projects Editor: Elizabeth Platt
Editorial Assistant: Amy L. Flagg
Associate Marketing Manager: Wendy Thayer
Composition: Appingo
Interactive Technology Manager: Dawn Mahon Priest
Cover Design: Anne Spencer
Printing and Binding: Courier
Cover Printing: Courier

ISBN-10: 0-7637-4222-8

ISBN-13: 978-0-7637-4222-5

6048

Printed in the United States of America
11 10 09 08 07   6 5 4 3 2

Contents

Introduction

Welcome to the study of human disease. Your textbook, *An Introduction to Human Disease,* was based on courses given to undergraduate and graduate students like you who have mastered the essential concepts of human disease. Many have gone on to careers in biology, medicine, nursing, and other health fields. Each chapter in your book begins with learning objectives, followed by a systematic survey of the pathology, pathophysiology, clinical manifestations, and principles of treatment of the important diseases considered in each chapter. Each chapter then finishes with an annotated bibliography that points you toward important articles in the medical literature related to the subjects considered in the chapter.

This workbook will help you navigate through the course. It includes diagrams, Power-Point presentations, and various types of exercises to test and reinforce your comprehension of the essential features of the diseases you will be studying. To get you started on your journey of discovery, the workbook begins with a listing of the important points considered in the first five chapters of your book. You will build on these concepts as you continue into other chapters dealing with specific organ system derangements.

I believe that you will be pleasantly surprised to find that the basic concepts relating to human disease are quite straightforward, easy to understand, and extremely interesting. You have undoubtedly completed a course in anatomy and physiology, and you already know that every organ system has key structural features and physiologic functions. All is well when the systems function properly. When you know normal structure and function, it is not hard to understand what happens when systems don't function properly, producing disease. Moreover, when you understand the anatomic and physiologic changes associated with a disease, you can usually deduce the clinical manifestations of the disease and can understand how treatment favorably influences its course and outcome.

The benefit you derive from the course will depend to a large extent on your own efforts. The course follows the class schedule closely. To get the most from the class, read over the material to be covered before you attend the lecture or classroom exercise so that you are familiar with what is to be covered. Then you will be in a better position to get more out of the lectures and other classroom activities dealing with the subjects considered in the assigned chapters. After the class, reread the material covered in class while the material is still fresh in your mind, and use the workbook material to help you. This approach will help you "nail down" your comprehension of the material. Such a systematic approach to learning the material will pay big dividends, and you will derive tremendous satisfaction from watching your knowledge base relating to human disease grow by "leaps and bounds" as you proceed through the course.

Enjoy your adventure. Have a pleasant journey.

Leonard Crowley

Chapter Outline

The chapter outline provides you with an organizational guide to the topics and ideas presented in this chapter of the text.

Introductory Concepts in Chapter 1

The following material is provided as a guide to some of the fundamental concepts in the first five chapters. It may help you organize the material as you get started in this course. You will build on these concepts as you begin to study diseases involving various organ systems.

1. Disease is a disturbance of the structure or function of the body.
2. Disease produces various manifestations: signs, symptoms, and abnormal laboratory test results.
3. The clinician's task is to determine the nature of the disease (make a diagnosis), estimate the probable outcome of the disease (prognosis), and then treat the patient (symptomatic and specific treatment).
4. Look over the various diagnostic procedures available to the physician, but learning the details of them is not necessary now.
5. We talk about screening for disease in a population. Screening requires three things: a "screenable population" (significant frequency of disease); a reliable, cost-effective test to identify the disease that can be performed without risk to the patient; and evidence that early detection of the disease will favorably influence outcome.

Study Questions

The following questions are provided as a test for comprehension and as a study guide for use with the text chapters. Additional study material is located at http://humandisease.jbpub.com/, which contains useful tools such as an A&P review, animated flashcards, an interactive online glossary, crossword puzzles, and web links.

Key Terms

Define the following terms:

1. Etiology _____

2. Symptom of disease _____

3. Sign of disease _____

4. Diagnosis _____

5. Prognosis _____

6. Specific treatment _____

7. Symptomatic treatment _____

8. Pathogen _____

9. Pathogenesis _____

Fill-in-the-Blank

1. A test based on echoes produced in tissues by high-frequency sound waves is _____.

2. A young woman has a skin rash caused by an allergic reaction to an antibiotic. This patient's condition would be classified as _____.

3. The opinion of a physician concerning the eventual outcome of a disease in a patient is called _____.

4. A disease in which the principal manifestation is an abnormal growth of cells leading to formation of tumors is called _____.

Identify

1. Identify the five major categories of diseases, and indicate the characteristic features of each type.

   a. _____

   b. _____

   c. _____

   d. _____

   e. _____

2. Identify the nine major categories of diagnostic tests and procedures available to help the physician or other health practitioner diagnose and treat a patient properly.

   a. _____

   b. _____

   c. _____

   d. _____

e. _____

f. _____

g. _____

h. _____

i. _____

3. Identify three tests that measure the electrical impulses associated with various body functions and activities.

   a. _____

   b. _____

   c. _____

4. Identify the tests or procedures that would be useful to assist the physician in evaluating the following conditions in a patient.

   a. Urinary tract infection _____

   b. Fractured wrist _____

   c. Possible "heart attack" _____

   d. A lump in the breast _____

   e. Amenorrhea in a young woman _____

   f. The maturity of a fetus and the location of the placenta within the mother's uterus _____
   _____

Discussion Questions

1. Describe the differences between a diagnosis and a prognosis. _____
   _____
   _____
   _____

2. Describe the steps a physician or other health practitioner uses to make a diagnosis of a specific disease or condition in a patient. _____
   _____
   _____
   _____

3. What is the difference between symptomatic treatment and specific treatment? _____
   _____
   _____
   _____

4. You wish to develop a program to screen for a specific disease, such as diabetes. Describe the requirements for a successful screening program. _____

_____

_____

_____

5. A middle-aged man consults his physician because of cough, fever, chest pain, and purulent sputum. What diagnostic measures will assist the physician in determining the cause of the patient's illness? _____

_____

_____

_____

6. A governmental agency proposes a pilot program to screen a population for a disease by means of a blood test. The characteristics of the disease and the screening test are listed here. Which of these characteristics indicate that the proposed screen is likely to be worthwhile, and which indicate that it is likely not to be worthwhile? Explain your answers.

a. The disease occurs with some frequency (1 per 1000 persons screened).

_____

b. The disease progresses slowly in affected persons.

_____

c. No specific method of treatment is available at the present time.

_____

d. The test can detect the disease in its early stage and is relatively inexpensive (about $42.50).

_____

e. The test is quite specific, producing few false-positive or false-negative results.

_____

An Introduction to

LEONARD V. CROWLEY, M.D.

Human Disease

PATHOLOGY AND PATHOPHYSIOLOGY CORRELATIONS

Seventh Edition

Chapter 1
General Concepts of Disease

Principles of Diagnosis

© 2007 Jones and Bartlett Publishers

Disease

A disturbance of body structure or function.

© 2007 Jones and Bartlett Publishers

Organic Contrasted with Functional Disease

- Organic Disease
- Associated with structural changes, lesions
- Examined through naked eye, *gross examination*
- Or through microscope, *histologic examination*

- Functional Disease
- Associated with *no* morphological abnormalities yet body functions are profoundly disturbed

© 2007 Jones and Bartlett Publishers

Pathology

- Study of disease: pathology
- Pathologist: physician who specializes in the *diagnosis* and *classification* of diseases, primarily by studying the morphology of cells and tissues
- Clinician: physician/health care professional that *cares* for patients

© 2007 Jones and Bartlett Publishers

Manifestations of Disease

- Subjective: *symptoms*, such as pain, weakness
- Objective: *signs* or *physical findings*, such as swelling, redness

© 2007 Jones and Bartlett Publishers

Manifestations Related to State of Disease

1. Symptomatic disease: *with* symptoms and/or signs
2. Asymptomatic disease: *without* symptoms and/or signs
- The distinction between one and the other is a matter of *degree*, depending on the extent
- In *early* stages of disease, usually *asymptomatic*
- When *not treated*, progresses to *symptomatic*

© 2007 Jones and Bartlett Publishers

Disease Terminology

- Etiology: *cause* of disease
- Etiologic agent: agent responsible for causing disease
- Pathogenesis: manner by which a disease develops
- Pathogen: any microorganism such as bacteria or virus that causes disease
- *Many diseases* fall into category of *unknown etiology* or cause

© 2007 Jones and Bartlett Publishers

Classifications of Disease

- Congenital and hereditary diseases
- Inflammatory diseases
- Degenerative diseases
- Metabolic diseases
- Neoplastic diseases

© 2007 Jones and Bartlett Publishers

Classifications of Disease

- Bases for classification of diseases
1. Similarity of lesions
2. Similarity of pathogenesis
- Diseases with similarities in a specific category may *not necessarily be closely related*

© 2007 Jones and Bartlett Publishers

_____

_____

_____

_____

_____

_____

_____

_____

_____

_____

_____

_____

_____

_____

_____

_____

_____

_____

_____

_____

_____

_____

_____

_____

_____

_____

_____

_____

_____

_____

_____

_____

_____

_____

_____

Health and Disease
Extremes of a <u>Continuum</u>

Good Health   Serious Illness

←——————————→

We are <u>all</u> somewhere on the line between health and illness (midpoint), and more specifically <u>between the midpoint and good health.</u>

© 2007 Jones and Bartlett Publishers

Continuum of Health
and Disease

- Good health – one extreme, an *ideal* good health, a state of complete physical and mental well-being
- Serious illness – other extreme, a *severe*, life-threatening, disabling illness
- Gradations of health and illness – between these two extremes are many *gradations* of health and disease, ranging from *mild* or short-term illness that limits activity to some extent, to *moderate* good health that falls short of the ideal state
- The *midpoint* is the "*neutral*" position, neither seriously ill nor in ideal good health

© 2007 Jones and Bartlett Publishers

Goal of Medicine

- The goal of *traditional medicine* is to *cure* or ameliorate disease
- Through the use of *antibiotics* to cure an infection
- Through *high technology treatments* such as a kidney transplant, heart surgery

© 2007 Jones and Bartlett Publishers

Health
vs.
Absence of Disease

- Advances of *modern medicine relieve suffering* and advance human welfare

However

- Modern medicine does *not guarantee* good health
- *Health is more* than the *mere absence* of *disease*

© 2007 Jones and Bartlett Publishers

Definition of Health

- Condition in which *mind* and *body* function efficiently and harmoniously as an integrated unit
- Requires *active participation* by assuming responsibility for our health
- Achieved by *good habits*, eating properly, exercising moderately, and avoiding harmful excesses such as overeating, smoking, heavy drinking, or using drugs

© 2007 Jones and Bartlett Publishers

Principles of Diagnosis
and Treatment

- Diagnosis
  - Clinical history
  - Physical examination
  - Differential diagnosis

- Treatment
  - Specific treatment
  - Symptomatic treatment

© 2007 Jones and Bartlett Publishers

_____

_____

_____

_____

_____

_____

_____

_____

_____

_____

_____

_____

_____

_____

_____

_____

_____

_____

_____

_____

_____

_____

_____

_____

_____

_____

_____

_____

_____

_____

_____

_____

_____

_____

Diagnosis
Prognosis
Treatment

- *Diagnosis*: determination of the *nature* and *cause* of a patient's *illness* by a physician based on:

    a. Patient's subjective symptoms
    b. Patient's physical findings
    c. Laboratory test results
    d. Other diagnostic procedures

- *Prognosis*: an *opinion* concerning the eventual *outcome* of the *disease*

- Treatment: measures to relieve symptoms (symptomatic treatment)

© 2007 Jones and Bartlett Publishers

Diagnosis
Clinical History

Diagnosis
Clinical History, Physical Exam, Differential Diagnosis

- Clinical History
1. Current Illness History
2. Past Medical History
3. Family History
4. Social History
5. Review of Symptoms

© 2007 Jones and Bartlett Publishers

Diagnosis
Clinical History

1. Current Illness History
- Severity, time of onset, and character of patient's symptoms
2. Past Medical History
- Details of patient's general health and previous illnesses, possibly shedding light on current problems
3. Family History
- Health of patient's parents and family members, some diseases run in families
4. Social History
- Patient's occupation, habits, alcohol and tobacco consumption, and similar data

© 2007 Jones and Bartlett Publishers

Diagnosis
Clinical History

5. Review of Symptoms
- Presence of symptoms other than those disclosed in History of present illness, suggesting other parts of the body affected by disease
- Possible dysfunctions of other organ systems are evaluated

© 2007 Jones and Bartlett Publishers

Diagnosis
Physical Examination

- Physical Exam
- Systematic examination of the patient, placing particular emphasis to parts of body affected by illness
- Abnormalities are correlated with the clinical history

© 2007 Jones and Bartlett Publishers

Diagnosis
Differential Diagnosis

- Differential Diagnosis
- Consideration of various diseases or conditions that would fit the clinical or physical findings
- More than one diagnosis may need to be considered
- Consideration of a number of diseases characterized by the patient's symptoms and signs
- List of diagnostic possibilities may be narrowed by selected laboratory tests or other diagnostic procedures
- Opinion of a medical consultant may be sought

© 2007 Jones and Bartlett Publishers

Treatment: Specific/Symptomatic

- Specific: exerts highly *specific* and favorable *effect* on the basic course of the disease, such as antibiotic for an infection, or insulin for diabetes
- Symptomatic: makes patient more comfortable by *alleviating symptoms* but does *not* influence the course of the underlying disease

Screening Tests

Screening Tests for Detection of Disease
- Detection of early *asymptomatic* diseases amenable to treatment, thereby preventing or minimizing late-stage organ damage
- Screening of some *genetic* diseases, such as sickle cell anemia, where the recessive sickle hemoglobin gene is inherited by a child born to two carriers of this gene

Requirements for Effective Screening

1. A *significant number* of persons must be at risk for the disease in the group being screened
2. A relatively *inexpensive* noninvasive test must be available to screen for the disease
3. Early identification and treatment of the disease will *favorably influence* the health or welfare of the person with the disease

Diagnostic Tests/Procedures

1. Clinical laboratory tests
- Determine the concentration of constituents in blood and urine
- Evaluate function of organs
2. Tests of electrical activity
- Record electrical impulses associated with bodily functions and activities
3. Radioisotope studies
- Administration of substance (radioisotope) to evaluate organ function

© 2007 Jones and Bartlett Publishers

Diagnostic Tests/Procedures

4. Endoscopy
- Tubular instrument to examine interior of body
5. Ultrasound
- Mapping of echoes produced by high-frequency sound waves transmitted into the body
6. X-ray examination
- X-rays are passed through body; rays leaving body expose an x-ray film

© 2007 Jones and Bartlett Publishers

Diagnostic Tests/Procedures

7. Computed tomography (CT)
- Production of images of body in cross section by rotating x-ray tube around patient at various levels
8. Magnetic resonance imaging (MRI)
- Similar to CT scan but uses ionizing radiation to construct images based on density of tissues

© 2007 Jones and Bartlett Publishers

Diagnostic Tests/Procedures

9. Positron emission tomography (PET)
- Injection of biochemical compound into patient, and assessing its distribution and metabolism by measuring the radiation produced
10. Cytologic and histologic examinations
- Abnormal cells have structural and cellular patterns recognized by the pathologist

© 2007 Jones and Bartlett Publishers

Diagnostic Tests/Procedures

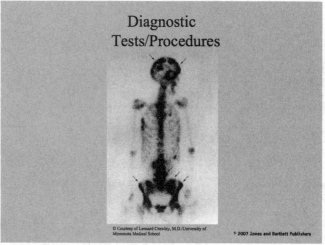

© Courtesy of Leonard Crowley, M.D./University of Minnesota Medical School

© 2007 Jones and Bartlett Publishers

Diagnostic Tests/Procedures

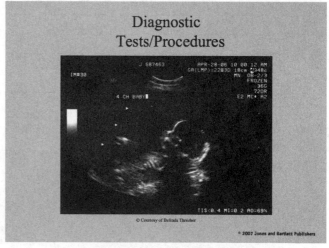

© Courtesy of Belinda Thresher

© 2007 Jones and Bartlett Publishers

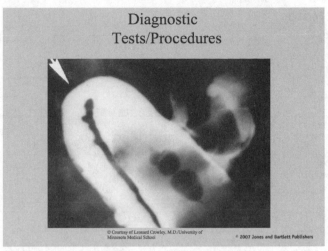

Diagnostic
Tests/Procedures

© Courtesy of Leonard Crowley, M.D./University of
Minnesota Medical School

© 2007 Jones and Bartlett Publishers

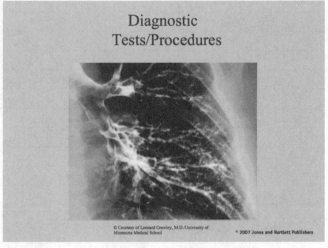

Diagnostic
Tests/Procedures

© Courtesy of Leonard Crowley, M.D./University of
Minnesota Medical School

© 2007 Jones and Bartlett Publishers

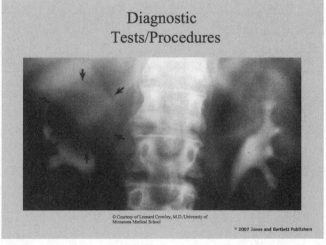

Diagnostic
Tests/Procedures

© Courtesy of Leonard Crowley, M.D./University of
Minnesota Medical School

© 2007 Jones and Bartlett Publishers

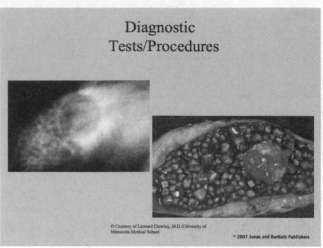

Diagnostic
Tests/Procedures

© Courtesy of Leonard Crowley, M.D./University of
Minnesota Medical School

© 2007 Jones and Bartlett Publishers

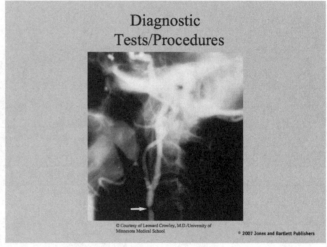

Diagnostic
Tests/Procedures

© Courtesy of Leonard Crowley, M.D./University of
Minnesota Medical School

© 2007 Jones and Bartlett Publishers

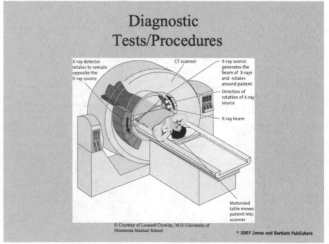

Diagnostic
Tests/Procedures

X-ray detector
rotates to remain
opposite the
X-ray source

CT scanner

X-ray source
generates the
beam of X-rays
and rotates
around patient

Direction of
rotation of X-ray
source

X-ray beam

Motorized
table moves
patient into
scanner

© Courtesy of Leonard Crowley, M.D./University of
Minnesota Medical School

© 2007 Jones and Bartlett Publishers

Notes

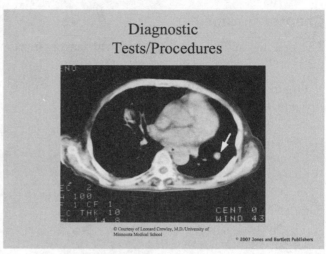

Diagnostic
Tests/Procedures

© Courtesy of Leonard Crowley, M.D./University of
Minnesota Medical School

© 2007 Jones and Bartlett Publishers

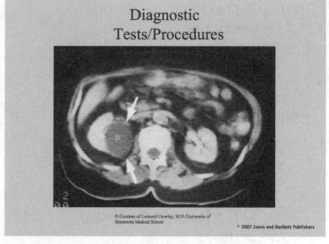

Diagnostic
Tests/Procedures

© Courtesy of Leonard Crowley, M.D./University of
Minnesota Medical School

© 2007 Jones and Bartlett Publishers

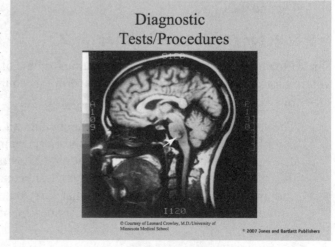

Diagnostic
Tests/Procedures

© Courtesy of Leonard Crowley, M.D./University of
Minnesota Medical School

© 2007 Jones and Bartlett Publishers

Chapter 2   Cells and Tissues: Their Structure and Function in Health and Disease

Chapter Outline

The chapter outline provides you with an organizational guide to the topics and ideas presented in this chapter of the text.

Organization of Cells
The Cell
    The Nucleus
    The Cytoplasm
Tissues
    Epithelium
    Connective and Supporting Tissues
    Muscle Tissue
    Nerve Tissue
Organs and Organ Systems
The Germ Layers and Their Derivatives
Cell Function and the Genetic Code
    The Structure of DNA
    Duplication (Replication) of DNA
    The Genetic Code
Movement of Materials Into and Out of Cells
    Diffusion and Osmosis
    Active Transport
    Phagocytosis and Pinocytosis
Adaptations of Cells to Changing Conditions
    Atrophy
    Hypertrophy and Hyperplasia
    Metaplasia
    Dysplasia
    Increased Enzyme Synthesis
Cell Injury, Cell Death, and Cell Necrosis
    Cell Injury
    Cell Death and Cell Necrosis
    Programmed Cell Death: Apoptosis
Aging and the Cell

Introductory Concepts in Chapter 2

The following material is provided as a guide to some of the fundamental concepts in the first five chapters. It may help you organize the material as you get started in this course. You will build on these concepts as you begin to study diseases involving various organ systems.

1. The cell is the basic structural and functional unit of the body. All cells have similar features (nucleus, cytoplasm, organelles), but many cells are specialized to perform specific functions.
2. The nucleus contains the genetic material (23 pairs of chromosomes = the genome) that directs the functions of the cell (via messenger RNA). The cytoplasm contains the various organelles (e.g., mitochondria, ribosomes, endoplasmic reticulum, lysosomes) that carry out the functions specified by DNA (see Fig. 2-8).
3. Groups of similar cells form tissues. Tissues are organized to form organs, and groups of organs form organ systems.

4. Epithelium covers the exterior of the body, lines the interior of organs such as the respiratory and GI tracts, lines body cavities, forms glands, and forms the functional cells of organs that have excretory or secretory functions (such as the liver and kidneys). Epithelium is classified on the basis of its structure (simple or stratified; squamous, transitional, or columnar). Connective tissue connects and supports. Muscle contracts, and nerve tissue conducts.

5. Materials move in and out of cells across cell membranes by active transport, phagocytosis, and pinocytosis (active processes that require the cell to expend energy) and by diffusion and osmosis (passive, non–energy-requiring processes).

6. Cells adapt to changing conditions (atrophy, hypertrophy, hyperplasia, metaplasia, dysplasia, increased enzyme synthesis).

7. Injured cells exhibit structural and functional abnormalities—swelling, fatty change, and necrosis, for example.

8. Normal cells don't last forever. They have a predetermined life span, and they wear out. (As we see later, some tumor cells can proliferate indefinitely. They are "immortal.")

Study Questions

The following questions are provided as a test for comprehension and as a study guide for use with the text chapter. Additional study material is located at http://humandisease.jbpub.com/, which contains useful tools such as an A&P review, animated flashcards, an interactive online glossary, crossword puzzles, and web links.

Key Terms

Define the following terms:

1. Genetic code _the info carried by the codons of DNA molecules in chromosomes_

2. Organelle _small structure present in cytoplasm_

3. Hyperplasia _____

4. Dysplasia _____

5. Osmosis _____

6. Diffusion _____

7. Metaplasia _____

True/False

Tell whether each statement is true or false. If false, explain why the statement is incorrect.

1. The nucleus directs the metabolic functions of the cell. _____

_____

2. Organelles are small chromosome fragments present in the nucleus. _____

_____

3. Lysosomes digest material brought into the cell by phagocytosis. _____

_____

4. All cells survive the same length of time within the body. _____

_____

5. Migration of water molecules from a more dilute solution to a more concentrated solution across the semipermeable membrane is called diffusion. _____

_____

Identify

1. Identify eight components within a typical cell, and indicate the function of each.

   a. _____

   b. _____

   c. _____

   d. _____

e. _____

f. _____

g. _____

h. _____

2. Identify the four major types of tissues, and briefly describe the functions of each type.

a. _____

b. _____

c. _____

d. _____

3. Identify the three germ layers that develop from the fertilized ovum, and indicate what structures develop from each layer. (*Hint:* see Fig. 2-5.)

a. _____

b. _____

c. _____

4. Identify the five ways in which cells adapt to changing conditions.

a. _____

b. _____

c. _____

d. _____

e. _____

Discussion Questions

1. Diagram the structure of a typical cell. Indicate the functions of the major organelles.

2. What is the difference between cell hyperplasia and dysplasia? _____

_____

_____

_____

3. How does the cell respond to injury? _____
_____
_____
_____

4. What are the major difference between epithelium and connective tissue? _____
_____
_____
_____

5. Briefly describe the structures and main functions of the various types of epithelium. _____
_____
_____
_____

6. List and describe the various ways that materials move in and out of cells across the cell membrane. _____
_____
_____
_____

7. Describe how osmosis differs from diffusion. _____
_____
_____
_____

8. Describe the difference between cell metaplasia and cell dysplasia. _____
_____
_____
_____

9. Describe some of the important changes that occur in an aging cell, and describe ways by which we can retard aging changes in cells. _____
_____
_____
_____

Notes

_____
_____
_____
_____
_____
_____
_____
_____
_____
_____
_____
_____
_____
_____
_____
_____
_____
_____
_____
_____
_____
_____
_____
_____
_____
_____
_____
_____
_____
_____
_____
_____

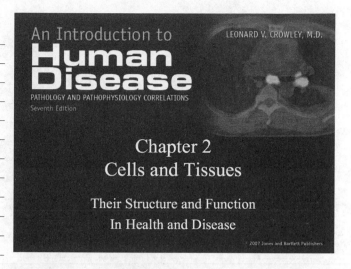

An Introduction to
Human Disease
LEONARD V. CROWLEY, M.D.
PATHOLOGY AND PATHOPHYSIOLOGY CORRELATIONS
Seventh Edition

Chapter 2
Cells and Tissues

Their Structure and Function
In Health and Disease

© 2007 Jones and Bartlett Publishers

Organization of Cells

- Cells
- Tissues
- Organs
- Organ Systems
- Functioning Organism

An abnormality at any level of organization can cause _disease_

© 2007 Jones and Bartlett Publishers

Basic Structure and Organization of Cells

1. <u>Nucleus:</u> contains genetic information, directs metabolic function of cells
2. <u>Cytoplasm:</u> its structures carry out directions of the nucleus

Organization of Cells
- <u>Cells:</u> basic unit of body
- <u>Tissues:</u> groups of similar cells to perform similar functions
- <u>Organs:</u> tissues grouped together in different proportions

© 2007 Jones and Bartlett Publishers

Basic Structure
Organization
Cells

- <u>Organ Systems:</u> groups of organs functioning together
- <u>Functioning Organisms:</u> integrated organ systems
- An abnormality at any level of organization can cause *disease*

© 2007 Jones and Bartlett Publishers

The Cell

- Nucleus
- Cytoplasm
  - Mitochondria
  - Endoplasmic reticulum
  - Golgi apparatus
  - Lysosomes
  - Centrioles
  - Cytoskeleton

© 2007 Jones and Bartlett Publishers

The Cell

© Courtesy of Leonard Crowley, M.D./University of Minnesota Medical School

© 2007 Jones and Bartlett Publishers

Nucleus and Cytoplasm

- Content of the Nucleus
- Two types of *nucleic acid* combined with *protein*
  - DNA (Deoxyribonucleic acid): contained in chromosomes
  - RNA (Ribonucleic acid): contained in nucleoli
- Cytoplasm: mass of *protoplasm* with its various *cytoplasm organelles*, surrounded by a *cell membrane*

© 2007 Jones and Bartlett Publishers

Cytoplasm Organelles

Cytoplasm Organelles

1. Mitochondria
2. Endoplasmic Reticulum
3. Golgi Apparatus
4. Lysosomes
5. Centrioles
6. Cytoskeleton (Tubules and Filaments)

Some *diseases* are associated with *characteristic abnormalities* in the cytoplasmic *organelles*

© 2007 Jones and Bartlett Publishers

Organelles

1. Mitochondria
- Sausage-shaped structure, containing enzymes that *convert food material* into *energy* by *oxidizing them*
- Cells use this energy to *manufacture* a high energy compound called *adenosine triphosphate (ATP)*, which is the *fuel* that powers the *chemical reactions* in the cell
2. Endoplasmic Reticulum
- An interconnected network of *tubular channels* enclosed by membranes, that *communicates* with both the *nuclear* and the *cellular membranes*

© 2007 Jones and Bartlett Publishers

Notes

_____
_____
_____
_____
_____
_____
_____
_____
_____
_____
_____
_____
_____
_____
_____
_____
_____
_____
_____
_____
_____
_____
_____
_____
_____
_____
_____
_____
_____
_____
_____
_____
_____
_____

Organelles

- Rough Endoplasmic Reticulum (RER): has *ribosomes* that *synthesize protein* that will be secreted by the cell
- Smooth Endoplasmic Reticulum (SER): has membranes containing enzymes that *synthesize lipids*
3. Golgi Apparatus
- Sacs near the nucleus that are *connected* with the tubules of the *rough endoplasmic reticulum*
- The *proteins produced* by the *ribosomes* pass through the *RER* tubules *into* the Golgi Apparatus
- Large *carbohydrate* molecules are *synthesized* and *combined* with the *proteins*

Organelles

- These molecules form into *secretory granules* that are eventually discharged by the cell
4. Lysosomes
- Cytoplasmic *vacuole* filled with *digestive enzymes*
- *Digest* material that has been *brought* into the cell by *phagocytosis*, *avoiding leakage* of *digestive enzymes* into the *cytoplasm* that cause *injury* to the cell
5. Centrioles
- Short cylindrical structures located adjacent to nucleus

Organelles

- They *move* to *opposite sides* during *cell division* to form the *mitotic spindle* which *attaches* to the *chromosomes* and cause them to *separate* in the course of cell division
6. Cytoskeleton (microtubules, microfilaments, intermediate filaments)
- Form the *structural framework* of the cell and are responsible for *cell movements*, such as *phagocytosis*
- Identification and characterization of *intermediate filaments* in cells often provide both *diagnostic and prognostic* information

_____
_____
_____
_____
_____
_____
_____
_____
_____
_____
_____
_____
_____
_____
_____
_____
_____
_____
_____
_____
_____
_____
_____
_____
_____
_____
_____
_____
_____

Tissues

- Epithelium
- Connective and supporting
  - Fibrous
  - Elastic
  - Reticular
  - Adipose
  - Cartilage
  - Bone
  - Hematopoietic
  - Lymphatic

- Muscle
- Nerve

© 2007 Jones and Bartlett Publishers

Tissues: Epithelium

- *Tissues*: a group of similar cells joined together to perform a *specific function*
- *Epithelium*:
a. Covers the *exterior* of the body
b. Lines the *interior body surfaces* that communicate with the outside, such as the gastrointestinal tract, urinary tract, and vagina
c. Forms *glands* such as the thyroid, pancreas, and parenchymal cells (functional cells) of excretory or secretory organs such as the liver and kidneys
d. Contains *no blood vessels*

© 2007 Jones and Bartlett Publishers

Tissues: Epithelium

- *Cells* are *nourished* by *diffusion* of material from the capillaries located in the underlying connective tissue
- There are different types of epithelium but they all perform a *protective* function
- Some types *absorb and secrete*, as in the lining of the intestinal tract
- Some types form *glands* that secrete mucus, sweat, oil, enzymes, hormones, and other products

© 2007 Jones and Bartlett Publishers

Tissues: Epithelium

- *Glands,* such as the pancreas, that discharge their secretions *through a duct* onto an epithelial surface are called *exocrine* glands
- *Glands* that discharge their secretions *directly into the bloodstream*, such as the thyroid and the adrenals, are called *endocrine* glands

© 2007 Jones and Bartlett Publishers

Tissues: Connective and Supportive Tissues

- Relatively small numbers of cells incorporated in a large amount of extracellular material called *matrix*, in which are embedded various types of *fibers*
- Three Types of Connective Tissue Fibers
1. Collagen fibers: contain protein called *collagen,* which is *strong* but does *not stretch*
2. Elastic fibers: contain protein called *elastin,* which is *not strong* but *stretches*
3. Reticulum fibers: *similar* to *collagen* but are quite thin and delicate

© 2007 Jones and Bartlett Publishers

Tissues: Connective and Supportive Tissues

Examples of Connective and Supportive Tissues
- Loose and dense fibrous tissues
- Elastic tissue
- Reticular tissue
- Adipose
- Cartilage
- Bone
- Hematopoietic (blood-forming)
- Lymphatic (lymphocyte-forming)
- Subcutaneous

© 2007 Jones and Bartlett Publishers

Tissues: Connective and Supportive Tissues

- Ligaments
- Tendons
- Blood vessel wall membranes
- Bronchi walls
- Trachea
- Supporting framework of organs such as liver, spleen and lymph nodes

© 2007 Jones and Bartlett Publishers

Tissues: Muscle

Three Types of <u>Muscle Tissue</u>
  1. Smooth
  2. Striated
  3. Cardiac

<u>Smooth Muscle</u>
- Located in the *walls* of hollow *internal organs* such as the gastrointestinal tract, biliary tract, reproductive tract, and blood vessels
- Functions *automatically*, *not* under conscious control

<u>Striated Muscle</u>
- Moves the *skeleton*
- Under *conscious control*

© 2007 Jones and Bartlett Publishers

Tissues Muscle

<u>Cardiac Muscle</u>
- Found *only* in the *heart*
- *Resembles striated* but has some features common to *both* smooth and striated muscle

© 2007 Jones and Bartlett Publishers

Tissues: Nerve

Nerve Tissue
- *Neurons* - nerve cells , transmit nerve impulses
- *Neuroglia* - supporting cells *(astrocytes, oligodendroglia, and microglia)*
  - Neuroglia are *more* numerous than neurons

© 2007 Jones and Bartlett Publishers

The Organs

- They are a group of different *tissues* that are integrated to perform a *specific function*
- One tissue performs the *primary* function
- Other tissues perform a *supporting* function
- Parenchyma cells: *primary functional* cells of an organ
- Parenchyma: *mass* of functional tissue
- Stroma: *supporting* framework of an organ

© 2007 Jones and Bartlett Publishers

Organ System

- A *group of organs* that are organized to perform *complementary functions*, such as the reproductive system, the respiratory system, and the digestive system
- Finally, the various *organ systems* are integrated into a *Functional Organism*

© 2007 Jones and Bartlett Publishers

Germ Layers

- The highly complex structure of the entire body evolves from a single cell, the *fertilized ovum*
- This occurs by a complex process that includes periods of *cell multiplication, differentiation, and organization* to form organs and organ systems
- As the *fertilized ovum grows*, its *cells differentiate* into two groups
  1. Trophoblast
  2. Inner Cell Mass

© 2007 Jones and Bartlett Publishers

Germ Layers

- Trophoblast- the *peripheral* group of cells, that form the *placenta* and other structures that will support and nourish the embryo

- Inner Cell Mass – *inner* group of cells, that will give rise to the *embryo*, becoming arranged into three distinct *germ layers*
  1. Ectoderm
  2. Mesoderm
  3. Entoderm

© 2007 Jones and Bartlett Publishers

Germ Layers

- Ectoderm: *outer* layer (external covering of body, nervous system, ears, eyes)

- Mesoderm: *middle* layer (connective tissue, muscle, bone, cartilage, heart, blood, blood vessels, and the major portions of the urogenital system)

- Entoderm: *inner* layer (epithelium of pharynx, respiratory tract, liver, biliary tract, pancreas, and some parts of the urogenital tract)

© 2007 Jones and Bartlett Publishers

Cell Function, DNA, Genetic Code

- Chromosomes are made up of DNA combined with proteins
- Structure of DNA: contains the *genetic code*, transmitted to each newly formed cell in cell division
- Duplication of DNA: the double strands of DNA *duplicate themselves* as the cell *prepares to divide*
- The Genetic Code: regulates the various *functions* of the *cells*

Cell Function, DNA, Genetic Code

The basic structural unit of DNA is called a *nucleotide*, consisting of
- a *phosphate* group
- linked to a *deoxyribose*
- joined to a *nitrogen*-containing *base*

There are two Different DNA bases
1. Purine base
2. Pyrimidine base

There are four Different bases in DNA
- Purine bases: adenine and guanine
- Pyrimidine bases: thymine and cytosine

Cell Function, DNA, Genetic Code

- Pairing Bases
- A DNA molecule consists of two strands of DNA that are held together by weak chemical attractions between the *bases* of the adjacent chains

The chemical structure of the bases is such that
- only adenine can pair with thymine
- only guanine can pair with cytosine

Cell Function, DNA, Genetic Code

- Genetic Coding

- The *DNA* in the nucleus "*tells the cell what to do*" by directing the synthesis of enzymes and other proteins by the ribosomes in the cytoplasm

- The *messenger RNA* (mRNA) *carries out* the "*instructions*" encoded in the DNA to the ribosomes in the cytoplasm

© 2007 Jones and Bartlett Publishers

Movement of Materials Into and Out of Cells

- For the cell to function properly, *oxygen* and *nutrients* must *enter* the cell and *waste products* must be *eliminated*

- These materials must all *cross* the *cell membrane* which *limits* the *passage* of some and is *freely permeable* to others

© 2007 Jones and Bartlett Publishers

Movement of Materials Into and Out of Cells

- Diffusion
- Osmosis
- Active transport
- Phagocytosis
- Pinocytosis

© 2007 Jones and Bartlett Publishers

Movement of Materials Into and Out of Cells

- <u>Diffusion</u>: The movement of *dissolved particles* (solute) from a *more concentrated* to a *dilute* solution
- <u>Osmosis</u>: The movement of *water molecules* from a *more dilute* solution to a *concentrated* solution
- <u>Active Transport</u>: The transfer of a *substance* across the cell membrane from a region of *low concentration* to one of *higher concentration*
- The process requires the cell to *expend energy* because the substance must *move against a concentration gradient*
- Many *metabolic processes* depend on *active transport* of ions and molecules

© 2007 Jones and Bartlett Publishers

Movement of Materials Into and Out of Cells

- <u>Phagocytosis</u>: The *ingestion* of *particles* that are *too large* to pass across the cell membrane.

- The cytoplasm flows around the particle and the cytoplasmic processes fuse, *engulfing* the particle within a vacuole in the cytoplasm of the cell

- <u>Pinocytosis</u>: Ingestion of *fluid* rather than solid material

© 2007 Jones and Bartlett Publishers

Alterations of Cells to Changing Conditions

- Atrophy
- Hypertrophy
- Hyperplasia
- Metaplasia
- Dysplasia
- Increased enzyme synthesis

© 2007 Jones and Bartlett Publishers

Notes

_____
_____
_____
_____
_____
_____
_____
_____
_____
_____
_____
_____
_____
_____
_____
_____
_____
_____
_____
_____
_____
_____
_____
_____
_____
_____
_____
_____
_____
_____
_____
_____
_____
_____
_____

Alterations of Cells to Changing Conditions

Atrophy: reduction in _size_ of cells in response to
- diminished function
- inadequate hormonal stimulation
- reduced blood supply

Examples
a. Reduction of skeletal muscle size when _extremity_ is _immobilized_ in a _cast_ for long period of times
b. Shrinkage of breasts and genitals following _menopause_ due to _inadequate estrogen stimulation_

© 2007 Jones and Bartlett Publishers

Alterations of Cells to Changing Conditions

Hypertrophy: an _increase_ in the _size_ of individual cells _without_ an actual _increase_ in their _numbers_

Examples
a. The large muscles of a _weight lifter_
b. The _heart_ of a person with _high blood pressure_ (heart must work harder in order to pump blood at a higher than normal pressure)

Hyperplasia: an _increase_ in the _size_ of a tissue or organ caused by an _increase_ in the _number_ of cclls
- It occurs in response to increased demand

© 2007 Jones and Bartlett Publishers

Alterations of Cells to Changing Conditions

Examples
- Glandular tissue of breasts during _pregnancy_ in preparation for _lactation_
- Endocrine glands such as the _thyroid_ may enlarge to increase their _output_ of _hormones_

Metaplasia: a _change_ from _one type_ of cell to _another_ type
Example
- The lining of the bladder chronically _irritated_ and _inflamed_

© 2007 Jones and Bartlett Publishers

Alterations of Cells to Changing Conditions

Dysplasia: a condition in which the *development* and *maturation* of cells is *disturbed* and *abnormal*

- The individual cells *vary* in *size* and *shape*
- Their *relationship* is also *abnormal*

Example

- Chronic irritation or inflammation of epithelial cells of *uterine cervix*; may progress to neoplasia (formation of tumor)

Increased Enzyme Synthesis:

- Adaptive response when cells are called upon to inactivate or detoxify drugs or chemicals

© 2007 Jones and Bartlett Publishers

Cell Injury, Cell Death, Cell Necrosis

- The *normal* cell actively transports *potassium into* the cell and moves *sodium out*
- When there is *cell injury*, the two most common changes are
  1. Cell swelling: sodium diffuses into the cell and water moves into the cell with the sodium
  2. Fatty changes: accumulation of fat droplets within the cytoplasm due to the impairment of the enzyme systems that metabolize fat

© 2007 Jones and Bartlett Publishers

Cell Injury, Cell Death, Cell Necrosis

- Cell death and cell necrosis
  - *All necrotic* cells are *dead*
  - *All dead* cells are *not necrotic*
- Programmed cell death – *apoptosis*

Apoptosis

- A form of *programmed self destruction* of cells. All normal cells have a *predetermined life span*
- The number of functional cells in all our body tissues is determined by a *balance* between proliferation of *new* cells and death of *older* "worn-out" cells

© 2007 Jones and Bartlett Publishers

_____

_____

_____

_____

_____

_____

_____

_____

_____

_____

_____

Cell Injury, Cell Death, Cell Necrosis

- Both *genetic* and *environmental* factors play a role in cell longevity
- *For example*, as the *red cell* ages and its enzyme systems gradually decline, it is less able to protect itself from injury than a young cell
- If the *red cells* are exposed to harmful drugs or antibodies that damage the cell membranes, the older cells bear the brunt of the damage and die
- Cells and organisms have a predetermined life span
- The aging of cells may be caused by damage to cellular DNA, RNA, and cytoplasmic organelles
- The more efficient the repair process, the greater the likelihood of survival

© 2007 Jones and Bartlett Publishers

Chapter 3: Chromosomes, Genes, and Cell Division

Chapter Outline

The chapter outline provides you with an organizational guide to the topics and ideas presented in this chapter of the text.

Introductory Concepts in Chapter 3

The following material is provided as a guide to some of the fundamental concepts in the first five chapters. It may help you organize the material as you get started in this course. You will build on these concepts as you begin to study diseases involving various organ systems.

1. Chromosomes occur in pairs: 22 matched pairs of homologous chromosomes called autosomes (non-sex chromosomes) and one pair of sex chromosomes (XX = females; XY = male). One member of each chromosome pair comes from each parent.

2. Genes occupy specific sites on chromosomes called *gene loci*. There are paired gene loci on the paired chromosomes. At any gene locus, any one of several related genes can occupy the locus. These alternative forms of genes are called *alleles* or *allelic genes*. A person is homozygous for a gene if both gene loci possess the same allelic gene; a person is heterozygous if the alleles are different. See the text for descriptions of dominant, recessive, codominant, and sex-linked genes and their effects.

3. There are two types of cell division: *mitosis,* characteristic of somatic cells, and *meiosis,* which occurs in germ cells. Each cell has already duplicated its DNA before it ever starts to divide.

4. Mitosis is simply a separation of already duplicated chromosomes. Each precursor (parent) cell produces two daughter cells, each one identical to the parent cell.

5. Meiosis is a two-phase process. In the *first division,* some intermixing of genetic material between homologous chromosomes occurs, and then the chromosomes separate without dividing. Each parent cell produces two daughter cells, each having only one member of each homologous pair of chromosomes (these homologous chromosomes are slightly different than those in the parents because of the intermixing of genetic material between homologous chromosomes). The *second division* is just like mitosis, but only 23 chromosomes separate. Each of the daughter cells from the first division, in turn, gives rise to two more daughter cells. The final result is that each precursor cell eventually gives rise to daughter cells in two divisions.

6. See the text for a description of the differences between spermatogenesis and oogenesis. These differences will be important when we consider chromosomal abnormalities such as Down syndrome.

7. The HLA (MHC) system is a system of interconnected (linked) genes located at gene loci on one pair of homologous chromosomes that determine specific proteins (self-antigens) called HLA or MHC proteins on the surface of cells. The HLA genes are transmitted in sets called *haplotypes,* with one set being provided by each parent (see Fig. 3-9). There are multiple possible alleles at each gene locus, and there are so many possible gene combinations that each individual has a unique set of HLA antigens (except identical twins, who possess identical genes). Certain HLA types appear to be associated with increased susceptibility to certain diseases.

Study Questions

The following questions are provided as a test for comprehension and as a study guide for use with the text chapters. Additional study material is located at http://humandisease.jbpub.com/, which contains useful tools such as an A&P review, animated flashcards, an interactive online glossary, crossword puzzles, and web links.

Key Terms

Define the following terms:

1. Allele _____

2. Dominant gene _____

3. Recessive gene _____

4. Homozygous _____

5. Heterozygous _____

6. Hemizygous _____

7. Human leukocyte antigen (HLA) _____

8. Haplotype _____

9. Gene therapy _____

True/False

Tell whether each statement is true or false. If false, explain why the statement is incorrect.

1. The human genome consists of about 3 billion pairs of DNA bases, and most of the DNA on chromosomes consists of genes that regulate cell structure and functions. _____

    _____

2. The Human Genome Project has identified all of the genes on the human chromosomes and has determined the function of each of these genes. _____

    _____

3. Minor variations in the sequence of the nucleotides within the same genes of different individuals (gene polymorphism) may lead to differences in the way the genes are expressed. _____

    _____

4. A gene inherited from a female parent does not always have the same effect as the identical gene inherited from the male parent. _____

    _____

5. Chromosomes normally exist in pairs called homologous chromosomes. _____

    _____

6. Certain HLA types appear to predispose a person to specific diseases. _____

    _____

7. Genes exist in pairs, and the members of each pair are located at corresponding sites (gene loci) on homologous chromosomes. _____

_____

8. An individual is heterozygous for a gene if the genes at the corresponding loci on homologous chromosomes are the same and homozygous for the gene if the genes are different. _____

_____

9. A dominant gene expresses itself in either the homozygous or heterozygous state. _____

_____

10. An X-linked gene is one that occurs in *only* the female. _____

_____

11. A defective X-linked gene may not cause clinical manifestations in the female, but may be associated with major clinical manifestations in the male. _____

_____

12. Tell whether each of the following statements regarding identification of inherited disease in newborn infants by screening tests is true or false. If false, explain why the statement is incorrect.

a. Screening is unlikely to be useful because most inherited diseases do not respond to treatment. _____

_____

b. Long-term harmful effects of inherited diseases can often be prevented by early treatment. _____

_____

c. Identification of a hereditary disease in a newborn may allow parents to make an informed decision regarding future pregnancies, based on the nature of the inherited disease and its prognosis. _____

_____

Discussion Questions

1. Describe the major differences between mitosis and meiosis. _____

_____

_____

_____

2. Describe how spermatogenesis differs from oogenesis. _____

_____

_____

_____

_____

3. What is the Human Genome Project? _____

_____

_____

_____

4. Describe the Lyon hypothesis relating to X chromosome inactivation. _____

_____

_____

_____

5. What is a karyotype? How is it determined? _____

_____

_____

_____

6. Describe what goals must be achieved for gene therapy to be successful. _____

_____

_____

_____

An Introduction to
Human Disease
PATHOLOGY AND PATHOPHYSIOLOGY CORRELATIONS
Seventh Edition

LEONARD V. CROWLEY, M.D.

Chapter 3

Hormones, Genes, and Cell Division

© 2007 Jones and Bartlett Publishers

Relationship of Genes, DNA, and Chromosomes

Genes
- Are the basic units of *inheritance*
- Are *segments* of the *DNA* chains that determine some property of the cell
- Each gene occupies a *specific site* on the chromosome called *locus* of gene
- Genes are arranged along the *chromosomes* "like beads on a string"
- Are *paired* the same way chromosomes are paired (*except* in the sperm and ova)

© 2007 Jones and Bartlett Publishers

Relationship of Genes, DNA, and Chromosomes

Genes
- Genes exist in *pairs* or *alleles* (*alternate* forms of a gene that can occupy the *same lotus*)
- Homozygous (*both alleles* are the *same*)
- Heterozygous (the *alleles* are *different*)
- Genes are *expressed* in a given cell, determining both its structure and functions

© 2007 Jones and Bartlett Publishers

Relationship of Genes, DNA, and Chromosomes

Genes
- *Expression* of genes
  - Dominant
  - Recessive
  - Codominant
- A *dominant* gene expresses itself in *either* the heterozygous or the homozygous state
- A *recessive* gene is one that produces an effect *only* in the *homozygous* state
- A *codominant* gene expresses itself when *both alleles* of a pair are *expressed*

© 2007 Jones and Bartlett Publishers

Relationship of Genes, DNA, and Chromosomes

Genes
- The *sum total* of all genes contained in a cell's chromosomes is called its *genome*
- Its genome is the *same* in all cells but *not* all genes are *expressed* (*active*) in all cells and *not* all genes are active *all the time*
- Only a very *small* percentage of the total DNA in the human genome consists of genes
- The *Human Genome Project* is an international collaboration that has constructed a *"road map"* of our genome by determining the *locations* of the individual *genes* on the *chromosomes*

© 2007 Jones and Bartlett Publishers

Relationship of Genes, DNA, and Chromosomes

Genes
- *Genomics* is the study of gene structure, attempting to *correlate* the *structure* with the *effects* of the genes (expression) in the individual

Chromosomes
- Present in the nucleus, chromosomes are composed of Double coils of *DNA* combined with protein
- Exist in *pairs* in *somatic cells* (cells *other than* those giving rise to eggs and sperm)

© 2007 Jones and Bartlett Publishers

Relationship of Genes, DNA, and Chromosomes

- One member of each pair is *derived* from the *male* parent and one member from the *female* parent
- *Except* for the *sex chromosomes*, *both members* of the pair are *similar* in size, shape and appearance and are called *homologous chromosomes*

Chromosomes
- In human beings, the normal chromosome component is *twenty-two pairs* of *autosomes* (chromosomes *other than* sex chromosomes) and *one pair* of *sex chromosomes*

© 2007 Jones and Bartlett Publishers

Relationship of Genes, DNA, and Chromosomes

- Sex chromosomes
  - Female XX chromosomes
  - Male XY chromosomes
- Any one chromosome can carry *only* one *allele* at a given *locus*

© 2007 Jones and Bartlett Publishers

Sex Chromosomes

- The cells of a normal *female* contain *two X* chromosomes
- The cells of a normal *male* contain *one X* and *one Y* chromosome
- The *small Y chromosome* consists almost entirely of genes concerned with the male *sexual* differentiation, carrying *few genes*
- The *large X chromosome* contains a large number of genes that direct many important *cell activities,* carrying *many genes*

© 2007 Jones and Bartlett Publishers

Lyon Hypothesis

- There is the *random inactivation* of the X chromosome in the *female*.
- The inactivated X chromosome appears as a small dense mass of chromatin attached to the nuclear membrane of somatic cells called a *sex chromatin body* or *Barr body*. The inactivated X is of *paternal origin* in some cells and of *maternal origin* in others.
- The percentages of inactivated paternal and maternal derived X chromosomes are *not necessarily equal*.

© 2007 Jones and Bartlett Publishers

Lyon Hypothesis

 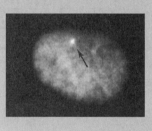

© Courtesy of Leonard Crowley, M.D./University of Minnesota Medical School

© 2007 Jones and Bartlett Publishers

Lyon Hypothesis

- The genes on the X chromosome that function in a woman's cell will *depend* on which *X chromosome* is *active* in the cell because the other X chromosome is inactivated and nonfunctional.
- According to the *Lyon Hypothesis*, a female is composed of a *mixture* of *two types of cells* with respect to the active X chromosome.
- This hypothesis has explained some of the *peculiarities* of the behavior of genes carried on the X chromosome in males and females, dealing with the *X-linked genetic diseases*.

© 2007 Jones and Bartlett Publishers

Notes

_____
_____
_____
_____
_____
_____
_____
_____
_____
_____
_____
_____
_____
_____
_____
_____
_____
_____
_____
_____
_____
_____
_____
_____
_____
_____
_____
_____
_____
_____
_____
_____
_____

Cell Division
Mitosis and Meiosis

- <u>Mitosis:</u> characteristic of *somatic* cells
  - Prophase
  - Metaphase
  - Anaphase
  - Telophase
- <u>Meiosis:</u> characteristic of *gametogenesis* (development of eggs and sperm)
  - 1st meiotic division
  - 2nd meiotic division

© 2007 Jones and Bartlett Publishers

Cell Division
Mitosis and Meiosis

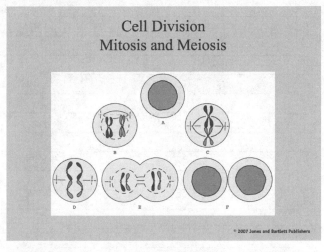

© 2007 Jones and Bartlett Publishers

Cell Division
Mitosis and Meiosis

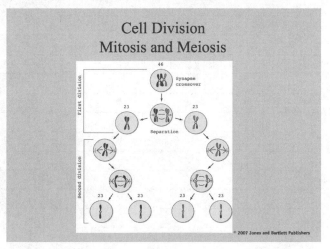

© 2007 Jones and Bartlett Publishers

Cell Division
Mitosis

- Each of the *two new cells* (*daughter* cells) resulting from the cell, receives the *same* number of chromosomes that were present in the *precursor cell* (*parent* cell)
- But *not* all mature cells are able to *divide*, such as cardiac, skeletal muscle and nerve cells
- *Others* such as connective tissue and liver cells *divide* as much *as needed*
- *Others divide constantly* such as those lining the testicular tubules that produce sperm cells
- *Others* in the bone marrow *continually replace* the circulating cells in the bloodstream

© 2007 Jones and Bartlett Publishers

Cell Division
Mitosis

- *Before* a cell begins *mitosis,* its *DNA* chains are *duplicated* to form a new chromosome material
- Each chromosome and its *newly duplicated counterpart* lie *side by side*
- The two members are called *chromatids*
- It is the process by which chromatids separate
- Each *chromosome duplicates* itself before beginning cell division
- There are normally forty-six *chromosomes* in each somatic cell

© 2007 Jones and Bartlett Publishers

Cell Division
Mitosis

- *Just prior* to cell *division*, there are actually the equivalent of *ninety-two* chromosomes in the cell
- When the chromosomes *shorten* during cell division, each chromosome can be seen to consist of *two separate chromosomes* that are still *partially joined* where the spindle fibers attach
- The term *chromatid* is applied to the *still-joined* chromosomes at this stage
- As soon as they *separate*, they are again called *chromosomes*

© 2007 Jones and Bartlett Publishers

Mitosis
Prophase, Metaphase,
Anaphase, and Telophase

Prophase
- Each chromosome shortens and thickens
- *Centrioles* move to *opposite poles* of the cell and form the *mitotic spindle* consisting of small fibers radiating in all directions
- Some fibers *attach* to the *chromatids*
- Nuclear membrane *breaks down*

© 2007 Jones and Bartlett Publishers

Mitosis
Prophase, Metaphase,
Anaphase, and Telophase

Metaphase
- Chromosomes *line up* in the *center* of the cell
- *Chromatids* are *partially separated* but remained joined at a constricted area called the *centromere*, which is the site where the *spindle fibers* are *attached*

© 2007 Jones and Bartlett Publishers

Mitosis
Prophase, Metaphase,
Anaphase, and Telophase

Anaphase
- *Chromatids separate* to form *individual chromosomes*, which are pulled to opposite poles of the cell by spindle fibers

© 2007 Jones and Bartlett Publishers

Notes

Mitosis
Prophase, Metaphase, Anaphase, and <u>Telophase</u>

<u>Telophase</u>
- *Nuclear membranes* of the two daughter cells *reform*
- The *cytoplasm divides*
- And the *two daughter cells* are *formed*, each an exact duplicate of the parent cell

Cell Division
<u>Meiosis</u>

- The process entails two separate divisions called the <u>*first*</u> and <u>*second meiotic divisions*</u>
- It leads to some *intermixing* of genetic material between *homologous* chromosomes
- In the *first division*, it reduces the number of chromosomes by *half* so that the *daughter cells* receive only *half* the *chromosomes* possessed by the parent cell and the chromosomes are *not* exact duplicates of those in the parent cell
- The *second division* is like a mitotic division but each cell contains only *twenty-three chromosomes*

Gametogenesis

- Gonads: *testes* and *ovaries*
- They contain *precursor* cells called *germ cells*, which are capable of developing into mature sperm or ova
- The *mature* germ cells are called *gametes*
- The *process* by which the gametes are formed is called *gametogenesis*

Gametogenesis

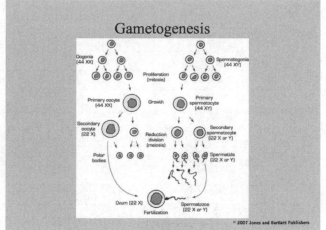

© 2007 Jones and Bartlett Publishers

Spermatogenesis and Oogenesis

Spermatogenesis: development of sperm
- The *precursor* cells in the *testicular tubes* are called *spermatogonia*

Oogenesis: development of ova
- The *precursor* cells of the *ova* are called *oogonia*

- *Both* processes are *similar* in many aspects

© 2007 Jones and Bartlett Publishers

Spermatogenesis

Spermatogonia form primary spermatocytes
↓
Secondary spermatocytes
↓
Spermatids
↓
Sperm

© 2007 Jones and Bartlett Publishers

Oogenesis

Oogonia form primary oocytes

↓

Oocytes form primary follicle

↓

Follicle matures - ovulated each month

↓

Primary oocyte

↓

Secondary oocyte

↓

Mature ovum

© 2007 Jones and Bartlett Publishers

Spermatogenesis and Oogenesis

• The development of sperm and that of ova is similar in many aspects but there are major *differences*

1. Each precursor cell produces *four* spermatozoa are in spermatogenesis
2. Only *one* ovum is produced in oogenesis; the other three are discarded as polar bodies
3. Spermatogenesis occurs *continually*, carried throughout completion in two months, seminal fluid always containing "fresh" sperm

© 2007 Jones and Bartlett Publishers

Spermatogenesis and Oogenesis

4. Oocytes are *not* produced *continually*; all oocytes form *before birth* and remain in a *prolonged prophase* of the *first mieotic* division from *fetal life* until they are *ovulated*

• This *may explain* why *congenital abnormalities* that result from abnormal separation of chromosomes in the course of *gametogenesis* are *more frequent* in *older women*

• These *ova* have been *exposed* for *many years* to *potentially harmful* radiation, chemicals, or other injurious agents, predisposing them to *abnormal separation* of chromosomes when *cell division* is resumed

© 2007 Jones and Bartlett Publishers

Histocompatibility Complex Genes

- Successful transplantation of organs from one person to another requires that the antigens present on the cells of the organ donor resemble as closely as those of the recipient
- Antigens present on cells are determined by a cluster of genes on *chromosome 6*
- This group of genes is called the *major histocompatibility complex (MHC complex)*
- In humans, these antigens were first identified on peripheral blood leukocytes, consequently named *human leukocyte antigens (HLA antigens)*
- A set of HLA genes on one chromosome is called *haplotype*

© 2007 Jones and Bartlett Publishers

Recombinant DNA Technology
Genetic Engineering
Gene Splicing

- Different *names* have been used for the same process
- Recombinant DNA Technology: genes from two different sources are recombined in a single organism
- Genetic Engineering: genes are being manipulated
- Gene Splicing: a piece of genetic material is being cut open and another piece of genetic material is being spliced into it

© 2007 Jones and Bartlett Publishers

Recombinant DNA Technology
Genetic Engineering
Gene Splicing

- Recent advances in DNA technology have led to the development of methods for large-scale production of many important biologic products such as insulin, growth hormone, and proteins that regulate the immune responses and proteins that activate the body's clot-dissolving mechanisms
- Applicable Principles:
a. Understanding the molecular basis of genetic disease
b. Prenatal diagnosis of genetic disease

© 2007 Jones and Bartlett Publishers

Gene Therapy

- *Gene Therapy* is an extension of the principles of *Recombinant DNA technology*

- In *Recombinant DNA technology*, a gene is inserted into a bacterial or yeast cell to make a protein

- In *Gene Therapy technology*, a normal gene is inserted into a defective cell lacking an enzyme or structural protein that the cell needs to function effectively and the inserted gene compensates for the missing or dysfunctional gene

© 2007 Jones and Bartlett Publishers

Goals for Successful Application of Gene Therapy

- Identify and select the *correct gene* to *insert* into the cell
- Choose the *proper cell* to *receive* the gene
- Select an *efficient means* of getting the gene into the cell
- Ensure that the newly inserted gene can *function effectively* enough within the cell to make the therapy worthwhile

© 2007 Jones and Bartlett Publishers

Chapter 19

Chapter Outline

The chapter outline provides you with an organizational guide to the topics and ideas presented in this chapter of the text.

The Inflammatory Reaction
>   Chemical Mediators of Inflammation
>   The Role of Lysosomal Enzymes in the Inflammatory Process
>   Inflammation Caused by Antigen–Antibody Interaction
>   Harmful Effects of Inflammation

Infection
>   Terminology of Infection
>   Factors Influencing the Outcome of an Infection

Introductory Concepts in Chapter 4

The following material is provided as a guide to some of the fundamental concepts in the first five chapters. It may help you organize the material as you get started in this course. You will build on these concepts as you begin to study diseases involving various organ systems.

1. The inflammatory reaction is a nonspecific stereotyped response to cell injury. The response is always the same because any tissue injury triggers the release of the same type of mediators of inflammation (see Fig. 4-1). Mediators come from *mast cells* (mostly histamine), *platelets* (serotonin), and *other injured cells* (prostaglandins, leukotrienes); they also come from blood plasma (bradykinins) and from activation of blood proteins called *complement*.

2. Lysosomes (packs of digestive enzymes in the cytoplasm of white cells) release their digestive enzymes when white cells degenerate at the site of inflammation. The released lysosomal enzymes then cause further tissue injury.

3. Sometimes the tissue injury caused by the inflammation is so marked that it is necessary to suppress the inflammatory process by means of corticosteroids (such as cortisone) or nonsteroidal anti-inflammatory drugs (such as aspirin or ibuprofen).

4. Inflammation is a general term. If the inflammation is caused by a pathogenic microorganism, we use the term *infection*. Various terms are used to describe an infection: *cellulitis* (localized infection in the tissues), *lymphangitis* (infection spreading into lymphatic channels draining the site of infection, with red streaks running up the arm), *lymphadenitis* (regional lymph nodes involved), *abscess* (necrosis of tissue with a pocket of pus), and *septicemia* (bloodstream infection).

5. The outcome of an infection depends on whether the pathogen or body defenses win or whether they are evenly matched and a chronic infection results (see Fig. 4-14).

Study Questions

The following questions are provided as a test for comprehension and as a study guide for use with the text chapters. Additional study material is located at http://humandisease.jbpub.com/, which contains useful tools such as an A&P review, animated flashcards, an interactive online glossary, crossword puzzles, and web links.

Key Terms

Define the following terms:

1. Exudate _____

2. Infection _____

3. Inflammation _____

4. Leukocytes _____

5. Pathogenic _____

6. Plasma _____

7. Lymphadenitis _____

8. Septicemia _____

9. Antibodies _____

10. Mediators of inflammation _____

11. Phagocytosis _____

12. Fibrinogen _____

13. Lysosome _____

Fill-in-the-Blank

1. _____ is a specialized connective-tissue cell containing granules filled with histamine and other chemical mediators.

2. A platelet is a component of the blood—a roughly circular or oval disk concerned with _____.

3. Serotonin is a _____ mediator of inflammation released from platelets.

4. _____ is a prostaglandin-like mediator of inflammation.

5. Bradykinin is a chemical mediator of inflammation derived from components in the _____.

6. _____ is an acute spreading inflammation affecting the skin or deeper tissues.

7. Lymphangitis is an inflammation of _____ draining a site of infection.

8. _____ is an infection in which large numbers of pathogenic bacteria are present in the bloodstream.

True/False

Tell whether each statement is true or false. If false, explain why the statement is incorrect.

1. Mediators of inflammation are produced primarily by neutrophils. _____

_____

2. The inflammatory reaction is a nonspecific response to any agent that injures cells. _____
_____

3. The inflammatory reaction concentrates leukocytes and antibodies at the site of inflammation. _____
_____

4. The plasma cell is the most important cell in acute inflammatory reaction. _____
_____

5. Lymphocytes phagocytize debris produced by the inflammatory process. _____
_____

6. A serous exudate resulting from an inflammation is yellow because it consists primarily of inflammatory cells. _____
_____

7. A fibrinous exudate is rich in fibrinogen, which coagulates to form fibrin and create a sticky film on the surface of the inflamed tissue. _____
_____

8. Extensive destruction of tissue secondary to inflammation is often followed by scarring. _____
_____

Discussion Questions

1. What is the inflammatory reaction? Describe its clinical manifestations. (*Hint:* see Fig. 4-1.) _____
_____
_____
_____

2. What are mediators of inflammation? _____
_____
_____
_____

3. What is the source of the mediators of inflammation? _____
_____
_____
_____

4. Describe what part lysosomal enzymes play in perpetuating and intensifying the inflammatory reaction. _____
_____
_____
_____

5. What is the difference between the terms "infection" and "inflammation"? _____
_____
_____
_____

6. What factors influence the outcome of an infection? (*Hint:* see Fig. 4-14.) _____
_____
_____
_____

7. List the possible outcomes of an inflammation produced by a pathogenic bacteria. _____
_____
_____
_____

8. What is the difference between serous and fibrinous exudates? _____
_____
_____
_____

An Introduction to

Human Disease

PATHOLOGY AND PATHOPHYSIOLOGY CORRELATIONS
Seventh Edition

LEONARD V. CROWLEY, M.D.

Chapter 4

Inflammation and Repair

© 2007 Jones and Bartlett Publishers

Inflammatory Reactions

- A *nonspecific response* to any *agent* that causes cell *injury*

Agents may be
- Physical (heat or cold)
- Chemical (concentrated acid)
- Microbiologic (bacterium or virus)

© 2007 Jones and Bartlett Publishers

Local and Systemic Effects of Inflammation

- Capillary dilatation: increased blood flow
- Increased capillary permeability: extravasation of fluid
- Attraction of leukocytes: migration of white cells to site of injury
- Systemic response: fever, leukocytes

© 2007 Jones and Bartlett Publishers

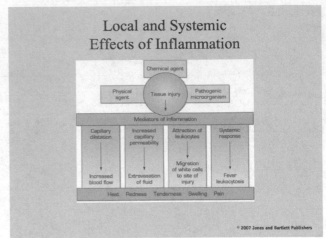

Clinical Manifestations of Inflammation

- Heat and redness
  - Dilated blood vessels and slowing of blood through vessels
- Swelling
  - Accumulation of fluid and exudate due to extravasation of plasma
- Tenderness and pain
  - Irritation of nerve endings

© 2007 Jones and Bartlett Publishers

Clinical Manifestations of Inflammation

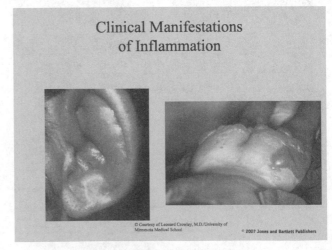

© Courtesy of Leonard Crowley, M.D./University of Minnesota Medical School   © 2007 Jones and Bartlett Publishers

Inflammatory Process

- *Acute* inflammatory process: most important cell involved is the *polymorphonuclear leukocyte* cell, being an actively *phagocytic* cell; later the *mononuclear cells* (monocytes, macrophages) that *clean* up the *debris*
- *Severe* inflammatory process: systemic effects become evident, i.e., feeling *ill* and *elevated temperature*; the bone marrow accelerates its production of leukocytes, which increase in bloodstream
- *Mild* inflammatory process: it *soon subsides*, tissues returning to normal (*resolution*)

© 2007 Jones and Bartlett Publishers

Outcome of Inflammation

- Resolution
- Repair
- Areas of destruction replaced by scar tissue
- Mediators intensify inflammatory process
- Mediators generate more mediators

© 2007 Jones and Bartlett Publishers

Chemical Mediators of Inflammation

- The *characteristic features* of the inflammatory reaction are *not* caused by the tissue damage itself
- They are caused by chemical agents *(chemical mediators)* formed when tissues are damaged
  - Some mediators are derived from *cells*
  - Some mediators are formed from *proteins* in the *blood plasma*

© 2007 Jones and Bartlett Publishers

Notes

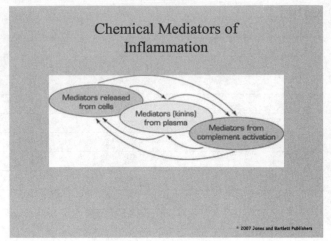

Chemical Mediators of Inflammation

Cell Derived Mediators

- <u>Mast cells</u>: widely distributed throughout connective tissue; their cytoplasm is filled with granules containing *histamine* (potent *vasodilator*)
- <u>Prostaglandins</u>: synthesized by cells from arachidonic acid present in *cell membranes*
- <u>Leukotrienes</u>: (*same* as above)

© 2007 Jones and Bartlett Publishers

Blood Plasma Mediators

- <u>Bradykinins (kinins)</u>: their formation is triggered by one of the proteins concerned with blood coagulation
- <u>Complement</u>: another group of blood proteins, consisting of nine separate protein components, that are activated when an antigen combines with an antibody or by other ways that do not require antigen-antibody interaction

© 2007 Jones and Bartlett Publishers

Harmful Effects of Inflammation

- The tissue *injury* results in part from the *injurious agent* and in part to the *inflammatory reaction* itself
- When the inflammatory reaction is *not self-limited* and persists, it is necessary to *suppress* it by administering *adrenal corticosteroid* hormones or other agents to reduce the tissue damage

© 2007 Jones and Bartlett Publishers

Infection

- An inflammatory process caused by disease-producing organisms
- "itis" is the suffix used with the name of the tissue or organ to indicate an infection or inflammatory process
- Examples: appendic*itis*, hepat*itis*, col*itis*
- *Cellulitis: acute spreading* infection at any site
- *Abscess*: infection associated with breakdown of tissues and formation of *pus*
- *Septicemia*: *overwhelming infection* where pathogenic bacteria gain access to bloodstream

© 2007 Jones and Bartlett Publishers

Infection

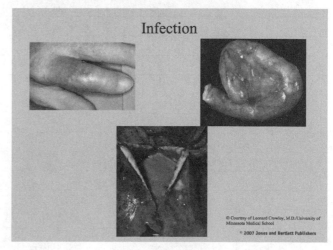

© Courtesy of Leonard Crowley, M.D./University of Minnesota Medical School

© 2007 Jones and Bartlett Publishers

Infection

- It involves the relationship between the *invading organism* and the *defenses* of the body
- Many microbiologic agents are *not* harmful to humans
- Those organisms that are capable of *causing human disease* are called *pathogenic agents*
- *Factors* influencing the *outcome*
  - *Virulence* of organism
  - *Numbers* of invading organisms
  - *Resistance* of host's body (infected individual)

© 2007 Jones and Bartlett Publishers

Factors Influencing Outcome of Infection Virulence

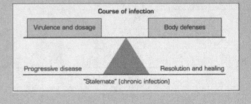

© 2007 Jones and Bartlett Publishers

Factors Influencing Outcome of Infection Virulence

- <u>Virulence</u> of organism: *ease* with which a *pathogenic organism* can *overcome* the *defenses* of the body
- <u>Highly virulent organism</u>: one that produces disease in the *majority* of *susceptible* individuals
- <u>Low virulence organism</u>: one that produces disease *only* in *highly susceptible* individuals under *favorable conditions*

© 2007 Jones and Bartlett Publishers

Notes

_____

_____

_____

_____

_____

_____

_____

_____

_____

_____

Chronic Infection

- State in which the pathogenic organism and the host are *evenly matched*
- Relatively *quiet, smoldering inflammation*, associated with repeated attempts at healing on the part of the host
- Lymphocytes, plasma cells, and monocytes are *predominant cells* in chronic inflammatory process.

© 2007 Jones and Bartlett Publishers

Chapter 5   Immunity, Hypersensitivity, Allergy, and Autoimmune Diseases

Chapter Outline

The chapter outline provides you with an organizational guide to the topics and ideas presented in this chapter of the text.

Introductory Concepts in Chapter 5

The following material is provided as a guide to some of the fundamental concepts in the first five chapters. It may help you organize the material as you get started in this course. You will build on these concepts as you begin to study diseases involving various organ systems.

1. Inflammation caused by a pathogenic microorganism (infection) differs from other types of inflammation caused by trauma or other types of tissue injury because the pathogen that causes the tissue injury is a *foreign substance* (non–self-antigen) that is introduced into the body. The body responds to its presence by generating an *immune response* to eliminate the foreign material in addition to giving rise to an inflammation.

2. The immune response may be *cell mediated* or *humoral*. Cell-mediated immunity is a property of T lymphocytes, which proliferate and accumulate around the foreign material, where they secrete destructive proteins called lymphokines. This is the main defense against viruses, fungi, parasites, and some bacteria such as the tubercle bacillus. Humoral immunity is a property of B lymphocytes. When stimulated by foreign material, they proliferate and "gear up" to produce large amounts of antibodies, which then combine with the foreign material. As B lymphocytes proliferate, they become transformed into cells with more cytoplasm that contains lots of ribosomes and rough endoplasmic reticulum. These cells are now called *plasma cells* and are very efficient "antibody-producing factories." This is our primary defense against most bacteria and bacterial toxins.

3. Several classes and types of antibodies (immunoglobulins) exist. See the fork analogy in the text (see Fig. 5-4). IgM, a large molecule, is the first antibody formed. IgG (gamma globulin) is formed soon thereafter and is the major immunglobulin. IgA is secreted by B lymphocytes in the mucosa of the GI and respiratory tracts and combines with inhaled or swallowed antigens so that they are not absorbed into the body. IgE is the allergy antibody. IgD is attached to the cell membranes of B lymphocytes; it has some special functions that need not be considered now.

4. Hypersensitivity reactions are important, and you should be familiar with them (see Table 5-1).

5. The IgE-mediated response triggers localized manifestations (allergy) or more serious systemic reactions to bee stings or penicillin reactions (anaphylaxis).

6. IgG-mediated hypersensitivity responses injure cells in two ways: by binding to cells and activating complement, which causes inflammation and tissue injury, or by forming antigen–antibody aggregates in tissues or in the circulation, which activates complement and induces inflammation.

7. A delayed hypersensitivity response (tuberculin-type hypersensitivity reaction) is a cell-mediated reaction and is not antibody related. Sensitized T lymphocytes accumulate at the site of contact with the foreign material and release lymphokines that attract macrophages and cytotoxic T lymphocytes. These attracted cells secrete cytokines (lymphokines and monokines) that cause the tissue injury and inflammation. A positive Mantoux test is an example of this type of reaction. Much of the tissue necrosis in tuberculosis is the result of a delayed hypersensitivity reaction to products of the tubercle bacillus.

8. Autoimmune disease occurs when the body develops an immune response to its own antigens (self-antigens), which damages the body's own cells and tissues. The nature of the autoimmune disease is determined by which organ or tissue is being attacked by the autoantibody.

9. Various mechanisms have been postulated to explain autoimmune disease (see Fig. 5-6). Defective regulation of the immune system by helper and suppressor lymphocytes is another mechanism of injury and one of the more important causes of autoimmune disease.

10. Table 5-2 provides examples of various autoimmune diseases, but the details of those diseases are not important now. Some examples will be illustrated in class.

Study Questions

The following questions are provided as a test for comprehension and as a study guide for use with the text chapters. Additional study material is located at http://humandisease.jbpub.com/, which contains useful tools such as an A&P review, animated flashcards, an interactive online glossary, crossword puzzles, and web links.

Key Terms

Define the following terms:

1. Acquired immunity _____

2. Cell-mediated immunity _____

3. Humoral immunity _____

4. Hypersensitivity _____

5. Active immunity _____

6. Passive immunity _____

7. Autoantibody _____

True/False

Tell whether the following statements are true or false as they apply to viral infections. If false, explain why the statement is incorrect.

1. Many viral infections cause acute cell necrosis and degeneration. _____

_____

2. Some viruses cause warts. _____

_____

3. Some viruses may persist indefinitely in the tissues of the host and become reactivated periodically, causing disease.

_____

4. Some viruses cause slowly progressive cell injury. _____

_____

5. Viruses are inhibited by adrenal corticosteroids. _____

_____

6. Some viruses respond to antiviral chemotherapeutic agents. _____

_____

Identify

1. Identify and describe the four major types of hypersensitivity reactions that cause tissue injury. (*Hint:* see Table 5-1.)

   a. _____

   b. _____

   c. _____

   d. _____

2. Identify and describe the four major categories of immunosuppressive agents used by physicians to treat autoimmune diseases or to perform organ transplants.

a. _____

b. _____

c. _____

d. _____

3. Identify and briefly describe three mechanisms postulated to explain the pathogenesis of autoimmune diseases.

a. _____

b. _____

c. _____

Discussion Questions

1. Describe the role of the lymphocyte in acquired immunity. (*Hint:* see Fig. 5-2.) _____

_____

_____

_____

2. Describe the role of the macrophage in acquired immunity. _____

_____

_____

_____

3. Describe the role of complement in immune responses. _____

_____

_____

_____

4. Draw and label a simple diagram of an immunoglobulin molecule. (*Hint:* see Fig. 5-4.)

5. List the major types of immunoglobulin molecules, and describe the function of each type.

_____

_____

_____

6. What is the difference between immunity and hypersensitivity? _____

_____

_____

7. What is the effect of autoantibody directed against the patient's own blood cells? _____

_____

_____

8. Describe what happens in a cell-mediated immune response secondary to a pathogenic microorganism. _____

_____

_____

9. Explain what happens when autoimmune diseases occur. How are they treated? _____

_____

_____

10. Describe what happens when a pathogenic organism enters the body. _____

_____

_____

11. Explain what happens when a person has a fungal infection. Are they treatable? _____

_____

_____

_____

Matching

Match the cell in the left column with its function or activity in the right column.

1. ____ Macrophage

2. ____ Antigenic determinant (epitope)

3. ____ MHC complex

4. ____ Cytotoxic T cell

5. ____ Helper T lymphocyte

A. Regulates immune response

B. A small fragment of an antigen to which the immune system responds

C. Destroys abnormal or infected body cells

D. A group of unique self-antigens on body cells

E. Antigen processing cell

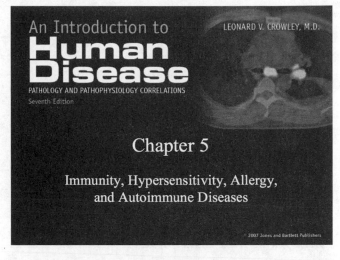

An Introduction to
Human Disease
PATHOLOGY AND PATHOPHYSIOLOGY CORRELATIONS
Seventh Edition

LEONARD V. CROWLEY, M.D.

Chapter 5

Immunity, Hypersensitivity, Allergy,
and Autoimmune Diseases

© 2007 Jones and Bartlett Publishers

The Body's Defense Mechanisms

- *Two* separate *mechanisms* that complement each other deal with pathogenic microorganisms
1. Inflammatory reaction: nonspecific response, phagocytosis of material by neutrophils and macrophages
2. Acquired immunity: depends on immune system, after contact with pathogenic organism, often associated with stage of altered reactivity to foreign material (*hypersensitivity*)

© 2007 Jones and Bartlett Publishers

The Body's Defense Mechanisms

- Two Types *Acquired Immunity*
1. Humoral immunity: production of *antibodies*; body's major defense against *bacteria* and bacterial toxins
2. Cell-mediated immunity: formation of a population of *lymphocytes* that attack and destroy foreign material; main defense against *viruses, fungi, parasites,* and *some bacteria*; the mechanism by which the body rejects *transplanted organs*; means of eliminating *abnormal cells* that arise spontaneously in *cell division*

© 2007 Jones and Bartlett Publishers

Acquired Immunity
Hypersensitivity

- An individual that displays *hypersensitivity* to an organism or its products, usually possesses some degree of *immunity* as well

- *However*, many diseases are associated with the development of an acquired immunity *without* demonstrable hypersensitivity

- *Normally*, a person develops an immune response *not* against cell proteins in his or her *own* cells and tissues but *only against foreign* antigens (*non-self antigens*), because the body has developed a *tolerance* to the self antigens present within it

© 2007 Jones and Bartlett Publishers

Acquired Immunity
Autoantibodies

- There are *diseases*, however, in which the patient forms *antibodies* to his or her *own* cells and tissues

- These *antibodies* may injure or destroy the patient's cells or tissues components

- This type of antibody is called an *autoantibody* and the diseases associated are called *autoimmune diseases*

© 2007 Jones and Bartlett Publishers

Immunity

- Role of Lymphocytes in Acquired Immunity
- Development of the Lymphatic System
- Response of Lymphocytes to Foreign Antigen
- Interaction of Cell-Mediated and Humoral Immunity
- Types of Responding T Cells
- Immune Response Genes
- Role of Complement in Immune Responses

© 2007 Jones and Bartlett Publishers

Notes

Acquired Immunity
Role of Lymphocytes

- Lymphocytes are the *important* cells of the immune system, together with the *macrophages* and related cells that process the antigen and "present" it to the lymphocyte
- They *respond* to *foreign antigens*
- The various cells of the immune system *communicate* with one another and produce many of their effects by secreting soluble protein *chemical messengers*
- Those messengers secreted by *lymphocytes* are called *lymphokines*

© 2007 Jones and Bartlett Publishers

Acquired Immunity
Role of Lymphocytes

- Those secreted by *monocytes* are called *monokines*
- *Cytokines* is a *general* term used to designate *any chemical messengers* involved in the immune system

- Some have specific names, such as,
  - *Interferons* (act by interfering with the multiplication of viruses within the cell)
  - *Interleukins* (send regulatory signals between cells of the immune system)
  - *Tumor necrosis factors* are cytokines that can destroy foreign or abnormal cells, including tumor cells

© 2007 Jones and Bartlett Publishers

Development of
Lymphatic System

- The *precursor* cells of the *lymphocytes* are formed initially from *stem cells* in the *bone marrow*
- They eventually develop into either of two groups, depending on *where* they undergo further *maturation*
1. Some of these precursor cells *migrate from* the *marrow* to the *thymus*, to form a specific type of lymphocyte called T lymphocyte (thymus-dependent)
2. Some *remain* within the *bone marrow*, to form a specific type of lymphocyte called B lymphocyte (bone marrow)

© 2007 Jones and Bartlett Publishers

Development of Lymphatic System

- *Before birth*, the *precursors* cells of *both T and B lymphocytes migrate* into the spleen, lymph nodes, and other sites
- Here they *proliferate* to form the masses of *mature lymphocytes* that populate the various lymphoid organs
- *Lymphocytes vary* in their *lifespan*, some having a *short* survival and some living for many *years*
- They do *not remain localized* within lymphoid organs, *continually circulating* between the *bloodstream* and the various *lymphoid tissues*
- About *two thirds* of the circulating lymphocytes are *T lymphocytes* and most of *the rest* are *B lymphocytes*

© 2007 Jones and Bartlett Publishers

Development of Lymphatic System

- About 10–15% of circulating lymphocytes have neither T nor B lymphocyte receptors
- These cells are called Natural Killer cells (NK cells)
- Their major *targets* are *virus-infected* cells and *cancer* cells
- They can destroy the target cells *as soon* as they are encountered
- In contrast, *T and B cells need time* to become activated and function effectively
- The *programming process* by which *lymphocytes* acquire *immune competence* involves a *rearrangement of genes* within the developing B and T lymphocytes

© 2007 Jones and Bartlett Publishers

Development of Lymphatic System

- Each programmed lymphocyte develops *antigen receptors* on its *cell membranes* that enable the lymphocyte to "*recognize*" and *respond* to a *specific antigen*
- When the *programming process* has been *completed*, many *millions of T and B cells* have formed, *each* programmed to *recognize* and *respond* to a *different antigen*
- *Although* a single lymphocyte can respond to *only* a single antigen, there is an *enormous population* of lymphocytes that can respond to *any antigen* an individual may encounter

© 2007 Jones and Bartlett Publishers

Response of Lymphocytes to Foreign Antigens

- Entry of a foreign antigen into the body triggers a *chain of events* that involves the *interactions* between *T and B Lymphocytes, and macrophages*, or similar antigen processing cells, summarized in three phases
1. *Recognition* of the foreign antigen
2. *Proliferation* of the lymphocytes programmed to respond to the antigen, forming a large group (clone) of cells
3. *Destruction* of the foreign antigen by the lymphocytes that have responded to the antigen

© 2007 Jones and Bartlett Publishers

Interaction of Cell-Mediated and Humoral Immunity

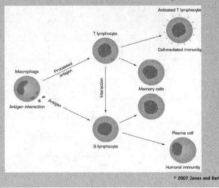

© 2007 Jones and Bartlett Publishers

Interaction of Cell-Mediated and Humoral Immunity

Figure 5-2 illustrates:

- The interaction of cell-mediated and humoral activity
- The *interaction* of *lymphocytes* with the *antigen* that they have been programmed to recognize
- That the *antigen* must first be "*processed*" and displayed on the *cell membrane* of the *antigen processing cell* before the immune response can be set in motion

© 2007 Jones and Bartlett Publishers

Interaction of Cell-Mediated and Humoral Immunity

- When appropriately stimulated,

  1) *B lymphocytes* proliferate and mature into antibody-forming plasma cells, and

  2) *T lymphocytes* proliferate to form a diverse population of cells that both regulate the immune response and generate a cell-mediated immune reaction to eliminate the antigenic material

- *Initial contact* with a foreign *antigen* is followed by a *lag phase* of a week or more before an *immune response* is demonstrated

© 2007 Jones and Bartlett Publishers

Interaction of Cell-Mediated and Humoral Immunity

- Once the body's *immune* mechanisms have *reacted* to a *foreign antigen*, however, some of the *lymphoid cells* retain a "*memory*" of the *antigen* that induced *sensitization*
- They *pass* this information to succeeding generations of *lymphocytes*
- Consequently, any *later contact* with the *same antigen* provokes a *renewed proliferation of sensitized lymphocytes or antibody-forming plasma cells*

© 2007 Jones and Bartlett Publishers

Types of Responding T cells

- They act to regulate the immune response and to act against the foreign antigens
- Regulator T cells: helper T cells that *regulate and control* the immune system by establishing a *balance* between promoting and inhibiting the immune response
- Effector T cells: involved in delayed hypersensitivity reactions
- In patients with AIDS, the causative virus *attacks* and *destroys helper T lymphocytes*

© 2007 Jones and Bartlett Publishers

Immune Response Genes

- They are closely related to the HLA complex on chromosome 6
- Control the immune response by regulating T cell and B cell proliferation
- Influence resistance to infection and resistance to tumors
- Influence the likelihood of acquiring an autoimmune disease

© 2007 Jones and Bartlett Publishers

Role of Complement

- When complement is *activated* along with the *immune system*, its components interact to accomplish several important functions:
1. They *act* as mediators of inflammation
2. They *coat* the surface of invading bacteria, making it easier for macrophages and neutrophils to phagocytose
3. They *generate* a large molecule called an attack complex, which destroys the target microorganism or abnormal cell by "punching holes" in its cell membrane

© 2007 Jones and Bartlett Publishers

Antibodies (Immunoglobulins)

- Types
  - Immunoglobulin M (IgM)
  - Immunoglobulin G (IgG)
  - Immunoglobulin A (IgA)
  - Immunoglobulin D (IgD)
  - Immunoglobulin E (IgE)

© 2007 Jones and Bartlett Publishers

Notes

_____

_____

_____

_____

_____

_____

_____

_____

_____

_____

_____

_____

_____

_____

_____

_____

_____

_____

_____

_____

_____

_____

_____

_____

_____

_____

_____

_____

_____

_____

_____

_____

Antibodies (Immunoglobulins)

- They are globulins produced by plasma cells
- Because of their structure, the antibody can react only with the specific antigen that induced its formation
- The arrangement of the Ig chains somewhat resembles the appearance of a fork

© 2007 Jones and Bartlett Publishers

Antibodies (Immunoglobulins)

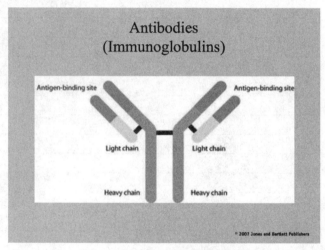

© 2007 Jones and Bartlett Publishers

Immunoglobulins IgM, IgG, IgA, IgD, and IgE

IgM
- Large antibody, called a macroglobulin
- Very efficient combining with fungi

IgG
- Smaller antibody
- Principal antibody molecule formed in response to the majority of infectious agents

© 2007 Jones and Bartlett Publishers

Notes

_____
_____
_____
_____
_____
_____
_____
_____
_____
_____
_____
_____
_____
_____
_____
_____
_____
_____
_____
_____
_____
_____
_____
_____
_____
_____
_____
_____
_____
_____
_____
_____
_____

Immunoglobulins
IgM, IgG, <u>IgA</u>, IgD, and IgE

<u>IgA</u>

- Produced by antibody-forming cells located in the respiratory and gastrointestinal mucosa
- It combines with harmful ingested or inhaled antigens, forming antigen-antibody complexes that cannot be absorbed
- In this way, it prevents the antigens from inducing sensitization

© 2007 Jones and Bartlett Publishers

Immunoglobulins
IgM, IgG, IgA, <u>IgD</u>, and <u>IgE</u>

<u>IgD</u>

- Found on cell membrane of B lymphocytes
- Present in minute quantities in blood

<u>IgE</u>

- Found in minute quantities in blood but its concentration is greatly increased in allergic individuals

© 2007 Jones and Bartlett Publishers

Hypersensitivity Reactions

- The immune system, while *protecting* us from foreign antigens, may also *damage* the tissues where the immune response occurs
- The *desirable* effect is *immunity*
- The *undesirable* effect is called *hypersensitivity*
- Both are manifestations of the same process
- There are four types
  - <u>Type I</u> – immediate hypersensitivity
  - <u>Type II</u> – cytotoxic hypersensitivity
  - <u>Type III</u> – tissue injury caused by immune complexes
  - <u>Type IV</u> – delayed hypersensitivity

© 2007 Jones and Bartlett Publishers

Type I: Immediate Hypersensitivity

- Allergy: immediate hypersensitivity reaction
- Anaphylaxis: widespread systemic reaction

Allergy

- Individuals who develop localized IgE-mediated reactions are predisposed to form specific IgE antibodies (become allergic) to ragweed, other plant pollens, and various other antigens that do not affect most people
- Atopic person: the allergy-prone individual
- Allergen: the sensitizing antigen
- Allergic manifestations: response of tissues exposed to the allergens

© 2007 Jones and Bartlett Publishers

Type I: Immediate Hypersensitivity

- Because histamine is one of the mediators released from IgE-coated cells, antihistamine drugs often relieve many of the allergic symptoms
- The sensitizing antigen is carried in the circulation throughout the body and triggers widespread mediator release from Ig-coated mast cells and basophils
- The release may lead to a fall in blood pressure, with circulatory collapse and often accompanied by severe respiratory distress

© 2007 Jones and Bartlett Publishers

Type I: Immediate Hypersensitivity

- Prompt treatment is required with epinephrine and other appropriate agents
- Anaphylaxis may be life-threatening

Examples:

- Anaphylaxis may occur when a sensitized individual takes penicillin
- Many persons are highly sensitive to bee stings
- Certain foods, particularly nuts, cause anaphylaxis in sensitive persons

© 2007 Jones and Bartlett Publishers

_____

_____

_____

_____

_____

_____

_____

_____

_____

_____

_____

_____

_____

_____

_____

_____

_____

_____

_____

_____

_____

_____

_____

_____

_____

_____

_____

_____

_____

_____

_____

_____

Type II: Cytotoxic Hypersensitivity

- The antibody formed against a cell or tissue antigen binds to the surface of the target cell or tissue
- This activates complement, and products of complement activation directly or indirectly damage the target
- This type of reaction occurs in response to:
  - the transfusion of incompatible blood
  - hemolytic disease in newborn infants caused by Rh incompatibility
  - some types of hemolytic anemia associated with autoantibodies directed against basement membranes of glomerular capillaries

© 2007 Jones and Bartlett Publishers

Type III: Tissue Injury Caused by Immune Complexes

- Antigen and antibody form clumps called immune complexes within the circulation that are deposited in the tissues
- This complex activates complement and its components and attracts inflammatory cells that damage the tissues
- This type of reaction occurs in:
  - A type of kidney disease called immune complex glomerulonephritis, in which the complexes are trapped within the glomeruli as the blood flows through the kidneys
  - Lupus erythematosus
    Rheumatoid arthritis

© 2007 Jones and Bartlett Publishers

Type IV: Delayed (Cell-Mediated)

- T lymphocytes rather than antibodies are responsible for tissue injury
- Happens with individuals that have been infected with the tubercle bacillus and have developed a cell-mediated immune reaction directed against the organism
- Other types of bacteria as well as fungi and parasites, evoke a similar response
- Unlike immediate hypersensitivity reactions, which are mediated by antibodies, a cell-mediated inflammatory reaction requires from 24–48 hours to develop

© 2007 Jones and Bartlett Publishers

Classification and Functions of Immune System Cells

TABLE 5-1

Classification and functions of immune system cells

CELL FUNCTION	CELL TYPE	ACTION OF CELL
Antigen processing	Macrophages, B lymphocytes, dendritic cells	Process antigen and present to lymphocytes
Regulate immune response	Helper T cells (CD4+)	Cytokines regulate immune system activity
Promote cytotoxic immune response	Cytotoxic T cells (CD8+)	Produce cytokines that destroy foreign or abnormal cells displaying antigen fragments combined with MHC Class I antigens
Promote delayed hypersensitivity response	Delayed hypersensitivity T cells (CD4+)	Respond to antigen processing cells presenting foreign antigen fragments combined with MHC Class II antigens; produce cytokines that activate and stimulate macrophages, cytotoxic T cells, and NK cells
Destroy virus-infected cells and cancer cells	NK cells	Cytokine-mediated cell destruction; no previous contact with antigen required
Produce antibodies	Plasma cells	Antigen processed by B lymphocytes and presented to responding T cells stimulates B lymphocytes to mature into plasma cells and make antibodies

© 2007 Jones and Bartlett Publishers

Suppression of the Immune Response
Reasons for Suppression

- Humoral and cell-mediated immune responses protect against potentially harmful microorganisms and other foreign substances
- These immunological mechanisms may at times have undesirable effects
- They may be directed against an individual's own cells or tissue components, leading to autoimmune diseases
- They are responsible for the rejection of transplanted organs
- They lead to Rh hemolytic disease in newborn infants

© 2007 Jones and Bartlett Publishers

Suppression of the Immune Response
Methods for Suppression

The main types of Immunosuppressive agents are
- Radiation
- Immunosuppressive drugs that impede cell division or cell function
- Adrenal corticosteroid hormones
- Gamma globulin preparations containing potent antibodies

© 2007 Jones and Bartlett Publishers

Pathogenesis of Autoimmune Diseases

- Alteration of the patient's own (self) antigens that causes them to become antigenic and provoke an immune reaction
- Formation of cross-reacting antibodies against foreign antigens that also attack the patient's own antigens
- Defective regulation of the immune response by regulator T lymphocyte

© 2007 Jones and Bartlett Publishers

Autoimmune Diseases

Examples

- Lupus erythematosus (systemic manifestations in various organs)
- Rheumatoid fever (inflammation in heart & joints)
- Glomerulonephritis (inflammation in renal glomeruli)
- Autoimmune blood diseases (anemia, leukopenia, or thrombocytopenia)
- Thyroiditis (hypothyroidism)
- Diffuse toxic goiter (hyperthyroidism)

© 2007 Jones and Bartlett Publishers

Etiology and Clinical Manifestations of Common Autoimmune Diseases

© 2007 Jones and Bartlett Publishers

Chapter Outline

The chapter outline provides you with an organizational guide to the topics and ideas presented in this chapter of the text.

Types of Harmful Microorganisms
Bacteria
    Classification of Bacteria
    Identification of Bacteria
    Major Classes of Pathogenic Bacteria
    Antibiotic Treatment of Bacterial Infections
    Antibiotic Sensitivity Tests
    Adverse Effects of Antibiotics
Chlamydiae
Rickettsiae and Ehrlichiae
Mycoplasmas
Viruses
    Classification of Viruses
    Mode of Action
    Bodily Defenses Against Viral Infections
    Treatment with Antiviral Agents
Fungi
    Superficial Fungal Infections
    Highly Pathogenic Fungi
    Other Fungi of Medical Importance
    Treatment of Systemic Fungal Infections

Study Questions

The following questions are provided as a test for comprehension and as a study guide for use with the text chapters. Additional study material is located at http://humandisease.jbpub.com/, which contains useful tools such as an A&P review, animated flashcards, an interactive online glossary, crossword puzzles, and web links.

Key Terms

Define the following terms:

1. Virus _____

2. Human papillomavirus _____

3. *Histoplasma capsulatum* _____

4. *Neisseria* _____

5. Latent virus infection _____

6. Hemolysis _____

7. Antigens _____

8. Pathogenic _____

True/False

1. Tell whether each statement is true or false as it applies to streptococci. If false, explain why the statement is incorrect.

   a. The organisms are classified based on the carbohydrate antigens present in their cell walls and on the type of hemolysis produced by the organism growing on a blood agar plate. _____
   _____

   b. Most alpha hemolytic streptococci are very pathogenic. _____
   _____

   c. Group A beta streptococci may cause serious respiratory tract infections such as streptococcal pharyngitis, and such infections may be followed by rheumatic fever. _____
   _____

   d. Group B beta streptococci may colonize the genital tract of pregnant women and may lead to an infection in the infant caused by the streptococcus acquired by the infant during delivery. _____
   _____

2. Tell whether each statement is true or false as it applies to the organism causing anthrax (*Bacillus anthracis*). If false, explain why the statement is incorrect.

   a. The organism is a gram-positive, spore-forming aerobic bacillus. _____
   _____

   b. The organism can be used as a bioterrorism–germ warfare agent. _____
   _____

c. Inhalation of anthrax spores may cause a severe pulmonary infection. _____

_____

d. Pulmonary anthrax caused by inhalation of anthrax spores can be prevented by a short (1- to 2-week) course of antibiotics because the organism is sensitive to antibiotics. _____

_____

Identify

1. Identify and briefly describe the four potentially harmful side effects of antibiotics.

   a. _____

   b. _____

   c. _____

   d. _____

2. Identify the important diseases caused by

   a. Pneumococci _____

   b. Gonococci _____

   c. Acid-fast bacteria _____

3. Identify two highly pathogenic fungi and the type of diseases they produce.

   a. _____

   b. _____

4. Identify five possible effects of a virus invasion of a susceptible cell. (*Hint:* see Fig. 6-4.)

   a. _____

   b. _____

   c. _____

   d. _____

   e. _____

5. List the four major factors used to classify bacteria.

   a. _____

   b. _____

   c. _____

   d. _____

Matching 1

Match the diseases in the right column with the responsible organisms in the left column.

1. _____ Group A beta streptococcus
2. _____ Group B beta streptococcus
3. _____ Hemolytic staphylococcus
4. _____ Human papillomavirus
5. _____ *Histoplasma capsulatum*
6. _____ Herpes virus
7. _____ Varicella zoster virus
8. _____ Mumps virus
9. _____ *Bacillus anthracis*
10. _____ Meningococcus (*Neisseria meningitidis*)

A. Severe throat infection
B. Warts
C. Infection of newborn infant
D. "Fever blisters"
E. Pulmonary infection
F. Germ warfare agent
G. Wound infection
H. Skin rash
I. Parotid gland infection
J. Meningitis

Matching 2

Match the organism in the left column with the disease or condition in the right column.

1. _____ *Brucella*
2. _____ *Borrelia*
3. _____ *Ehrlichia*
4. _____ *Babesia*
5. _____ *Yersinia*

A. A malaria-like parasite transmitted by ticks
B. A febrile illness transmitted to people from unpasteurized milk or tissues of infected animals
C. Causes a febrile illness with a skin rash
D. Causes bubonic plague
E. A tick transmitted rickettsia-like agent that infects white blood cells

Discussion Questions

1. How is the Gram stain used to classify bacteria?_____
_____
_____

2. How do antibiotics inhibit the growth of bacteria? (*Hint*: see Fig. 6-2.)_____
_____
_____

3. How does penicillin kill bacteria? _____
_____
_____

4. How do bacteria become resistant to an antibiotic? _____

_____

_____

_____

5. What factors render a patient susceptible to an infection by a fungus of low pathogenicity? _____

_____

_____

_____

An Introduction to
Human Disease
LEONARD V. CROWLEY, M.D.

PATHOLOGY AND PATHOPHYSIOLOGY CORRELATIONS
Seventh Edition

Chapter 6

Pathogenic Microorganisms

© 2007 Jones and Bartlett Publishers

Types of Harmful Microorganisms

Bacteria
Chlamydiae
Rickettsiae and Ehrlichiae
Mycoplasmas
Viruses
Fungi

© 2007 Jones and Bartlett Publishers

Classification of <u>Bacteria</u>

Based on four major characteristics
1. Shape
2. Gram-stain reaction
3. Biochemical and cultural characteristics
4. Antigenic structure

<u>Shape</u>
- Coccus (spherical)
  - Staphylococci (grow in clusters)
  - Diplococci (grow in pairs)
  - Streptococci (grow in chains)
- Bacillus (rod shaped)
- Spiral

© 2007 Jones and Bartlett Publishers

Classification of <u>Bacteria</u>

<u>Gram stain</u>
- A dried fixed suspension of bacteria prepared on a microscopic slide is
- stained *first* with a *purple* dye
- *then* with an *iodine* solution
- *then* the slide is *decolorized* with alcohol or another solvent
- and *last* it is stained with a *red* dye

  - Gram-positive: bacteria that resists decolorization and *retain purple* stain
  - Gram-negative: bacteria that accept the decolorization and *accept red*

© 2007 Jones and Bartlett Publishers

Classification of <u>Bacteria</u>

<u>Biochemical and cultural characteristics</u>
- Some bacteria are quite fastidious and can be grown only on enriched media under carefully controlled conditions of temperature and acidity (pH)
- Other bacteria are hardy and capable of growing on relatively simple culture media under a wide variety of conditions
- Most bacteria have distinct biochemical characteristics, each having its own "biochemical profile," which aids in its identification

© 2007 Jones and Bartlett Publishers

Classification of <u>Bacteria</u>

<u>Antigen structure</u>
- Each type of bacterium contains a large number of antigens associated with the cell body, the capsule of the bacteria, and the flagella in some

- The antigenic structure can be determined by special methods, defining a system of antigens unique for each group of bacteria

© 2007 Jones and Bartlett Publishers

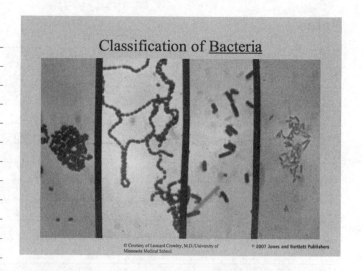

Classification of Bacteria

© Courtesy of Leonard Crowley, M.D./University of
Minnesota Medical School   © 2007 Jones and Bartlett Publishers

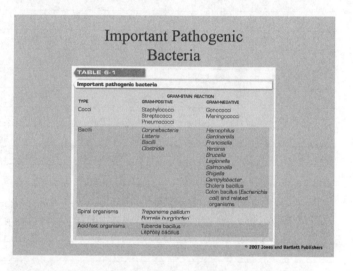

Important Pathogenic
Bacteria

TABLE 6-1

Important pathogenic bacteria

| TYPE | GRAM-STAIN REACTION | |
	GRAM-POSITIVE	GRAM-NEGATIVE
Cocci	Staphylococci Streptococci Pneumococci	Gonococci Meningococci
Bacilli	Corynebacteria Listeria Bacilli Clostridia	Hemophilus Gardnerella Francisella Yersinia Brucella Legionella Salmonella Shigella Campylobacter Cholera bacillus Colon bacillus (Escherichia coli) and related organisms
Spiral organisms	Treponema pallidum Borrelia burgdorferi	
Acid-fast organisms	Tubercle bacillus Leprosy bacillus	

© 2007 Jones and Bartlett Publishers

Characteristics of Bacteria

- *Aerobic* organisms: bacteria that grow best in the *presence of oxygen (O₂)*
- *Anaerobic* organisms- bacteria that only grow in the *absence of oxygen (O₂)* or under extremely low oxygen tension
- *Other* bacteria grow equally well under *either conditions*
- *Flagella*: hair-like processes covering the surface of some bacteria, giving it its *motility*
- *Spores*: spherical structures that some bacteria form, which allows them to *survive* under conditions that would kill an actively growing bacterium

© 2007 Jones and Bartlett Publishers

Characteristics of Bacteria

- Spores may be considered a *dormant, extremely resistant* bacterial modification that forms under adverse conditions
- Spores can *germinate* and give rise to *actively growing bacteria* under favorable conditions

© 2007 Jones and Bartlett Publishers

Identification of Bacteria

- An illustration shows how the methods of *classifying bacteria* can be applied to the identification of a *specific bacterium*
1. An organism is isolated from blood of patient with febrile illness
2. By means of the Gram stain reaction, the organism has been identified as a Gram-negative bacillus (shape)
3. The biochemical and cultural characteristics indicate that it is not a fastidious organism and that it is capable of growing on a wide variety of cultural media at various temperatures
4. It grows well under the presence or absence of oxygen

© 2007 Jones and Bartlett Publishers

Identification of Bacteria

5. The organism is motile and does not form spores
- At this point, the number of possible organisms consistent with these characteristics has been reduced to relatively few Gram-negative bacteria
- The number of possibilities is narrowed still further by various biochemical tests indicating that the bacterium does not ferment lactose but is capable to ferment glucose and certain other sugars
- These and other biochemical tests support the conclusion that the organism is *Salmonella*, found in the GI tract and capable of causing a typhoid-like febrile illness

© 2007 Jones and Bartlett Publishers

Pathogenic Bacteria: Staph and Strep

Staphylococci
- Are normal inhabitants of the skin and nasal cavity
- Are normally not pathogenic
- Some are pathogens and some strains are extremely virulent

Streptococci
- There are many kinds
- They are classified based on
1. Serological characteristics (*Lancefield* system)
2. Type of *hemolysis* produced

© 2007 Jones and Bartlett Publishers

Pathogenic Bacteria: Staph and Strep

- The *Lancefield* system consists of *20 major groups* based on differences in the carbohydrate antigens present in their cell walls
- These groups are designated *A through H* and *K through V*; most of the *medically important* Strep are in groups *A, B and D*
- The *hemolysis* classification is based on the type of hemolysis they produce when cultured on a solid medium containing blood
- They can be classified as *alpha* hemolysis, *beta* hemolysis, or *no* hemolysis
- Usually *both* the Lancefield group and the type of hemolysis are specified when *describing a Strep*

© 2007 Jones and Bartlett Publishers

Chlamydiae
Characteristics and Diseases

Characteristics
- Gram-negative nonmotile bacteria
- Live only as parasites inside cell
- Form inclusion bodies in infected cells

Diseases
- Nongonococcal urethritis
- Inflammation of uterine cervix
- Inclusion conjunctivitis
- Pulmonary infections
- Lymphogranuloma venereum

© 2007 Jones and Bartlett Publishers

Notes

Rickettsiae and Ehrlichiae Characteristics and Diseases

<u>Characteristics</u>
- Intracellular parasite
- Parasite of insects transmitted to humans
- Rickettsiae multiply in endothelial cells of blood vessels
- Ehrlichiae multiply in neutrophils or monocytes
- Respond to some antibiotics

<u>Diseases</u>
- Typhus
- Rocky Mountain spotted fever
- Ehrlichiosis

© 2007 Jones and Bartlett Publishers

Mycoplasmas and Viruses

<u>Mycoplasmas</u>
- Fragile bacteria lacking cell wall
- Cause primary atypical pneumonia
- Respond to some antibiotics

<u>Viruses</u>
- Either DNA or RNA
- Genome enclosed in capsid
- Size and complexity of genome varies
- Lack metabolic enzymes
- Rely on metabolic processes of host for survival

© 2007 Jones and Bartlett Publishers

Virus Classification Viral Mode of Action

<u>Classification</u>
- Nucleic acid structure
- Size
- Structural configuration
- Biologic characteristics

<u>Mode of Action</u>
- Invasion of susceptible cell. Many form inclusion bodies
  - Asymptomatic latent viral infection
  - Acute cell necrosis and degeneration
  - Cell hyperplasia and proliferation
  - Slowly progressive cell injury
  - Neoplasia

© 2007 Jones and Bartlett Publishers

Notes

_____
_____
_____
_____
_____
_____
_____
_____
_____
_____
_____
_____
_____
_____
_____
_____
_____
_____
_____
_____
_____
_____

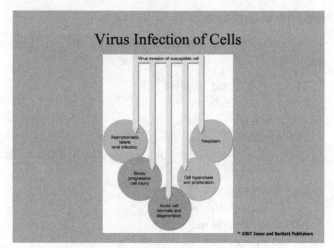

Virus Infection of Cells

© 2007 Jones and Bartlett Publishers

Fungi
Types of Fungal Infections

Fungi
- Plantlike organisms without chlorophyll
  - Yeasts, molds
- Treated with antifungal antibiotics

Infections
- Superficial fungal infections
- Mucous membranes – *Candida*
- Histoplasmosis, coccidioidomycosis
- Blastomycosis, cryptococcus

© 2007 Jones and Bartlett Publishers

Chapter Outline

The chapter outline provides you with an organizational guide to the topics and ideas presented in this chapter of the text.

The Parasite and Its Host
Protozoal Infections
    Malaria
    Amebiasis
    Genital Tract Infections Caused by Trichomonads
    Giardiasis
    Toxoplasmosis
    Cryptosporidiosis
Metazoal Infections
    Roundworms
    Tapeworms
    Flukes
Arthropods

Study Questions

The following questions are provided as a test for comprehension and as a study guide for use with the text chapters. Additional study material is located at http://humandisease.jbpub.com/, which contains useful tools such as an A&P review, animated flashcards, an interactive online glossary, crossword puzzles, and web links.

Key Terms

Define the following terms:

1. Protozoa _____

2. Metazoa _____

3. *Toxoplasma gondii* _____

4. *Pneumocystis carinii* _____

Fill-in-the-Blank

1. _____ is the large roundworm that lives in the intestinal tract of humans and that is acquired from ingestion of worm eggs.

2. _____ is the small (1 cm long) roundworm that inhabits the colon of infected children and periodically migrates out of the anus at night to deposit eggs on the perianal skin.

3. _____ is the small roundworm that forms cysts in the muscles of infected animals and may cause a serious systemic illness in persons who ingest the cysts contained in incompletely cooked meat.

4. _____ is the long ribbon-like worm that lives in the intestinal tract and that is acquired by eating the flesh of infected animals or fish.

5. _____ is the fluke infestation that causes an itchy skin rash, as a result of swimming in a lake containing the infectious form of the parasite.

6. _____ is the sexually transmitted parasite that causes an intense itching of the pubic skin.

7. _____ is a parasite that infests many birds and animals and that can be transmitted to humans by ingestion of incompletely cooked meat (such as hamburgers) or by contact with infected cats that excrete an infectious form of the parasite in their feces.

Identify

1. Indicate the name of the parasite that causes the following diseases or conditions:

   a. A protozoal disease transmitted by mosquitoes _____

   b. An intestinal infection caused by a pathogenic amoeba _____

   _____

   c. A sexually transmitted infection caused by a small motile parasite that does not form cysts _____

   _____

   d. An intestinal infection caused by a small pear-shaped parasite that causes intestinal cramps and diarrhea

   _____

e. A parasitic infection that may be transmitted from a recently infected pregnant woman to her fetus _____

_____

f. A parasitic infection that may be acquired by contact with cats _____

_____

g. A small parasite that forms highly resistant cysts that may contaminate municipal water supplies, lakes and rivers, and swimming pools; ingestion of the cysts causes cramps and diarrhea _____

_____

h. A small parasite that causes a skin rash _____

2. Identify the three large groups of metazoal parasites.

   a. _____

   b. _____

   c. _____

Matching

Match the parasite in the right column with the clinical manifestation or condition in the left column. Some letters may be used more than once, and some may not be used:

1. _____ "Swimmer's itch"   A. Pinworms

2. _____ Profuse vaginal discharge   B. *Plasmodium* species

3. _____ Injures the fetus of a pregnant woman   C. Crab louse

4. _____ Severe life-threatening diarrhea in an   D. *Ascaris* larvae
         immunocompromised person

5. _____ Fever, cough, and pulmonary inflammation   E. *Trichomonas*

6. _____ Diarrhea from swimming in chlorinated   F. *Cryptosporidium*
         swimming pool

7. _____ Chills and fever   G. Tapeworm

8. _____ Perianal itching awakening a child at night   H. *Toxoplasma*

9. _____ Itching of pubic skin   I. *Schistosomes*

10. _____ Severe pulmonary infection in an   J. *Pneumocystis*
          immunocompromised person

Parasite and Host

- Animal parasites are organisms that have become adapted to living within or on body of another animal, called the *host*
- These organisms are *no* longer capable of *free-living existence*
- Many animal parasites have a *complex* life cycle
- Many animal parasites live within the *intestinal tract* and discharge *eggs* in the *feces*
- *Transmission* is *favored* by conditions of *poor sanitation* and by relatively *high temperature* and *humidity*
- Many *parasitic infections* are *common* in *tropical climates* and are much *less frequent* in *cold* or *temperate climates*

© 2007 Jones and Bartlett Publishers

Animal Parasites

- Protozoa
  - One-celled organisms
- Metazoa
  - Multicellular structures
  - Roundworms, tapeworms, flukes
- Arthropods
  - Small insects

© 2007 Jones and Bartlett Publishers

Protozoal Infections

- <u>Malaria</u>: caused by various species of *Plasmodium*
- <u>Amebic dysentery</u>: caused by pathogenic ameba, *Entamoeba histolytica*
- <u>Genital tract trichomonad</u>: caused by parasite *Trichomonas vaginalis*
- <u>Giardiasis</u>: caused by *Giardia lamblia*, which infects the *small intestine*
- <u>Toxoplasmosis</u>: caused by *Toxoplasma gondii*, which may infect the *fetus* of a pregnant woman and cause *congenital malformations*

© 2007 Jones and Bartlett Publishers

Protozoal Infections

- <u>Cryptosporidiosis</u>: caused by a parasite called *Cryptosporidium parvum*, which parasitizes the *intestinal tract* and can cause *severe diarrhea*

- <u>Pneumocystic pneumonia</u>: caused by *Pneumocystis carinii*, which does *not* cause disease in *immunocompetent* persons but causes a severe, sometimes fatal *pulmonary infection* in persons with *AIDS*

© 2007 Jones and Bartlett Publishers

Metazoal Infections

- <u>Roundworm</u>: the three most important ones that parasitize human beings are
  1. <u>*Ascaris*</u>: large roundworm that lives within *intestinal tract* and eggs discharge in feces
  2. <u>Pinworms</u>: small roundworm that migrates out of *colon* through the *anus* while the infected individual is *asleep* and deposits its eggs on the *perianal skin*; *frequent* in *children* and *spreads* through a *family*
  3. <u>*Trichinella*</u>: small roundworm that parasitizes *human and animals*; most people become infected by eating *improperly cooked pork*

© 2007 Jones and Bartlett Publishers

Notes

_____

_____

_____

_____

_____

_____

_____

_____

_____

_____

_____

_____

_____

_____

_____

_____

_____

_____

_____

_____

_____

_____

_____

Metazoal Infections

- <u>Tapeworms</u>: long, ribbonlike worms that grow to a *length of several feet* that inhabit the *intestinal tract*; humans become infected by eating the flesh of an infected animal that contains the larvae of the parasite
- <u>Flukes</u>: thick, fleshy, short worms with *suckers to attach* to the *host;* some live within the *intestinal tract*, the *liver*, the *lungs*, the *venous portal system*. Some animal flukes (schistosomes) may infect skin.

© 2007 Jones and Bartlett Publishers

Arthropod Infections

- Transmitted by close *physical* contact and often spread by *sexual contact*
- <u>Scabies</u>: small parasite that burrows in the *superficial layers* of the *skin*, where it lays eggs that hatch in a few days
- <u>Crab louse:</u> lives in the *anal* and *genital hairs*, which causes *intense itching*

© 2007 Jones and Bartlett Publishers

Chapter Outline

The chapter outline provides you with an organizational guide to the topics and ideas presented in this chapter of the text.

Methods of Transmission and Control
Methods of Transmission
Methods of Control
    Immunization
    Identification, Isolation, and Treatment of Infected Persons
    Control of Means of Indirect Transmission
    Requirements for Effective Control
Sexually Transmitted Diseases
    Syphilis
    Gonorrhea
    Herpes
    Genital Chlamydial Infections
Human Immunodeficiency Virus Infections and AIDS
    HIV and Its Target
    Early Manifestations of HIV Infection
    Late Manifestations of HIV Infection
    Measurements of Viral RNA and CD4 Lymphocytes as an Index of Disease Progression
    Complications of AIDS
    Prevalence of HIV Infection and AIDS in High-Risk Groups
    Prevention and Control of HIV Infection
    Treatment of HIV Infection

Study Questions

The following questions are provided as a test for comprehension and as a study guide for use with the text chapters. Additional study material is located at http://humandisease.jbpub.com/, which contains useful tools such as an A&P review, animated flashcards, an interactive online glossary, crossword puzzles, and web links.

Key Terms

Define the following terms:

1. Communicable disease _____

2. Chlamydia _____

3. HIV _____

4. AIDS _____

5. Opportunistic infections _____

True/False

Tell whether each statement is true or false. If false, explain why the statement is incorrect.

1. Currently, about 18 percent of all AIDS cases occur in women. _____

_____

2. Among young persons ages 13 to 19 years, most HIV infections occur in males.

_____

3. The drug zidovudine (ZDV), when given to a pregnant HIV-infected mother, significantly reduces the risk of mother-to-infant HIV transmission. _____

_____

4. A newborn infant born to an HIV-infected mother is also treated with ZDV for several weeks after delivery. _____

_____

5. A newborn infant born to an HIV-infected mother may be breastfed because the virus cannot be transmitted by breast milk.

_____

6. Delivery of an HIV-infected mother by cesarean section reduces the risk of mother-to-infant HIV transmission.

_____

Identify

1. Identify the four major sexually transmitted diseases. Indicate in tabular form the major clinical manifestations of each disease and method of treatment.

Disease	Manifestation	Treatment
a.		
b.		
c.		
d.		

2. Identify the three major classes of drugs used to treat HIV infection. Indicate briefly how each class acts to interrupt the replication of HIV.

a. _____

b. _____

c. _____

Discussion Questions

1. Describe how communicable diseases are transmitted. _____

_____

_____

_____

2. Describe how communicable diseases are controlled. _____

_____

_____

_____

3. A woman has been infected with the genital herpes virus (type 2). Describe how she can reduce the risk of transmission of the infection to her sexual partner. _____

_____

_____

_____

4. An HIV-infected woman wishes to become pregnant. What steps can she take to minimize the risk of transmitting the infection to her infant when she becomes pregnant? _____

_____

_____

_____

5. A woman had a test performed for a chlamydial infection, and the test was positive. She is concerned about the consequences of the infection. What would you tell her about the consequences of the infection, the risk of infecting her partner, and steps she should take to eradicate the infection? _____

_____

_____

_____

6. Can an HIV infection be treated? Can it be cured? _____

_____

_____

_____

7. What should an HIV-infected person do to slow the progression of the infection and to prevent transmission of the infection to other persons? _____
_____
_____
_____

8. An HIV-positive woman is considering becoming pregnant. What factors should she consider when she makes a decision as to whether to undertake a pregnancy? _____
_____
_____

9. What are the initial and late manifestations of HIV infection? _____
_____
_____
_____

10. What groups are at high risk of HIV infection? _____
_____
_____
_____

11. How can HIV transmission be reduced or prevented? _____
_____
_____
_____

12. Explain whether each of the following descriptors applies to AIDS. Why or why not?

   a. Occurs frequently in homosexual females _____
   _____

   b. Occurs frequently in homosexual males _____
   _____

   c. Often fatal as a result of opportunistic infections _____
   _____

   d. Caused by a virus that damages the immune system _____
   _____

   e. May be contracted by blood transfusions _____
   _____

   f. Usually responds to corticosteroids, which stimulate the immune system _____
   _____

13. Explain whether each of the following descriptors applies to herpes infection of the genital tract. Why or why not?

a. A sexually transmitted disease _____

_____

b. Initial attack confers permanent immunity _____

_____

c. May predispose to cervical carcinoma _____

_____

d. Patient may transmit herpes infection from the oral cavity to the genital tract by autoinoculation _____

_____

e. Infected woman may transmit virus to her infant during childbirth _____

_____

f. Cannot be transmitted to sexual partner unless active lesions present in the genital tract _____

_____

An Introduction to
Human Disease
LEONARD V. CROWLEY, M.D.
PATHOLOGY AND PATHOPHYSIOLOGY CORRELATIONS
Seventh Edition

Chapter 8
Communicable Diseases

© 2007 Jones and Bartlett Publishers

Communicable Diseases and Methods of Transmission

- Endemic
  - *Small* number of cases are *continually present* in the population
- Epidemic
  - Relatively *large* numbers of *people infected*
- Direct transmission
  - Physical contact
  - Droplet spread (coughing, sneezing)
- Indirect transmission
  - Contaminated food or water
  - Insects

© 2007 Jones and Bartlett Publishers

Methods of Control Communicable Diseases

- Disease perpetuates itself by continuous transmission of the infectious agent
- To eradicate or control the disease, the chain of transmission must be broken
1. Immunization
- Used to control or eliminate some communicable diseases by protecting people against transmission
- Also used for persons traveling to a geographic area where a disease is endemic
- Smallpox, polio have been eliminated due to widespread immunization

© 2007 Jones and Bartlett Publishers

Methods of Control

2. <u>Identification, Isolation, and Treatment</u>
- Approach used when immunization is not possible; sometimes disease is difficult to control because infection may not be obvious, thus is untreated and spreads (TB, STDs, etc.)

3. <u>Control of Means of Indirect Transmission</u>
Examples
- Chlorination of water supplies
- Effective sewage treatment facilities
- Standards for handling, manufacture & distribution of commercially prepared foods
- Eradication or control of insects and animals that spread disease

© 2007 Jones and Bartlett Publishers

Methods of Control

- The application of *effective control measures* requires knowing the *cause* of the disease and its method of *transmission*
- For example, during the *bubonic plague* or "black death" of the Middle Ages, it was not known that plague is a *disease carried by rats* and other rodents, *transmitted to people by insects*

© 2007 Jones and Bartlett Publishers

Methods of Control

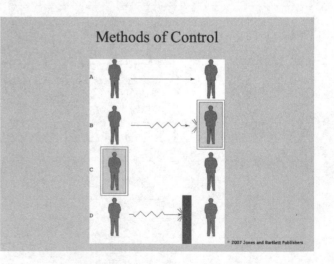

© 2007 Jones and Bartlett Publishers

Sexually Transmitted Diseases

Transmitted through *sexual relations*
The four *major STDs are:*

1. Syphilis (*Treponema pallidum*)
2. Gonorrhea (*Neisseria gonorrhoeae*)
3. Herpes *(Herpesvirus)*
4. Chlamydia (*Chlamydia trachomatis*)

© 2007 Jones and Bartlett Publishers

Sexually Transmitted Diseases: Syphilis

Syphilis = Treponema pallidum infection
Clinical Manifestations
a. Chancre (Primary)
b. Systemic infection with skin rash and enlarged lymph nodes (Secondary)
c. Late destructive lesions in internal organs (Tertiary)

© 2007 Jones and Bartlett Publishers

Sexually Transmitted Diseases: Syphilis

Diagnostic Tests
1. Demonstration of treponemas in chancre
2. Serologic tests (antigen-antibody reactions in a test tube)
Treatment
• Antibiotics
Major Complication
• Damage to cardiovascular and nervous system in tertiary syphilis, which may be fatal

© 2007 Jones and Bartlett Publishers

Sexually Transmitted Diseases: Gonorrhea

Gonorrhea = Neisseria gonorrhoeae infection

Clinical Manifestations

1. Urethritis (inflammation of passage through which urine is discharged from bladder)
2. Cervicitis (inflammation of cervix)
3. Pharyngitis (inflammation of pharynx)
4. Infection of rectal mucosa (proctitis)

Tests for Diagnosis

- Culture of organisms from sites of infection

Treatment

- Antibiotics

© 2007 Jones and Bartlett Publishers

Sexually Transmitted Diseases: Gonorrhea

Major Complications

1. Disseminated blood-stream infection
2. Tubal infection with impaired fertility
3. Spread of infection to prostate and epididymides (structures adjacent to testes, that provides storage, transit and maturation for spermatozoa)

© 2007 Jones and Bartlett Publishers

Sexually Transmitted Diseases: Herpes

Herpes = Herpesvirus infection

Major Clinical Complications

1. Superficial vesicles and ulcers on external genitalia and in genital tract
2. Regional lymph nodes often enlarged, tender

© 2007 Jones and Bartlett Publishers

Sexually Transmitted Diseases:
<u>Herpes</u>

<u>Tests for Diagnosis</u>
1. Demonstration of intranuclear inclusions in infected cells
2. Virus cultures
3. Serologic tests in some cases

<u>Treatment</u>
• Antiviral drug shortens infection but not curative

<u>Major Complication</u>
• Spread from infected mother to infant

© 2007 Jones and Bartlett Publishers

Sexually Transmitted Diseases:
<u>Chlamydia</u>

Chlamydia = *Chlamydia trachomatis* infection

<u>Clinical Manifestations</u>
1. Cervitis
2. Urethritis

<u>Tests for Diagnosis</u>
1. Detection of chlamydial antigens in cervical/urethral secretions
2. Fluorescence microscopy
3. Cultures

© 2007 Jones and Bartlett Publishers

Sexually Transmitted Diseases:
<u>Chlamydia</u>

<u>Treatment</u>
• Antibiotics

<u>Major Complications</u>
1. Tubal infection with impaired fertility
2. Epididymitis

© 2007 Jones and Bartlett Publishers

Notes

_____

_____

_____

_____

_____

_____

_____

_____

_____

_____

_____

_____

_____

_____

_____

_____

_____

_____

_____

_____

_____

_____

_____

_____

_____

_____

_____

_____

_____

_____

_____

_____

_____

_____

_____

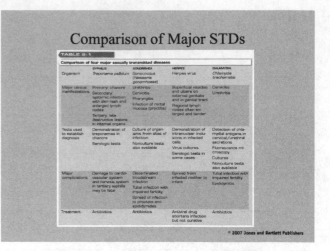

Comparison of Major STDs

© 2007 Jones and Bartlett Publishers

Sexually Transmitted Diseases

In addition to the *four major STDs*, other *common* but *less serious STDs* are

1. Anal and genital warts (condylomas)
2. Vaginitis (caused by *Gardenella*)
3. Triconomal vaginitis (caused by *Trichonomas vaginalis*)
4. Scabies and crabs
5. Some intestinal infections

© 2007 Jones and Bartlett Publishers

Sexually Transmitted Diseases: AIDS

In a class by itself is <u>AIDS</u>

1. In addition to *sexual transmission*, it can also be transmitted by *blood* and *secretions* from infected persons
2. It has high *mortality*
- It is a devastating disease that cripples the body's immune system by attacking and *destroying T lymphocytes*, making the person *susceptible* to unusual *infections* and *malignant tumors*

© 2007 Jones and Bartlett Publishers

Sexually Transmitted Diseases: AIDS

- AIDS is the *end stage* and most serious manifestation caused by a virus called *human immunodeficiency virus* or *HIV*
- HIV is an *RNA virus* that belongs to a class of viruses called *retroviruses*

There are *two viruses* that cause AIDS

1. HIV-1: responsible for AIDS in most parts of the world
2. HIV-2: responsible for AIDS mostly in Africa
3. *First cases* of AIDS were identified in *1981* by CDC (Center for Disease Control) in a small group of homosexual men with an unusual opportunistic lung infection

© 2007 Jones and Bartlett Publishers

Sexually Transmitted Diseases: AIDS

- *HIV* was *identified* in *1983*
- A *blood test* to detect HIV infection became available in *1985*
- The disease *continues to spread* because we do *not know how to eradicate the virus*, although we *can slow the multiplication of the virus* and arrest the progression of the disease that it causes

© 2007 Jones and Bartlett Publishers

Sequence of Events in HIV Infections and Their Significance

TABLE 8-2

Sequence of events in HIV infections and their significance

EVENT	SIGNIFICANCE
HIV invades CD4+ cells and becomes part of cell DNA	Individual is infected for life
Virus proliferates in infected cells and sheds virus particles	Virus present in blood and body fluids
Body forms anti-HIV antibody	Antibody is a marker of infection but is not protective
Progressive destruction of helper T cells	Compromised cell-mediated immunity
Immune defenses collapse	Opportunistic infections Neoplasms

© 2007 Jones and Bartlett Publishers

Distribution of AIDS Cases by Risk Group

TABLE 8-4

Distribution of AIDS cases by risk group

RISK GROUP	PERCENTAGE OF TOTAL AIDS CASES
Homosexual and bisexual men	46
Homosexual and bisexual men who are also intravenous drug users	6
Heterosexual drug abusers	25
Heterosexual contacts of HIV-infected persons	11
Hemophiliacs	1
Blood transfusion recipients	1
Other sources of infection	10

Source: Centers for Disease Control and Prevention. AIDS cases reported through December 2001. HIV/AIDS Surveillance Report. Volume 13, No. 2.

© 2007 Jones and Bartlett Publishers

HIV Target

- HIV like other viruses, requires a *host* cell to *reproduce*
- However, because HIV is a retrovirus, it carries the *genetic material* in ribonucleic acid (*RNA*), rather than in deoxyribonucleic acid (DNA)
- During *replication*, this genetic material in the RNA must be *converted* into *DNA*
- Although it is characterized by gradual destruction of *cell-mediated* (T-cell) immunity, it also affects *humoral immunity* as well as cell mediated immunity because of the central role of the CD4+ (helper) T lymphocyte in immune reactions

© 2007 Jones and Bartlett Publishers

HIV Consequences

- The *resulting immunodeficiency* makes the patient *susceptible* to opportunistic infections, cancers, and other abnormalities that define AIDS

AIDS Opportunistic Infections
- *Pneumocystis carinii* pneumonia
- *Mycobacterium avium-intracellulare*
- *Parasitic* infections
  - Toxoplasmosis
  - Cryptosporidiosis

© 2007 Jones and Bartlett Publishers

HIV Consequences

Malignant Tumors in AIDS Patients
- Kaposi's sarcoma
- Malignant tumors of B lymphocytes
- Cancers of oral cavity and rectum

© 2007 Jones and Bartlett Publishers

Antibody Response to HIV and Signs/Symptoms

Antibody Response to HIV
- *Antibodies* are formed within *one to six months*
- Detection of *antibodies* provide *evidence* of HIV *infection*
- Antibodies do *not* eradicate the virus
- The virus is detectable *only* by laboratory tests

Signs and Symptoms of AIDS
- HIV infection shows itself in many ways
- After a high- risk exposure and inoculation, the infected person usually experiences a *mononucleosis-like syndrome*, which may be attributed to flu or another virus

© 2007 Jones and Bartlett Publishers

Antibody Response to HIV and Signs/Symptoms

- Infected person may remain *asymptomatic* for years
- In this *early stage*, the only sign of HIV infection is laboratory evidence of *sero-conversion*

When symptoms appear, they take many forms
- Persistent *generalized lymphadenopathy* caused by impaired function of CD4+ cells
- *Nonspecific symptoms*, including weight loss, fatigue, night sweats, fevers related to altered function of CD4+ cells
- *Immunodeficiency*
- Infection of *other* CD4+ antigen-bearing cells
- *Neurologic* symptoms resulting from HIV encephalopathy and infection of neuroglial cells

© 2007 Jones and Bartlett Publishers

Early and Late Manifestations of HIV Infection

Early
- Asymptomatic
- Mild febrile illness

Late
- Generalized lymph node enlargement
- Non-specific symptoms
  - Fever, weakness, chronic fatigue, weight loss, thrombocytopenia
- AIDS

© 2007 Jones and Bartlett Publishers

HIV Transmission

- Sexual contact
- Blood and body fluids
- Mother to infant

The HIV virus may enter the body by any of several routes involving the transmission of blood or bodily fluids

1. *Direct inoculation* during intimate sexual contact, especially linked to the mucosal trauma of receptive rectal intercourse
2. *Transfusion* of contaminated blood or blood products (a risk lessened by routine testing of all blood products)

© 2007 Jones and Bartlett Publishers

HIV Transmission

3. *Sharing* of contaminated injection needles
4. *Transplacental or postpartum* transmission from infected mother to fetus (by cervical or blood contact at delivery and in breast milk

Over twenty years of research data suggest that HIV is *not transmitted* by *casual* household or social contacts

© 2007 Jones and Bartlett Publishers

Notes

Treatment of HIV Infections/AIDS

- <u>No cure</u> has yet been found for AIDS
- Primary therapy includes the use of various combinations of *three* different types of *antiretroviral agents* to try to gain the maximum benefit of *inhibiting HIV viral replication* with the *fewest adverse reactions*
- Treatment schedules are revised continually as new drugs are developed and as the advantages and side effects of various drug combinations are recognized

© 2007 Jones and Bartlett Publishers

Treatment of HIV Infections/AIDS

The drugs include:
- Protease inhibitors to block the action of viral protease required for an important phase of viral replication (reducing the number of new virus particles produced)
- Reverse-transcriptase inhibitors to interfere with the copying of viral RNA into DNA by the enzyme reverse transcriptase

Additional treatment may include:
- *Supportive therapy*, including nutritional support, fluid and electrolyte replacement therapy, pain relief, and psychological support

© 2007 Jones and Bartlett Publishers

Treatment of HIV Infections/AIDS

Many drugs are given in combination to target different phases of the virus life cycle.

- Main groups are
1. Non-nucleoside reverse transcriptase inhibitors
2. Nucleosides reverse transcriptase inhibitors (nucleoside analogs)
3. Protease inhibitors
4. Another class of drugs called integrase inhibitors is under development

© 2007 Jones and Bartlett Publishers

Chapter Outline

The chapter outline provides you with an organizational guide to the topics and ideas presented in this chapter of the text.

Causes of Congenital Malformations
Chromosomal Abnormalities
    Sex Chromosome Abnormalities
    Autosomal Abnormalities
Genetically Determined Diseases
    Autosomal Dominant Inheritance
    Autosomal Recessive Inheritance
    Codominant Inheritance
    X-Linked Inheritance
Intrauterine Injury
    Harmful Drugs and Chemicals
    Radiation
    Maternal Infections
Multifactorial Inheritance
Prenatal Diagnosis of Congenital Abnormalities

Study Questions

The following questions are provided as a test for comprehension and as a study guide for use with the text chapters. Additional study material is located at http://humandisease.jbpub.com/, which contains useful tools such as an A&P review, animated flashcards, an interactive online glossary, crossword puzzles, and web links.

Key Terms

Define the following terms:

1. Sex chromosome body _____

2. Chromosome nondisjunction _____

3. Chromosome translocation _____

4. Chromosome deletion _____

5. Trisomy 21 _____

Fill-in-the-Blank

1. _____ is a hereditary blood disease or condition transmitted by codominant inheritance.

2. _____ is a hereditary disease in which transmission follows an autosomal recessive inheritance pattern.

3. _____ is a hereditary disease in which transmission follows an autosomal dominant inheritance pattern.

4. _____ is a hereditary disease in which the mutant gene is transmitted on the X chromosome.

5. The incidence of congenital malformations in aborted embryos and fetuses is approximately _____.

6. Absence of chromosome 21 is called _____.

7. Most cases of Down syndrome result from _____.

True/False

Tell whether each statement is true or false. If false, explain why the statement is incorrect.

1. Some congenital abnormalities (such as congenital absence of the kidneys) may be incompatible with life after delivery. _____
_____

2. Chromosomal abnormalities in the fetus can usually be determined by amniocentesis. _____
_____

3. Cleft palate often results from interaction of genetic and environmental factors. _____
_____

4. German measles acquired by the mother during pregnancy leads to *chromosomal* abnormalities in the fetus.
_____

5. Infants born with Down syndrome usually have an extra X chromosome. _____
_____

6. Patients born with genetically determined defects (such as phenylketonuria) have normal chromosome karyotypes._____

7. Fertilized ova contain 23 chromosomes. _____

_____

8. Spermatozoa usually have more chromosomes than do unfertilized ova. _____

_____

9. Most persons with Turner's syndrome have only a single X chromosome (45,X). _____

_____

10. A pregnant woman with phenylketonuria does not need to adhere to a phenylalanine-restricted diet because the high concentration of phenylalanine in the woman's blood does not harm the fetus. _____

_____

11. An increased concentration of alpha fetoprotein in maternal blood or amnionic fluid suggests that the fetus has Down's syndrome. _____

_____

12. Most infants with Down syndrome are born to mothers who are carriers of chromosome 21, which is attached to another chromosome (translocation carrier). _____

_____

13. A neural tube defect (anencephaly or spina bifida) usually can be identified in an affected fetus by means of an ultrasound examination performed at about 16 weeks, gestation. _____

_____

Identify

1. Identify the four main causes of congenital abnormalities.

   a. _____

   b. _____

   c. _____

   d. _____

2. Identify three maternal infections that may lead to congenital abnormalities in the fetus.

   a. _____

   b. _____

   c. _____

Matching

Match the chromosomal abnormality in the right column with the clinical condition in the left column.

1. ____ Turner's syndrome   A. 47,XXX

2. ____ Klinefelter's syndrome   B. 45,X

3. ____ Triple X syndrome   C. Trisomy of chromosome 21

4. ____ Down syndrome   D. 47,XXY

Discussion Questions

1. What is the difference between mitosis and meiosis? _____
_____
_____
_____

2. What is the difference between a sex chromosome and an autosome? _____
_____
_____
_____

3. What is a karyotype? How is it determined? _____
_____
_____
_____

4. What is the incidence of congenital abnormalities? _____
_____
_____
_____

5. What is the significance of a reciprocal translocation of chromosome fragments between two nonhomologous chromosomes? (*Hint:* see Case 9-1.) _____
_____
_____
_____

6. What is Down syndrome? Under what conditions may this syndrome occur? _____
_____
_____

7. Describe the role of amniocentesis or chorionic villus sampling in the prenatal diagnosis of Down syndrome.

_____

_____

_____

8. Describe the effect of thalidomide taken by the mother on the development of the fetus. Is this drug still available?

_____

_____

_____

9. Describe how drugs are classified on the basis of possible risk to the fetus when taken by the pregnant woman.

_____

_____

_____

10. What does the term "multifactorial inheritance" mean? Give examples of diseases or conditions transmitted in this way. _____

_____

_____

_____

11. Describe the role of amniocentesis in prenatal detection of fetal abnormalities. Indicate what type of congenital abnormalities can be detected by this method, and indicate in which group of patients the method is most widely used. _____

_____

_____

_____

12. What methods can provide information about the number of X chromosomes possessed by an individual? _____

_____

_____

_____

13. What syndromes and conditions result from an abnormal number of sex chromosomes? _____

_____

_____

_____

14. Explain whether each of the following conditions or situations affecting the mother may lead to congenital malformations in the developing fetus.

a. Heavy cigarette smoking _____

_____

b. Heavy alcohol consumption _____

_____

c. Ingestion of a tetracycline antibiotic _____

_____

d. Penicillin tablets (ampicillin) given to a mother to treat a urinary tract infection _____

_____

e. Dilantin taken by the mother to prevent epileptic seizures _____

_____

f. Excessive use of chewing gum _____

_____

g. Maternal infection by virus of German measles _____

_____

h. Maternal *Toxoplasma* infection _____

_____

i. Excessive consumption of egg salad sandwiches _____

_____

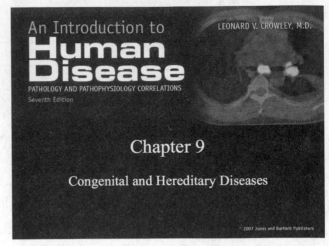

An Introduction to
Human Disease

PATHOLOGY AND PATHOPHYSIOLOGY CORRELATIONS

Seventh Edition

LEONARD V. CROWLEY, M.D.

Chapter 9

Congenital and Hereditary Diseases

© 2007 Jones and Bartlett Publishers

Hereditary and Congenital Malformations

- There are many congenital and hereditary diseases
- A *congenital* disease is abnormality *present at birth*, even though it may not be detected until some time after birth
- A *hereditary* or *genetic* disease may be defined as one resulting from a *chromosome abnormality* or a *defective gene*

© 2007 Jones and Bartlett Publishers

<u>Review:</u> Genetics, Chromosomes, Genes, Cell Division

- Genetics: the study of <u>heredity</u>, the passing of physical, biochemical and physiologic traits from biological parents to their children
- In this transmission, *disorders* can be transmitted by gene *mutations* that can result in *disability or death*
- Genetic information is carried in *genes*, which are strung together on the strands of the deoxyribonucleic acid (*DNA*) double helix structure to form *chromosomes*
- Every normal human cell (*except* reproductive cells) has *46 chromosomes*

© 2007 Jones and Bartlett Publishers

Notes

_____

_____

_____

_____

_____

_____

_____

_____

_____

_____

_____

_____

_____

_____

_____

_____

_____

_____

_____

_____

_____

_____

_____

_____

_____

_____

_____

_____

_____

_____

_____

_____

_____

_____

_____

_____

_____

Review Genetics Chromosomes, Genes, Cell Division

- There are two *sex chromosomes* (a *pair* of *X's* in *females* and an *X and a Y in males*)
- A representation of a person's *individual set* of *chromosomes* is called the person's *karyotype*
- The *activities of cells* are controlled by the *chromosomes* present in the nucleus
- In *somatic* cells (cells *other* than those that give rise to eggs and sperm), *chromosomes* exist in *pairs*
- One member of each pair is derived from the *male* parent and one from the *female* parent

© 2007 Jones and Bartlett Publishers

Review: Genetics, Chromosomes, Genes, Cell Division

- There are twenty-two *paired* chromosomes called *autosomes*
- *Except* for the sex chromosomes, both members of the pair are *similar* in size, shape, and appearance, called homologous chromosomes
- In human beings, the normal chromosome component is *twenty-two pairs* of *autosomes* and *one pair* of *sex chromosomes*
- Chromosomes are composed of double coils of DNA
- Genes are segments of the DNA chains
- The sum total of all the genes contained in a cell's chromosomes is called its *genome* and is the *same* in all cells

© 2007 Jones and Bartlett Publishers

Review: Genetics, Chromosomes, Genes, Cell Division

- *Not* all genes are expressed (*active*) in all cells, and *not* all genes are *active all the time*
- *Mitosis* is the cell division of *somatic* cells
- Each of the *two new cells* called *daughter* cells, receives the *same chromosomes* as the precursor cell called *parent* cell
- *Meiosis* is a specialized type of cell division that occurs during the development of *egg and sperm*
- The number of chromosomes is *reduced* so that the daughter cells receive only *half* the chromosomes possessed by the parent cell

© 2007 Jones and Bartlett Publishers

Review: Genetics, Chromosomes, Genes, Cell Division

- *DNA ultimately controls* the formation of essential substances throughout the life of every cell in the body
- It does this through the *genetic code*, the precise sequence of AT and CG pairs on the DNA molecule

© 2007 Jones and Bartlett Publishers

Review: Genetics, Chromosomes, Genes, Cell Division

- *Genes* not only control hereditary traits, but also *cell reproduction* and the *daily functions* of all cells
- Genes control cell function by controlling the *structures* and *chemicals* that are made within the cell
- Genes control the formation of *RNA*, which in turn controls the formation of specific proteins, most of which are enzymes that assist chemical reactions in the cells

© 2007 Jones and Bartlett Publishers

Genetics
Trait Predominance

- *Each parent* contributes *one set* of *chromosomes* (and therefore one set of genes) so that every child has *two genes* for every *locus* (location on the chromosome) on the autosomal chromosomes
- Some characteristics, or traits, of the child are determined by *one gene* that may have *many variants*, such as is the case with *eye color*

© 2007 Jones and Bartlett Publishers

Genetics
Trait Predominance

- Others called *polygenic traits*, require the *interaction* of one or more genes
- In addition, *environmental factors* may affect how a gene or genes are expressed
- *Variations* in a *particular gene*, such as brown, blue, or green eye color, are called *alleles*
- A person who has *identical alleles* on each chromosome is *homozygous* for that gene
- If the *alleles* are *different*, the person is said to be *heterozygous*

© 2007 Jones and Bartlett Publishers

Genetics
Trait Predominance

- Children will *express* a *dominant allele* when *one or both chromosomes* in a pair carry it
- A *recessive allele* won't be expressed *unless both chromosomes* carry the *recessive alleles*
- For example, a child may *receive* a gene for *brown* eyes from *one parent* and a gene for *blue* eyes from the *other* parent
- The gene for *brown eyes* is *dominant* and the gene for *blue eyes* is *recessive*
- Because the *dominant* gene is more likely to be *expressed*, the child is more likely to have brown eyes

© 2007 Jones and Bartlett Publishers

Trait Predominance
Autosomal Inheritance

Autosomal Inheritance

- For unknown reasons, on autosomal chromosomes, one allele may be *more influential* than the other in determining a specific trait
- The more powerful or *dominant gene* is more likely to be *expressed* than the recessive gene

© 2007 Jones and Bartlett Publishers

Trait Predominance
Sex-linked Inheritance

Sex-linked Inheritance

- The X and Y chromosomes aren't literally a pair because the *X chromosome* is *much larger* than the *Y*
- The *male* has *less functioning genetic material* than the female because one X chromosome is inactivated (see Lyon Hypothesis), which means he has *only one copy of most genes on the X chromosome*
- Inheritance of those genes is called *X-linked*
- A *man* will transmit *one copy* of *each X-linked* gene to his *daughters* and *none* to his *sons*
- A *woman* will transmit *one copy to each daughter* or *son*

© 2007 Jones and Bartlett Publishers

Trait Predominance
Multifactorial Inheritance

Multifactorial Inheritance

- *Environmental* factors can affect the *expression* of some genes
- *Height* is a classic *example*, where although it will be in *range* between the height of the two parents, environmental factors also influence development
- *Such factors* include *nutritional patterns* and *health care*
- The better *nourished, healthier* children of two *short parents* may be *taller* than either

© 2007 Jones and Bartlett Publishers

Genetically Determined
Diseases

- Genetically determined diseases are the result of abnormalities of *individual genes* on the chromosomes
- The *chromosomes* themselves *appear normal*
- Some defects arise *spontaneously*, whereas others may be caused by *environmental teratogens* (agent or influence that causes physical defects in the developing embryo)
- A *permanent change* in genetic material is a <u>mutation</u>, which may occur spontaneously or after exposure of a *cell* to radiation, certain chemicals, or viruses

© 2007 Jones and Bartlett Publishers

Factors in Congenital Malformations

- A *genetic* or *hereditary* disorder or disease caused by *abnormalities* in an individual's genetic material (*genome*)
- A *congenital* disease or malformation is any abnormality present at birth
- There are four factors in congenital malformation
1. Chromosomal abnormalities
2. Abnormalities of individual genes
3. Intrauterine injury to embryo or fetus
4. Environmental factors

© 2007 Jones and Bartlett Publishers

Causes of Congenital Malformations

- *2-3%* of all newborn infants have *congenital* defects

- An *additional 2-3%* defects are *not* recognized at *birth, showing* developmental defects as infants grow *older*

- *25-50%* of *spontaneous aborted* embryos and fetuses and stillborn infants have *major malformations*

© 2007 Jones and Bartlett Publishers

Chromosomal Abnormalities

- Failure of homologous chromosomes in germ cells to separate (*nondisjunction*), in either the *first* or *second meiotic* division
- Nondisjunction may involve either *sex chromosomes or autosomes*
- It causes *abnormalities* in the distribution of chromosomes between germ cells
- One of the two germ cells derived from the abnormal chromosome division has an *extra chromosome*, and the other *lacks* a chromosome

© 2007 Jones and Bartlett Publishers

Notes

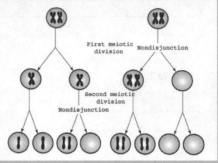

Chromosomal Abnormalities

© 2007 Jones and Bartlett Publishers

Chromosomal Abnormalities

Monosomy, Trisomy, Deletions, Translocations

- Monosomy: *absence* of a chromosome in a cell
- Trisomy: the presence of an *extra* chromosome in a cell
- Deletions: when a chromosome *breaks* during meiosis and the *broken piece* is *lost*
- Translocations: when a *misplaced* chromosome or part of it, *attaches* to *another* chromosome

© 2007 Jones and Bartlett Publishers

Sex Chromosome Abnormalities

- *Variations* from the *normal number* of *sex chromosomes* are often associated with some *reduction* of *intelligence*
- The *Y chromosome* directs *masculine* sexual differentiation, its presence associated with the *male body* configuration, *regardless* of the number of X chromosomes present
- An *extra Y* does *not* make a *big difference* because it mainly carries genes concerned with male sexual differentiation
- *However*, if the *Y* chromosome is *absent*, the *body* configuration is *female*

© 2007 Jones and Bartlett Publishers

Sex Chromosome Abnormalities

- The effect of *extra X chromosomes* has *little effect* on the *female* because the *extra ones* are *inactivated* and appear as extra sex chromatin bodies attached to the nuclear membrane of the cell
- The effect of *extra X chromosomes* in the *male* adversely affects *male development*

Several <u>syndromes</u> result from abnormalities in the number or structure of the *sex chromosomes*

The two most common ones in the female

1. Turner's Syndrome: absence of one X chromosome
2. Triple X Syndrome: extra X chromosome

© 2007 Jones and Bartlett Publishers

Sex Chromosome Abnormalities

The two most common ones in the *male*

- Klinefelter's Syndrome: extra X chromosomes
- XYY Syndrome: extra Y chromosome

The principal characteristics of these syndromes are summarized in Table 9-1

- Fragile X Syndrome: not related to an excess or a deficiency of sex chromosomes
- It is associated with a *characteristic abnormality* of the *X chromosome*
- It is only *second to Down Syndrome* as a major cause of *mental deficiency*

© 2007 Jones and Bartlett Publishers

Sex Chromosome Abnormalities

TABLE 9-1

Syndromes resulting from an abnormal complement of sex chromosomes

	USUAL GENOTYPE	APPROXIMATE INCIDENCE	UNUSUAL NUMBER OF BARR BODIES	UNUSUAL NUMBER OF Y FLUORESCENT BODIES	FERTILITY
Turner's syndrome	45,X	1:2500 females	0	0	Sterile
Triple X syndrome	47,XXX	1:850 males	2	0	Usually not impaired
Klinefelter's syndrome	47,XXY	1:750 males	1	1	Usually sterile
XYY syndrome	47,XYY	1:850 males	0	2	Usually not impaired

© 2007 Jones and Bartlett Publishers

Autosomal Abnormalities

- *Absence* of an *autosome* results in the *loss* of so *many genes* that *development* is generally *not possible* and the *embryo* is *aborted*
- *Deletion* of a *small part* of an *autosome* may be *compatible* with *development but* it usually results in *multiple severe congenital abnormalities*
- Most common chromosomal abnormality (autosomal trisomy) is *Down Syndrome*

© 2007 Jones and Bartlett Publishers

Down Syndrome

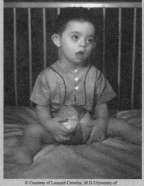

© Courtesy of Leonard Crowley, M.D./University of Minnesota Medical School

© 2007 Jones and Bartlett Publishers

Autosomal Abnormalities

- Trisomy of the small chromosome 21; many fetuses are aborted early in pregnancy (70%)
- Liveborn trisomy 21 fetuses have Down Syndrome
- Trisomy of a chromosome 13 or chromosome 18
- Associated with severe congenital malformations
- Both 13 and 18 trisomies are usually fatal in the neonatal period or in early infancy

© 2007 Jones and Bartlett Publishers

Transmission of Genetically Determined Diseases

- Autosomal dominant inheritance
- Autosomal recessive inheritance
- Codominant inheritance
- X-linked inheritance
- *Most* hereditary diseases are transmitted on *autosomes*
- *Few* are carried on *sex chromosomes*

© 2007 Jones and Bartlett Publishers

TABLE 9-2

Mode of inheritance, pathogenesis, and major manifestations of some common genetic diseases

ABNORMALITY	MODE OF INHERITANCE	DEFECT	MANIFESTATIONS
Phenylketonuria	Recessive	Phenylalanine hydroxylase deficiency	Mental retardation
Tay-Sachs disease	Recessive	Hexosaminidase A deficiency	Mental retardation, motor weakness, blindness
Cystic fibrosis of pancreas	Recessive	Dysfunction of mucous and sweat glands; thick mucus obstructs bronchioles, pancreatic ducts, and bile ducts	Chronic broncho-pulmonary infections as a result of bronchial obstruction by mucus; pancreatic and liver dysfunction as a result of thick mucous obstruction of excretory ducts
Achondroplasia	Dominant	Disordered bone growth at ends of long bones (epiphyses)	Dwarfism with disproportionately short limbs
Congenital polycystic kidney disease (one type)	Dominant	Maldevelopment of nephrons and collecting tubules causes formation of multiple cysts in kidneys	Renal failure
Multiple neurofibromatosis	Dominant	Multiple tumors arise from peripheral nerves	Disfigurement and deformities caused by tumors; predisposition to malignant change in tumors
Sickle cell trait	Codominant	Red cells contain mixture of normal (A) and sickle (S) hemoglobin	None
Sickle cell anemia	Codominant	Red cells contain no normal hemoglobin	Severe anemia and obstruction of blood flow to organs by masses of sickled red cells
Hemophilia	X-linked recessive	Deficiency of protein required for normal coagulation of blood	Uncontrolled bleeding into joints and internal organs after minor injuries

© 2007 Jones and Bartlett Publishers

Intrauterine Injury

Causes of Injury
- Harmful drugs and chemicals (refer Table 9-3)
- Radiation
- Maternal infections (refer Figure 9-11)
  - Rubella, cytomegalovirus, *toxoplasma gondii*
  - The *embryonic period* from the *third* to the *eighth week* after conception, when the organ systems are forming, is the time when the *embryo* is most *vulnerable* to *injury*

© 2007 Jones and Bartlett Publishers

Notes

Categories of Drugs Harmful to Fetus

TABLE 9-3

Five categories of all drugs used in the United States rated by the FDA according to degree of possible risk to the fetus

CATEGORY	INTERPRETATION
A	No risk to fetus demonstrated in well-controlled studies in humans.
B	No evidence of risk to fetus. Either animal studies show risk but human studies do not or there are no adequate human studies but animal studies do not indicate risk.
C	Risk to fetus cannot be ruled out. No human studies available to assess risk. Animal studies either are not available or indicate possible risk.
D	Positive evidence of risk to fetus; however, drug is needed to treat patients, and no safer alternative drug is available. Potential benefit to patients outweighs risk to fetus.
X	Absolutely contraindicated in pregnancy. Severe risk to fetus greatly outweighs any possible benefit to patients.

© 2007 Jones and Bartlett Publishers

Newborn Disease via Maternal Infection

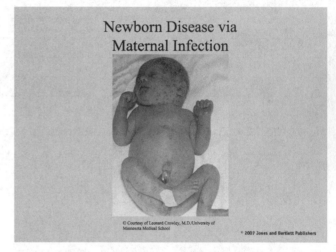

© Courtesy of Leonard Crowley, M.D./University of Minnesota Medical School

© 2007 Jones and Bartlett Publishers

Multifactorial Inheritance

- *The combined effect of multiple genes interacting with environmental agents*
- Congenital abnormalities
  - Cleft lip, cleft palate, cardiac malformations, clubfoot, dislocation of hip, anencephaly, spina bifida

© 2007 Jones and Bartlett Publishers

Prenatal Diagnosis of Congenital Abnormalities

- Examination of fetal cells: determination of biochemical abnormalities in fetal cells
- Examination of amnionic fluid: products secreted into fluid by fetus that may indicate fetal abnormality
- Ultrasound examination: detection of major structural abnormalities
- Fetal DNA analysis: determination of biochemical abnormalities by analysis of DNA of fetal cells

© 2007 Jones and Bartlett Publishers

Amniocentesis

- *Alpha fetoprotein*: high concentration in amniotic fluid is suggestive of a *neural tube defect*
- Amniotic fluid for study is obtained by a technique called *transabdominal amniocentesis* (refer Figure 9-15)
- It is usually performed between the *fourteenth* and *eighteen week of pregnancy*
- The main use is for prenatal detection of a chromosomal abnormality in *women over age of 35 because of the higher incidence of Down Syndrome in infants born to older women* (refer to Table 9-4)

© 2007 Jones and Bartlett Publishers

Amniocentesis

© 2007 Jones and Bartlett Publishers

Notes

_____

_____

_____

_____

_____

_____

_____

_____

_____

_____

_____

Indications for Amniocentesis

TABLE 9-4

Main indications for amniocentesis or chorionic villus sampling

1. Maternal age over 35 years
2. Previous infant born with Down syndrome or other chromosomal abnormality
3. Known translocation chromosome carrier, or other chromosome abnormality in either parent
4. Risk of fetal genetic disease that can be detected by fetal cell biochemical or DNA analysis
5. Maternal blood tests (triple screen) indicating increased risk of fetal chromosome abnormality

© 2007 Jones and Bartlett Publishers

Chapter Outline

The chapter outline provides you with an organizational guide to the topics and ideas presented in this chapter of the text.

Study Questions

The following questions are provided as a test for comprehension and as a study guide for use with the text chapters. Additional study material is located at http://humandisease.jbpub.com/, which contains useful tools such as an A&P review, animated flashcards, an interactive online glossary, crossword puzzles, and web links.

Key Terms

Define the following terms:

1. Teratoma _____

2. Lymphoma _____

3. Precancerous condition _____

4. In situ carcinoma _____

5. Adjuvant chemotherapy _____

6. Carcinoma _____

7. Nevus _____

8. Melanoma _____

9. Multiple myeloma _____

10. Leukemia _____

True/False

Tell whether each statement is true or false. If false, explain why the statement is incorrect.

1. Some neoplasms in humans may be caused by viruses. _____

_____

2. A mutation is a cancer-causing chemical. _____

_____

3. A Pap smear is a screening test used to detect cervical cancer. _____

_____

4. A tumor-associated antigen is a carbohydrate–protein complex secreted by tumor cells that can be used to monitor tumor growth. _____

_____

5. A hormone-dependent tumor is one that produces sex hormones. _____

_____

6. Anticancer drugs injure normal cells as well as cancer cells. _____

_____

7. Adjuvant chemotherapy is used in an attempt to prevent late recurrences of cancer by destroying small foci of metastatic carcinoma before they grow to large size. _____

_____

8. Some types of acute leukemia can be cured by chemotherapy. _____

_____

9. Myeloma is often associated with small areas of bone destruction. _____

_____

10. Some chemotherapy drugs impede tumor cell growth by blocking growth factor receptors on the tumor cells so that the tumor cells are unable to respond to the growth factors that stimulate cells to divide. _____

_____

Identify

1. Give an example for each of the following:

   a. In situ carcinoma _____

   b. Teratoma _____

   c. Precancerous condition _____

2. In this list of common prefixes used to name tumors, write the meaning of the prefix after the name:

   a. Adeno _____

   b. Angio _____

   c. Chondro _____

   d. Fibro _____

   e. Lipo _____

   f. Myo _____

   g. Neuro _____

   h. Osteo _____

   i. Lymphangio _____

   j. Hemangio _____

3. Three large groups of genes play important roles in regulating cell functions, and dysfunctions of these genes may lead to tumors. Identify these three groups of genes.

   a. _____

   b. _____

   c. _____

4. Identify four methods used to treat tumors.

   a. _____

   b. _____

   c. _____

   d. _____

5. How would you name the following neoplasms?

a. A benign tumor of fibrous connective tissue _____

b. A malignant tumor of fat cells _____

c. A benign tumor of pigment-forming cells in the skin _____

d. A neoplasm of plasma cells _____

e. A malignant tumor of mature lymphocytes _____

f. A malignant tumor of blood vessels _____

g. A malignant tumor of lymph vessels _____

h. A tumor of lymph nodes containing Reed-Sternberg cells intermixed with lymphocytes, plasma cells, and eosinophils _____

i. A noninvasive malignant tumor of cervical squamous epithelium _____
_____

j. A malignant tumor of lymphocytes _____

k. A leukemia in which the circulating cells are immature lymphocytes _____
_____

l. A benign tumor of the ovary composed of many different types of mature tissues _____
_____

m. A benign tumor of cartilage _____

n. A benign pedunculated tumor arising from the epithelium of the colon _____
_____

o. A malignant noninvasive tumor arising from the squamous epithelium of the cervix _____
_____

Discussion Questions

1. What are the major differences in growth rate, circumscription, cell differentiation, and spread between benign and malignant tumors? Give your comparison in tabular form.

	Benign Tumor	Malignant Tumor
Growth rate		
Cell differentiation		
Growth characteristics		
Spread (metastasis)		

2. Describe how tumors are named. _____
_____
_____
_____

3. What is a Pap smear? What is its application to the early diagnosis of tumors? What is the significance of a Pap smear containing atypical cells? _____

_____

_____

_____

4. What are tumor suppressor genes? What happens if one member of the pair of tumor suppressor genes fails to function normally? _____

_____

_____

_____

5. What is the Philadelphia chromosome? With what conditions is it associated? _____

_____

_____

_____

6. Describe the role of heredity in tumors. _____

_____

_____

_____

7. The eye tumor retinoblastoma is caused by mutations of both members of the paired RB genes within a single retinal cell. Explain the difference between a hereditary retinoblastoma and a sporadic retinoblastoma. (*Hint:* see Fig. 10-22.) _____

_____

_____

_____

8. Describe a simple classification of leukemia based on cell type and maturity of the leukemic cells. How is leukemia classified? _____

_____

_____

_____

9. How does our immune system protect us from cancer? _____

_____

_____

_____

10. What is the significance of an abnormal cervical Pap smear in a 32-year-old woman? What further diagnostic or therapeutic measures would you recommend? _____

_____

_____

_____

11. What clinical, hematologic, and radiologic abnormalities often occur in persons with multiple myeloma? What abnormal laboratory test results often occur? _____

_____

_____

_____

12. A patient has a blood disease characterized by a greatly increased white blood cell count consisting of mature lymphocytes, with anemia and thrombocytopenia. What is the most likely diagnosis? _____

_____

_____

_____

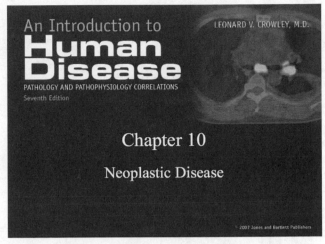

Neoplasm/Tumor Classification

- A neoplasm (*new growth*) is an *overgrowth* of cells that serves *no* useful purpose
- Neoplasms appear *not* to be subject to the *control mechanisms* that normally regulate cell growth and differentiation
- *Neoplasm* and *Tumor* are *terms* that may be used *interchangeably*

Classification (refer Table 10-1 for comparison)
- Benign
- Malignant (cancer)
  - Carcinoma
  - Sarcoma
  - Leukemia

© 2007 Jones and Bartlett Publishers

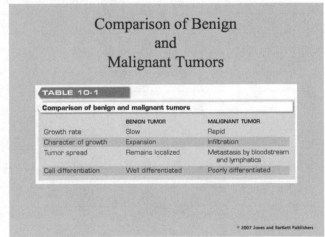

Comparison of Benign and Malignant Tumors

TABLE 10-1

Comparison of benign and malignant tumors

	BENIGN TUMOR	MALIGNANT TUMOR
Growth rate	Slow	Rapid
Character of growth	Expansion	Infiltration
Tumor spread	Remains localized	Metastasis by bloodstream and lymphatics
Cell differentiation	Well differentiated	Poorly differentiated

© 2007 Jones and Bartlett Publishers

Notes

Neoplasm Classification

- As they *grow*, tumor cells acquire properties that allow them to *flourish* at the *expense* of surrounding *normal* cells
- They *secrete enzymes* that *break down* normal cell and tissue *barriers*, allowing them to *infiltrate* into adjacent tissues, *invade* lymphatic channels and blood vessels, and eventually *spread* throughout the body
- Moreover, the proliferating tumor cells do *not "wear out"* and die *after* a specific number of cell *divisions, as normal cells do*
- They become "*immortal*" and can *proliferate indefinitely*

© 2007 Jones and Bartlett Publishers

Neoplasms: Lymphomas Classifications

Lymphomas: neoplasms of *lymphoid* tissue
- With extremely *rare exceptions*, these tumors are *usually malignant*
- Therefore, the *term lymphoma without classification* refers to a malignant, *not* a *benign* tumor
- Often to *avoid confusion*, the *term malignant lymphoma* rather than simply lymphoma, is *used*

There are two major classifications
1. Hodgkin's Lymphoma (Hodgkin's disease)
2. Non-Hodgkin's Lymphoma

© 2007 Jones and Bartlett Publishers

Neoplasms: Lymphomas

- *Another classification* is based on whether they *infiltrate* the *lymph nodes diffusely*
- Still *another description* is used based on its *prognosis*, such as *low, intermediate,* or *high grade*
- All these *three classifications* are *used* to describe lymphomas
- *Low-grade* lymphoma: patients have a *favorable* prognosis
- *Intermediate-grade* lymphoma: patients do *not do nearly as well*
- *High-grade* lymphoma: patients do *poorly*

© 2007 Jones and Bartlett Publishers

Neoplasms: Lymphomas

- A more *recent classification* scheme divides lymphomas into *four* large groups based on the *type of cells* (T cells, B cells, NK cells, histiocytes), *giving rise* to the tumor, and the *maturity* of the cells, with *many subgroups* within each of the four major groups
- About *75%* percent of lymphomas arise from *B lymphocytes*
- Most of the *remainder* originate from *T lymphocytes*

© 2007 Jones and Bartlett Publishers

Lymphomas: Hodgkin's and Non-Hodgkin's

Lymphomas are divided in two major groups
1. Hodgkin's
2. Non-Hodgkin's

Hodgkin's disease: variable histologic appearance consisting of large cells called *Reed-Sternberg cells* intermixed with lymphocytes, plasma cells, eosinophils, and fibrous tissues

- *Reed Sternberg cell:* large cell with abundant cytoplasm containing *two nuclei* appearing as *mirror images.* Some may contain only a single nucleus. Each nucleus contains a *large nucleolus* surrounded by a *clear halo.*

© 2007 Jones and Bartlett Publishers

Neoplasms: Lymphomas

- *Four* different *histologic types* of *Hodgkin's* disease are recognized, and they *differ* somewhat in their *clinical behavior* and *prognosis*

Non-Hodgkin's lymphomas: *all other lymphomas* are generally grouped together under this category

- Are quite *variable* in *appearance* and *behavior*
- *One classification* system is based on the *size, shape,* and *growth pattern* of the malignant cells
- *Another classification* is based on the *shape* of their *nuclei* and *nuclear membranes*

© 2007 Jones and Bartlett Publishers

Notes

Terminology of Tumors

- *Tumors* are *named* and *classified* according to the *cells* and *tissues* from which they *originate*
- Tumor *nomenclature* is *not completely uniform*, but certain *generalizations* are possible

Exceptions are encountered in the *naming* of

- Lymphoid tumors
- Skin tumors arising from pigment-producing cells within the epidermis
- Certain tumors of mixed cellular components
- Certain types of tumors composed of primitive cells seen in children

© 2007 Jones and Bartlett Publishers

Common Prefixes in Tumor Names

TABLE 10-2

Common prefixes used to name tumors

PREFIX	MEANING
Adeno-	Gland
Angio-	Vessels (type not specified)
Chondro-	Cartilage
Fibro-	Fibrous tissue
Hemangio-	Blood vessels
Lymphangio-	Lymph vessels
Lipo-	Fat
Myo-	Muscle
Neuro-	Nerve
Osteo-	Bone

© 2007 Jones and Bartlett Publishers

Principles of Naming Tumors

TABLE 10-3

General principles of naming tumors

GENERAL TERM	MEANING
Polyp, papilloma	Any benign tumor projecting from surface epithelium.
___ + oma (suffix)	A benign tumor. The prefix designates primary tissue of origin.
Carcinoma	Malignant tumor arising from surface, glandular, or parenchymal epithelium (but not endothelium or mesothelium).
Sarcoma	Malignant tumor of any primary tissue other than surface, glandular, and parenchymal epithelium.
Leukemia	Neoplasm of blood cells.

© 2007 Jones and Bartlett Publishers

Notes

Comparison of Benign and Malignant Tumors

TABLE 10-1

Comparison of benign and malignant tumors

	BENIGN TUMOR	MALIGNANT TUMOR
Growth rate	Slow	Rapid
Character of growth	Expansion	Infiltration
Tumor spread	Remains localized	Metastasis by bloodstream and lymphatics
Cell differentiation	Well differentiated	Poorly differentiated

© 2007 Jones and Bartlett Publishers

Skin Tumors

Most skin tumors arise from
- Either the keratin-forming cells or the pigment-producing cells of the epidermis
- Keratinocytes: the *keratin*-forming cells
- Basal cells: *deepest* layer of *keratinocytes* adjacent to the dermis
- Squamous cells: *upper* layer of cells that arise from the *proliferation* of *basal cells*
- Melanocytes: (interspersed among the keratinocytes) skin cells that normally produce *pigment* and are responsible for normal skin color, producing the *dark-brown pigment* called *melanin*

© 2007 Jones and Bartlett Publishers

Skin Tumors

- Melanocytes
  - Benign – <u>nevus</u> ("birthmark" in Latin)
  - Malignant – <u>melanoma</u>
- Keratinocytes
  - Benign – <u>keratoses</u>
  - Malignant – <u>basal cell carcinoma, squamous cell carcinoma</u>

  Melanocytes
  - Nevus: common benign pigmented skin lesion derived from melanin-producing cells
  - Melanoma: malignant tumor of melanocytes

© 2007 Jones and Bartlett Publishers

Notes

_____
_____
_____
_____
_____
_____
_____
_____
_____
_____
_____
_____
_____
_____
_____
_____
_____
_____
_____
_____
_____
_____
_____
_____
_____
_____
_____
_____
_____
_____
_____

Malignant Skin Tumors

Basal Cell Carcinoma

- Composed of clusters of *infiltrating cells* that *resemble* the *normal basal cells* of the epidermis
- It is a rather *indolent, slowly* growing tumor that can be *locally destructive* but *rarely metastasizes*

Squamous Cell Carcinoma

- Composed of *abnormal infiltrating squamous* cells
- It is a *more aggressive* tumor that *sometimes metastasizes*
- Both types generally can be *cured* by *surgical excision*, carrying a very *good prognosis*

© 2007 Jones and Bartlett Publishers

Malignant Skin Tumors and Teratomas

- Excessive sunlight exposure predisposes one to *all types of skin cancer*, including the potentially lethal *melanoma*, and the development of some types of *keratoses*

Teratoma

- Tumor derived from cells that have *potential* of *differentiating* into many different types of tissues, such as bone, muscle, glands, epithelium, brain tissue, hair
- Tumor of *mixed* components, *poorly organized*
- *Frequently* occur in *reproductive tract*, but may develop in *other areas*
- Must specify as *benign* or *malignant* based on maturity of cells

© 2007 Jones and Bartlett Publishers

Primitive Cell Tumors

- Arise from persistent groups of primitive cells
- They may arise in *children*
- Brain
- Retina (eye)
- Adrenal gland
- Kidney
- Liver
- Genital tract
- Are named from the *site* of origin with the *suffix -blastoma* added
- *Example*: tissue of origin (retina) + blastoma *retinoblastoma*

© 2007 Jones and Bartlett Publishers

Tumors: Blood Supply and Necrosis

- *Tumors derive* their blood supply from the *tissues* they *invade*
- *Malignant* tumors frequently *induce new blood vessels* to proliferate in the adjacent normal tissues to supply the demands of the growing tumor
- However, a *malignant* tumor may *outgrow its blood supply*, in which case the parts of the tumor with the poorest blood supply, undergo *necrosis*
- Depending on the *location* of the *tumor*, the *blood supply* will be *rich or poor*

© 2007 Jones and Bartlett Publishers

Tumors: Blood Supply and Necrosis

- If tumor is *growing within* the *lung,* surrounded by normal tissue, the *blood supply* is *best* at the periphery of the tumor and *poorest* in its *center*
- If the tumor is *growing outward* from an *epithelial surface* such as the *colon,* the *best* blood supply is at its *base* and the *poorest* at its *surface*
- Often, *small blood vessels* are exposed in the *ulcerated base* of a *tumor*
- *Blood* may *ooze* continuously from the vessels, eventually leading to *anemia* from chronic blood loss
- *Sometimes,* the ulcerated tumor may be the source of a *severe hemorrhage*

© 2007 Jones and Bartlett Publishers

Noninfiltrating (in Situ) Carcinoma

- Arise from the surface epithelium and remain localized within the epithelium for many *years*
- Can occur in many locations of the body
- Cervix
- Breast
- Urinary tract
- Colon
- Skin

© 2007 Jones and Bartlett Publishers

_____
_____
_____
_____
_____
_____
_____
_____
_____
_____
_____
_____
_____
_____
_____
_____
_____
_____
_____
_____
_____
_____
_____
_____
_____
_____
_____
_____
_____
_____
_____
_____
_____
_____

Precancerous Condition

- *A nonmalignant condition with a tendency to become malignant*
  - Actinic keratoses: small, crusted, scaly patches that develop on the *sun-exposed* skin, which if untreated *may develop* into *cancer*
  - Lentigo maligna: *frecklelike* proliferation of *melanin*-producing cells in the skin that may also develop on the *sun-exposed* skin, that may transform later into *melanoma*
  - Leukoplakia: thick *white patches* in the mucous membranes of the *mouth* as a result of exposure to *tobacco tars* from pipe or cigar smoking, or from use of smokeless tobacco (snuff or chewing tobacco)

© 2007 Jones and Bartlett Publishers

Precancerous Condition

- Leukoplakia may give rise to *squamous* cell cancers of the oral cavity
- *Precancerous conditions* should always be *treated* appropriately to *prevent malignant* change, which *occurs* in *many but not* in all cases

© 2007 Jones and Bartlett Publishers

Etiologic Factors in Neoplastic Disease

- Viruses
- Gene and chromosomal abnormalities
- Failure of immunologic defenses
- Heredity

Viruses

- *Some cancers* in humans appear to be *caused* by *viruses*
- Some *unusual* types of *leukemia* and *lymphoma* are caused by a virus called the *human T cell leukemia-lymphoma virus (HTLV-1)*, which is *related* to the *virus* that causes *AIDS*

© 2007 Jones and Bartlett Publishers

Etiologic Factors in Neoplastic Disease

- *Kaposi's sarcoma* in *AIDS* patients is caused by a *herpes virus, human herpesvirus 8 (HHV-8)*
- Some strains of the *papilloma virus* that cause *genital condylomas* appear to *predispose* to *cervical carcinoma*
- *Chronic viral hepatitis* predisposes to *primary carcinoma of the liver*
- Some types of *nasopharyngeal carcinoma* and some types of *lymphoma* appear to be *related* to *Epstein-Barr virus infections*, which is the virus that causes infectious *mononucleosis*

© 2007 Jones and Bartlett Publishers

Etiologic Factors in Neoplastic Disease

Gene and Chromosomal Abnormalities
- There are *three* large *groups* of *genes* that play an important role in *regulating cell functions,* and *derangements* of these are associated with the formation of *tumors*
1. Proto-oncogenes
2. Tumor-suppressor genes
3. DNA repair genes

© 2007 Jones and Bartlett Publishers

Etiologic Factors Neoplastic Disease

1. Proto-oncogenes
- Normal "*growth genes*" in the human chromosomes, that promote some aspects of cell growth, differentiation, or mitotic activity
- If a proto-oncogene undergoes a mutation or is translocated to another chromosome, it can become an *oncogene*
- An *oncogene* is an *abnormally functioning gene* that will stimulate *cell growth excessively*, leading to *unrestricted cell proliferation*

© 2007 Jones and Bartlett Publishers

Etiologic Factors in Neoplastic Disease

2. Tumor Suppressor Genes
- They function to suppress cell proliferation
- *Loss* of their *function* by mutation or other event can also lead to *unrestrained cell growth*
- They *exist in pairs* at corresponding *gene loci* on *homologous chromosomes*, and *both* suppressor genes *must cease* to function *before* the *cell malfunctions*

© 2007 Jones and Bartlett Publishers

Etiologic Factors in Neoplastic Disease

3. DNA Repair Genes
- They regulate the processes that *monitor* and *repair* any *errors in DNA* duplication during cell *division*, or caused by DNA damage from radiation, chemicals, or other environmental agents
- *Any change* in the normal arrangement of DNA nucleotides on the DNA chain constitutes a *DNA mutation*
- *Failure* of DNA repair gene function *increases* the likelihood of *DNA mutations* within the cell

© 2007 Jones and Bartlett Publishers

Etiologic Factors in Neoplastic Disease

Failure of immunologic defenses
- In most cases, *cancers do not* result from *mutations* of a *single gene*
- They result from *multiple genetic "insults"* to the genome
- It is characterized by *activation* of *oncogenes* along with *loss of function* of one or more *tumor suppressor genes*
- Once a *cell* has been *deregulated* and has formed a *tumor, additional random genetic changes* may take place in the tumor cells, *indicative* of the *instability* of the *tumor cell genome*

© 2007 Jones and Bartlett Publishers

Etiologic Factors in Neoplastic Disease

- A *mutant cell* often produces *different cell proteins* not present in a normal cell
- These proteins are *recognized* as *abnormal* by the *immune system*
- It *attempts* to *destroy* the *abnormal cells* by means of various *cell-mediated* and *humoral* mechanisms
- Apparently, *mutations leading to neoplastic transformation* of cells are relatively *common*
- The *body recognizes them and destroys them*
- *Therefore*, one may consider a *tumor to manifest* in part a *failure* of the *body's immune defenses*

© 2007 Jones and Bartlett Publishers

Etiologic Factors in Neoplastic Disease

Heredity and Tumors

- There is *no strong hereditary predisposition* to most common malignant tumors
- *Hereditary factors do play a role* in *some* common tumors
- The *predisposition* is apparently the result of *multifactorial inheritance pattern* in which the *individual at risk* has *inherited set of genes* that influence some *hormonal- or enzyme-regulated biochemical process* within the body that *slightly increases* the *susceptibility* to a specific cancer

© 2007 Jones and Bartlett Publishers

Diagnosis of Tumors

1. Early recognition through warning signs and symptoms (refer to *Table 10-5*)
2. Abnormal smear: *slides* containing *abnormal cells* shed from surface of tumors
3. Cytologic diagnosis: from *smears, needle aspiration, biopsy*
4. Frozen-section: cutting a thin *section* of tissue, at *subzero* temperature, with a *microtome*, then preparing and *staining* the slides (provides a *rapid histologic diagnosis*)
5. Tumor associated antigen tests: some cancers *secrete* substances called *tumor-associated antigens* that can be detected in the bloodstream by laboratory tests

© 2007 Jones and Bartlett Publishers

Early Recognition and Warning Signs

TABLE 10-5

American Cancer Society warning signals

1. Change in bowel or bladder habits
2. A sore that does not heal
3. Unusual bleeding or discharge
4. A thickening or lump in the breast or elsewhere
5. Indigestion or difficulty in swallowing
6. An obvious change in wart or mole
7. A nagging cough or hoarseness

© 2007 Jones and Bartlett Publishers

Diagnosis of Tumor-Associated Antigens and Other Products

- CEA (carcinoembrionic antigen): a well-known <u>tumor-associated antigen</u> that, although *not secreted* by *all tumors* or *specific* for any type, may be present in *amounts related* to the *size* of tumor and its *possible spread*

- CEA is produced by most *malignant* tumors of the *GI tract, pancreas,* and *breast*

© 2007 Jones and Bartlett Publishers

Diagnosis of Tumor-Associated Antigens and Other Products

Other products secreted by tumor cells
- Alpha fetoprotein: *normally* produced by *fetal tissues* in the placenta but *not normally produced by adult cells*; this product is usually *elevated* in patients with *primary carcinoma of the liver*
- Human chorionic gonadotropin: *normally* produced by *placenta; elevated* in *testicular carcinoma*
- Acid-phosphatase: *normally* produced by *prostate epithelial cells,* may be *elevated* in *prostate cancer*

© 2007 Jones and Bartlett Publishers

Diagnosis of Tumors

Next step in diagnosing tumors:

- A complete medical history and physical examination by the physician to evaluate suspected abnormalities
- The *physical* may include special studies
1. Examination of the rectum and colon by special instruments
2. Vaginal examination and Pap smear in women
3. Examination of the esophagus and stomach with special devices
4. Various types of x-ray studies

Treatment of Tumors

- Surgery
- Radiotherapy
- Hormones
- Anticancer drugs
- Adjuvant chemotherapy
- Immunotherapy

Leukemia

- A neoplasm of *hematopoietic* tissue
- Leukemic cells *diffusely infiltrate* the *bone marrow* and lymphoid tissues, *spill over* into the *bloodstream,* and *infiltrate* throughout the *various organs* of the body
- Cells may be *mostly mature* or they may be extremely *primitive*
- The *overproduction* of *white cells* may be revealed in the *peripheral blood* by a very *high white blood count*
- The white cells *may be confined* to the *bone marrow,* and the *number* in the *peripheral blood* is *normal or decreased;* called aleukemic leukemia

Notes

_____

_____

_____

_____

_____

_____

_____

_____

_____

_____

_____

_____

_____

_____

_____

_____

_____

_____

_____

_____

_____

_____

_____

_____

_____

_____

_____

_____

_____

_____

_____

_____

Leukemia: Classification

- Any type of hematopoietic cells can give rise to leukemia, but the most common types are:
1. Granulocytic
2. Lymphocytic
3. Monocytic

Basis for Classification of Leukemia
1. By Cell type
   - Granulocytic, lymphocytic, monocytic
2. By Maturity of Leukemic cells
   - Acute, chronic

© 2007 Jones and Bartlett Publishers

Clinical Features
Leukemia

Manifestations caused by impairment of bone marrow function

- Overgrowth of leukemic cells that crowds out normal cells, causing:
- Anemia: inadequate red cell production
- Thrombocytopenia (low blood platelets): causes bleeding
- Infections resulting from inadequate number of normal white cells

© 2007 Jones and Bartlett Publishers

Clinical Features: Leukemia

2. Those caused by infiltration of the viscera by leukemic cells, causing:
- Splenomegaly: enlarged spleen
- Hepatomegaly: enlarged liver
- Lymphadenopathy: enlarged lymph nodes
- In *chronic* leukemia: evolution of disease proceeds at a *relatively slow pace* and often can be *controlled*
- In *acute* leukemia: a *rapidly progressive* disease, more difficult to control

© 2007 Jones and Bartlett Publishers

Myelodysplasia (Preleukemia)

- Disturbed growth and maturation of *marrow cells*
  - Anemia: reduced number of erythrocytes
  - Leukopenia: reduced number white cells
  - Thrombocytopenia: reduced number of platelets
- *Although* it has been *called preleukemia*, *not all* patients with bone marrow disturbances of this type *develop leukemia*
- Recently these *conditions* have been *grouped* together under the general term, *myelodysplastic syndromes*
- In general, the *more severe* the *maturation disturbance* in the bone marrow, the greater the *likelihood* the *leukemia will occur*

© 2007 Jones and Bartlett Publishers

Multiple Myeloma

- A *neoplasm* that arises from *plasma cells* within the *bone marrow*
- In many ways, it *resembles leukemia*, but the *cell proliferation* is *confined* to the *bone marrow*
- *Infiltration* of the *viscera* is *unusual*
- *Outpouring* of large number of *plasma cells* into the *peripheral blood* is also *uncommon*
- The *abnormal plasma cells* either may *infiltrate the bone marrow* diffusely or may *form discrete tumors* that weaken the bone
- Leads to *spontaneous fractures, pain,* and *disability*

© 2007 Jones and Bartlett Publishers

Survival of Neoplastic Disease

- The *curability* of the various types of cancer can be *assessed* in terms of *five-year survival rates*
- *Survival rates* vary *from 4%* to more than *95%*
- *Cancer* is *second* only *to heart disease* as a *cause of death in the US*
- *One in every 4* people will eventually *develop cancer*
- *Lung cancer* is the most *common* cancer affecting *males*
- *Breast cancer* is the most *common* cancer affecting *women*

© 2007 Jones and Bartlett Publishers

Notes

_____

_____

_____

_____

_____

_____

_____

_____

_____

_____

_____

_____

Survival of Neoplastic Disease

- *Early diagnosis* and *treatment* may *enhance survival*
- The *chances* for *survival* are significantly *reduced* if the tumor has *metastasized* to the regional lymph nodes or to distant sites
- *Five-year survival does not* necessarily mean that the patient is *cured*
- Some types of malignant tumors *may recur* and may prove *fatal* many years after initial treatment, such as *breast carcinoma and malignant melanomas*

© 2007 Jones and Bartlett Publishers

Chapter Outline

The chapter outline provides you with an organizational guide to the topics and ideas presented in this chapter of the text.

Hemostasis
Factors Concerned with Hemostasis
    Blood Vessels and Platelets
    Plasma Coagulation Factors
    Coagulation Inhibitors and Fibrinolysins
    Calcium and Blood Coagulation
Clinical Disturbances of Blood Coagulation
    Abnormalities of Small Blood Vessels
    Abnormalities of Platelet Numbers or Function
    Deficiency of Plasma Coagulation Factors
    Liberation of Thromboplastic Material into the Circulation
    Relative Frequency of Various Coagulation Disturbances
Laboratory Tests to Evaluate Hemostasis
Case Studies

Study Questions

The following questions are provided as a test for comprehension and as a study guide for use with the text chapters. Additional study material is located at http://humandisease.jbpub.com/, which contains useful tools such as an A&P review, animated flashcards, an interactive online glossary, crossword puzzles, and web links.

Key Terms

Define the following terms:

1. Hemostasis _____

2. Platelets _____

3. Blood coagulation _____

4. Hemophilia A _____

5. Von Willebrand's disease _____

6. Thrombocytopenia _____

7. Hemorrhage _____

8. Coagulation factors _____

9. Thromboplastin _____

Identify

1. Identify the four factors required for normal hemostasis.

   a. _____

   b. _____

   c. _____

   d. _____

Discussion Questions

1. Construct a simple system to describe the sequence of events involved in normal blood coagulation. (*Hint:* see Fig. 11-1.)

2. Describe the role of platelets in blood coagulation. _____

   _____

   _____

   _____

3. Describe the characteristic appearance of the bleeding associated with platelet deficiency. _____

_____

_____

4. Describe the differences between hemophilia A and von Willebrand's disease. _____

_____

_____

_____

5. What is the disseminated intravascular coagulation syndrome? _____

_____

_____

_____

6. What factors initiate the disseminated intravascular coagulation syndrome? _____

_____

_____

_____

7. List some of the readily available laboratory tests commonly used to evaluate the functions of the various factors involved in blood coagulation. Indicate what each test measures. _____

_____

_____

_____

8. What is the consequence of liberation of thromboplastic material into the circulation? _____

_____

_____

_____

9. What types of diseases produce abnormalities in the first phase of blood coagulation? _____

_____

_____

_____

10. What conditions lead to disturbances in the second phase of blood coagulation? _____

_____

_____

_____

11. What types of diseases are associated with thrombocytopenia? _____
_____
_____
_____

12. What are the major types of blood coagulation disturbances? _____
_____
_____
_____

13. A 5-year-old male child experiences frequent areas of hemorrhage into joints and muscles after minor trauma. Laboratory tests reveal a reduced concentration of a plasma coagulation factor that is concerned with the early stage of the coagulation mechanism (formation of thromboplastin). What is the most likely diagnosis?
_____
_____
_____

Notes

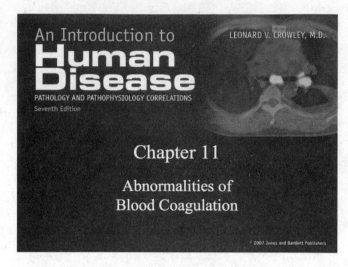

An Introduction to
Human Disease
PATHOLOGY AND PATHOPHYSIOLOGY CORRELATIONS
Seventh Edition

LEONARD V. CROWLEY, M.D.

Chapter 11

Abnormalities of Blood Coagulation

© 2007 Jones and Bartlett Publishers

Hemostasis

Hemostasis
- The *arrest of bleeding* caused by activation of the blood coagulation mechanism

Factors Concerned with Hemostasis
1. Integrity of small blood vessels
2. Adequate numbers of platelets
3. Normal amounts of coagulation factors
4. Normal amounts of coagulation inhibitors
5. Adequate amounts of calcium ions in the blood

© 2007 Jones and Bartlett Publishers

Factors Concerned with Hemostasis

1. Integrity of Small Vessels
- *Small vessels* are the *first line of defense* in the body
- If *injured*, they *constrict* (narrowing the caliber), which facilitates its *closure* by a *clot*
- As the small vessel is injured, there is *disruption of endothelium*, exposing the underlying connective tissue which activates the coagulation mechanism

2. Adequate Number of Platelets
- This is the *next step* where *platelets accumulate and adhere*, performing *three* important functions
a. *Plug* defect in the vessel wall

© 2007 Jones and Bartlett Publishers

Factors Concerned with Hemostasis

b. *Liberate* chemical compounds (vasoconstrictors) and compounds that cause platelets to aggregate

c. *Release* substances (phospholipids) that initiate the process of coagulation

Platelets

- Are *small* fragments of *cytoplasm* from large precursor cells in the bone marrow called *megakaryocytes*

- Platelets' average *survival* in the circulation is *10 days*

© 2007 Jones and Bartlett Publishers

Factors Concerned with Hemostasis

- When platelets *wear out*, they are *removed* by *macrophages* in the *spleen*

- The *activation of platelets* starts the blood *coagulation process*

3. Normal Amounts of Coagulation Factors

- The coagulation factors are *proteins* contained in the *blood plasma* which are *designated* by *name* and *Roman numerals*

  (Refer to Table 11-2 for the list of coagulation factors)

- When these *factors* are *activated,* they interact to *produce* a blood *clot*

© 2007 Jones and Bartlett Publishers

Factors Concerned with Hemostasis

- The process of blood coagulation is a *chain reaction* in which *each component* of the chain is formed from an *inactive precursor* in the blood, and each activated component in turn *activates* the *next* member of the chain

4. Normal Amounts of Coagulation Inhibitors

- They counterbalance the *coagulation factors by restricting the* clotting process to a *limited area*

- An *important one* is, for example, *antithrombin III* which inhibits thrombin and other activated coagulation factors generated in the clotting process

- *Another important* control system is the one that *dissolves fibrin* after it is formed

© 2007 Jones and Bartlett Publishers

Factors Concerned with Hemostasis

5. Adequate Amounts of Calcium Ions (Ca^{2+}) in the blood

- *There are no conditions in which low calcium levels lead to impaired blood coagulation because levels* low enough to affect blood coagulation are *incompatible with life*

© 2007 Jones and Bartlett Publishers

Blood Coagulation Process

Coagulation is chain reaction (like a *chain of dominoes*) that is highly complex

Phase 1

- Formation of *thromboplastin* by either the interaction of *intrinsic factors* (platelets and plasma factors) within the blood or by the *extrinsic factors* from components outside the circulatory system

Phase 2

- *Conversion of prothrombin into thrombin* (*after* the *thromboplastin interacts* with other substances to *form prothrombin activator*, which makes the *conversion*)

© 2007 Jones and Bartlett Publishers

Blood Coagulation Process

Phase 3

- *Conversion of fibrinogen into fibrin* by *thrombin*
- *Thrombin splits off a part* of the fibrinogen and forms a *smaller molecule called fibrin monomer.* They become *joined* end to end, into long strands of fibrin, which also become linked together side to side
- Then the *fibrin stabilizing factor* acts by *strengthening* the bonds between the fibrin molecules, increasing the strength of the fibrin clot
- The *blood clot* is the *end stage* in the clotting process, consisting of an interlacing meshwork of *fibrin threads* containing entrapped *plasma, red cells, white cells, and platelets*

© 2007 Jones and Bartlett Publishers

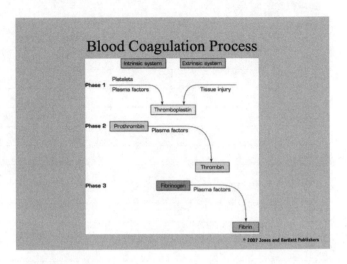

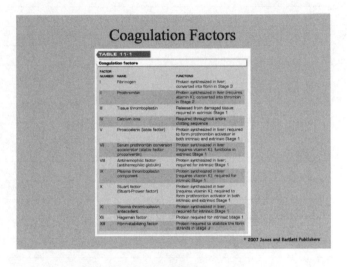

Disturbances of Blood Coagulation

Classification: Four categories
- Abnormalities of *small blood vessels*
- Abnormality of *platelet* formation
- *Deficiency* of one or more plasma *coagulation factors*
- *Liberation* of *thromboplastic* material into circulation

Abnormality of small blood vessels
- This has caused some rare diseases characterized by *abnormal bleeding* resulting from abnormal function of the small blood vessels, which do *not contract after tissue injury*, to help seal the defect by a blood clot

© 2007 Jones and Bartlett Publishers

Notes

_____
_____
_____
_____
_____
_____
_____
_____
_____
_____
_____
_____
_____
_____
_____
_____
_____
_____
_____
_____
_____
_____
_____
_____
_____
_____
_____
_____
_____
_____
_____
_____
_____
_____
_____
_____

Disturbances of Blood Coagulation

Abnormality of platelet formation

- *Thrombocytopenia* (decrease in platelets) may be caused by:

1. Injury or disease of the *bone marrow*, which damages the megakaryocytes (precursors of platelets)

2. The *bone marrow* is *infiltrated* by *leukemic* cells or *cancer* cells that have spread to the skeletal system, *crowding out the megakaryocytes*

© 2007 Jones and Bartlett Publishers

Disturbances of Blood Coagulation

3. *Antiplatelet antibodies destroy* the *platelets* in the peripheral blood (as seen in autoimmune diseases)

4. *Abnormal function of platelets* even though they are normal in quantities

Bleeding associated with defective or inadequate platelets is generally manifested by *small petechial hemorrhages*

Deficiency of one or more coagulation factors

- They often lead to *large areas* of *hemorrhage* called *hematomas*

© 2007 Jones and Bartlett Publishers

Clinical Disturbances of Blood Coagulation

- *Deficiencies* of *factors* concerned with *Phase 1* of the coagulation process are usually *hereditary* and are *relatively rare except*
1. Hemophilia A
2. Hemophilia B
3. von Willebrand's disease

Liberation of Thromboplastic Material into the Circulation

- Products of *the following* have *thromboplastic* activity, liberated into circulation and leading to widespread *intravascular coagulation*
1. Diseases associated with shock and tissue necrosis
2. Overwhelming bacterial infections
3. Other causes of tissue necrosis

© 2007 Jones and Bartlett Publishers

Notes

_____

_____

_____

_____

_____

_____

_____

_____

_____

_____

_____

_____

_____

_____

_____

_____

_____

_____

_____

_____

_____

_____

_____

_____

_____

_____

_____

_____

_____

_____

_____

_____

Hemophilia A, Hemophilia B, and von Willebrand's Disease

Hemophilia
- An _x-linked_ hereditary disease affecting _males_
- The _most common_ and _best known_
- Characterized by _episodes_ of _hemorrhage_ in _joints_ and _internal organs_ after _minor injury_

There are two forms of hemophilia

1. Hemophilia A
- The _classic_ hemophilia, characterized by a _decrease_ in _coagulation factor VIII (antihemophilic factor)_

© 2007 Jones and Bartlett Publishers

Hemophilia A, Hemophilia B, and von Willebrand's Disease

2. Hemophilia B
- Called _Christmas_ disease (named after affected _patient_)
- Characterized by a _decrease_ in _coagulation factor IX_ (_Christmas_ factor)

von Willebrand's disease
- Results from a _deficiency_ of a _large protein molecule_ that is produced by endothelial cells lining the blood vessels
- This _factor_ is _required_ in order for _platelets to adhere_ to the vessel wall at the site of injury
- This _protein_ is also _released_ into the bloodstream where it forms a _complex_ with _factor VIII_

© 2007 Jones and Bartlett Publishers

Hemophilia A, Hemophilia B, and von Willebrand's Disease

- This complex is _needed_ to maintain a _normal level of factor VIII_ in the blood

- _von Willebrand's factor functions_ by adhering to the vessel wall where the endothelium is disrupted, forming a framework that allows platelets and coagulation factors to adhere, interact, and form a clot

- von Willebrand's patients _synthesize factor VIII but_ an _adequate amount_ of _von Willebrand's factor_ is required to form a _complex_ with _factor VIII_ and maintain a _normal level_ of _factor VIII_ in the circulation

© 2007 Jones and Bartlett Publishers

Hemophilia A, Hemophilia B, and von Willebrand's Disease

- The excessive bleeding is *not* in the joints, as is in Hemophilias A and B
- Patients with these three diseases can be *treated with factor concentrates*

© 2007 Jones and Bartlett Publishers

Clinical Disturbances of Blood Coagulation

- *Disturbances affecting Phase 2* of the coagulation process result from a *deficiency* of *prothrombin* or *factors required* for the *conversion* of *prothrombin into thrombin*
- These *factors* are produced in the *liver*
- *Vitamin K* is required for s*ynthesis* of most of these factors
- *Vitamin K* is synthesized by *intestinal bacteria*
- *Bile* is required for its *absorption*

© 2007 Jones and Bartlett Publishers

Clinical Disturbances of Blood Coagulation

These disturbances may be caused by
1. Administration of anticoagulant drugs
2. Inadequate synthesis of vitamin K
3. Inadequate absorption of vitamin K
4. Severe liver disease

How it happens
- *Anticoagulant drugs* precisely act by inhibiting the synthesis of biochemically active vitamin K-dependent factors
- Inadequate synthesis of vitamin K can occur if the *intestinal bacteria* has been *eradicated* with *prolonged use* of *antibiotics*

© 2007 Jones and Bartlett Publishers

Clinical Disturbances of Blood Coagulation

- Inadequate uptake of Vitamin K may occur in *blockage of the common bile duct* by a gallstone or tumor, preventing the bile from entering the intestine to promote absorption of the vitamin
- Severe liver disease impairs the *synthesis* of *adequate* amounts of *coagulation factors*

© 2007 Jones and Bartlett Publishers

Causes of Thrombocytopenia

- Result of injury or disease of the bone marrow
- Due to infiltration of bone marrow by leukemic or cancer cells
- Antiplatelet antibody destroys platelets in the peripheral blood

© 2007 Jones and Bartlett Publishers

Disseminated Intravascular Coagulation Syndrome

- Abnormal bleeding state resulting from the net effect of various events that lead to
- Activation of the coagulation mechanism due to
  - diseases associated with shock
  - overwhelming bacterial infection
  - extensive necrosis of tissue
- Products of tissue necrosis and other substances with thromboplastic activity are liberated into the circulation

© 2007 Jones and Bartlett Publishers

Disseminated Intravascular Coagulation Syndrome

- In the process of *clotting*, *platelets* and the *plasma coagulation factors* are *utilized*, and the *levels* of these in the *blood rapidly drop*
- The *body* then *activates* the *fibrinolysin system* to defend itself against widespread intravascular clotting, *dissolving clots* and *preventing* potentially the *lethal obstruction* of the *circulatory* system
- The net effect is Disseminated Intravascular Coagulation

© 2007 Jones and Bartlett Publishers

Disseminated Intravascular Coagulation Syndrome

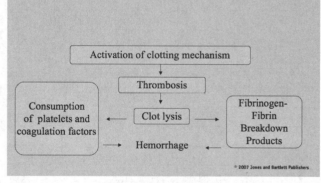

© 2007 Jones and Bartlett Publishers

Laboratory Tests to Evaluate Hemostasis

- Platelet count
- Examination of blood smear for platelet numbers
- Bleeding time
- Clotting time of whole blood
- Partial thromboplastin time
- Prothrombin time

© 2007 Jones and Bartlett Publishers

Laboratory Tests to Evaluate Hemostasis

These tests evaluate the overall efficiency of the coagulation process
- Platelet Count: counting platelets in blood smear
- Bleeding Time: the time it takes for a small skin lesion to stop bleeding, used to evaluate the function of the capillaries in the hemostatic process
- Clotting Time: time it takes for blood to clot in a test tube
- Partial Thromboplastin Time: the time it takes for blood plasma to clot after a lipid substance is added to the plasma sample

© 2007 Jones and Bartlett Publishers

Laboratory Tests to Evaluate Hemostasis

- Prothrombin time: the measurement of the time of the combined second and third phases of coagulation
- There are several tests for the presence of inhibitors of coagulation
- The function of platelets is measured with other tests

© 2007 Jones and Bartlett Publishers

Tests Measuring Phases of the Clotting Mechanism

Formation of intrinsic thromboplastin	Conversion of prothrombin	Conversion of fibrinogen
Phase 1	Phase 2	Phase 3

Whole blood clotting time
Partial thromboplastin time

© 2007 Jones and Bartlett Publishers

Notes

_____
_____
_____
_____
_____
_____
_____
_____
_____
_____
_____
_____
_____
_____
_____
_____
_____
_____
_____
_____
_____
_____

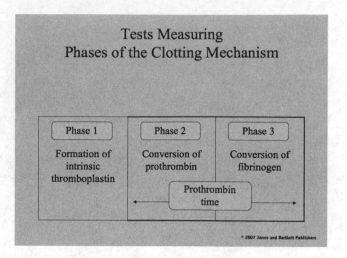

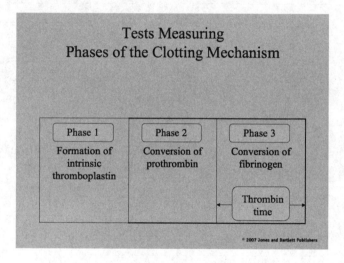

Chapter Outline

The chapter outline provides you with an organizational guide to the topics and ideas presented in this chapter of the text.

Study Questions

The following questions are provided as a test for comprehension and as a study guide for use with the text chapters. Additional study material is located at http://humandisease.jbpub.com/, which contains useful tools such as an A&P review, animated flashcards, an interactive online glossary, crossword puzzles, and web links.

Key Terms

Define the following terms:

1. Edema _____

2. Thrombus _____

3. Embolus _____

4. Infarct _____

Fill-in-the-Blank

1. Reduced capillary osmotic pressure can be caused by _____.

2. Increased capillary permeability can be caused by _____.

3. _____ results in increased capillary hydrostatic pressure.

4. _____ results in obstruction of lymphatic channels.

5. If the capillary hydrostatic pressure exceeds the osmotic pressure, _____ will result.

True/False

Tell whether each of the following statements is true or false. If false, explain why the statement is incorrect.

1. Rapid release of thromboplastic material into the circulation activates the blood coagulation and fibrinolytic systems and leads to a disseminated intravascular coagulation syndrome. _____

   _____

2. Slow release of thromboplastic material into the circulation activates the blood coagulation and fibrinolytic systems and leads to a disseminated intravascular coagulation syndrome. _____

   _____

3. Slow release of thromboplastic material into the circulation activates the blood coagulation and fibrinolytic systems but also causes a compensatory increase in platelets and blood proteins concerned with blood coagulation (coagulation factors), which predisposes the person to intravascular thromboses. _____

   _____

4. Formation of blood clots within leg veins results primarily from slowing or stasis of blood in leg veins. _____

   _____

5. A large pulmonary embolus that completely blocks both pulmonary arteries causes infarction of both lungs.

   _____

Identify

1. Identify the four main causes of edema.

   a. _____

   b. _____

   c. _____

   d. _____

2. Identify the three conditions that may lead to the formation of blood clots within the heart.

   a. _____

   b. _____

   c. _____

3. Identify three diagnostic measures that may assist the clinician in making the diagnosis of a pulmonary infarct.

   a. _____

   b. _____

   c. _____

Matching

Several factors predispose to the formation of blood clots within blood vessels:

A. Sluggish blood flow within a blood vessel
B. Damage to the wall of a blood vessel
C. Increased coagulability of the blood

Write the letter of the factor that is of greatest importance in the following situations next to each statement:

1. _____ A thrombus formed in a coronary artery in which the lining (intima) is roughened by accumulation of cholesterol and other lipids in the arterial wall

2. _____ A thrombus formed in an artery of a healthy young woman taking birth control pills

3. _____ A thrombus in a leg vein of a healthy middle-aged man who had recently completed a 10-hour nonstop airplane flight

Discussion Questions

1. What factors regulate the flow of fluid into and out of the capillaries? (*Hint:* see Fig. 12-9.) _____

   _____

   _____

   _____

2. Why do some patients with cancer develop blood clots within their circulation because they have a higher than normal level of platelets and blood coagulation factors? _____

   _____

   _____

   _____

3. What is the difference between a thrombus and an embolus? _____

_____

_____

4. What factors predispose a person to venous thrombosis? What are the major complications of a thrombus in a leg vein? _____

_____

_____

_____

5. What factors predispose a person to arterial thrombosis? _____

_____

_____

_____

6. What conditions predispose a person to thrombosis by increasing the coagulability of the blood? _____

_____

_____

_____

7. What is the usual source of pulmonary emboli? _____

_____

_____

_____

8. A 6-year-old child has marked edema of the legs and edema fluid within the abdominal cavity (ascites). The child's blood protein and albumin levels are much lower than normal. The urine contains large amounts of protein. What is the most likely cause of the edema? _____

_____

_____

_____

9. A 58-year-old woman sustains a large pulmonary embolus that completely blocks the main pulmonary artery. Explain whether each of the following descriptors applies to the condition. Why or why not?

    a. Patient experiences severe pleuritic chest pain. _____

    _____

    b. Patient becomes short of breath. _____

    _____

    c. Lung scan is abnormal. _____

    _____

d. Chest x-ray is abnormal. _____

   _____

e. Patient had pulmonary infarct. _____

   _____

f. Patient coughs up blood. _____

   _____

10. What populations have a greater than normal risk of developing thromboembolic disease? _____

   _____

   _____

   _____

11. What factors predispose a person to postoperative venous thromboses? _____

   _____

   _____

   _____

12. What conditions may result from a blood clot that forms in the left ventricle after a myocardial infarction? _____

   _____

   _____

   _____

Chapter 12

Circulatory Disturbances

© 2007 Jones and Bartlett Publishers

Intravascular Blood Clots

Normally, blood does *not* clot within the vascular system

- Intravascular clotting occurs
  1. Slowing or <u>stasis</u> of blood flow
  2. Damage to <u>wall</u> of blood vessel
  3. Increased <u>coagulability</u> of blood
- Thrombosis
  - Intravascular clot; it can occur in any vessel or within the heart itself
- Embolus
  - *Detached clot* carried in circulation, either in the pulmonary or in the systemic circulation

© 2007 Jones and Bartlett Publishers

Intravascular Blood Clots

  - An embolism plugs a vessel of *smaller caliber* than the diameter of the clot, which *blocks* the *blood flow* to the tissue beyond the obstruction, and the tissue may undergo *necrosis*
- Infarct
  - Tissue necrosis caused by interruption of blood supply

© 2007 Jones and Bartlett Publishers

Venous Thrombosis

- Caused by the formation of blood clots within *leg veins*
  - Prolonged bed rest
  - Cramped position for long periods
  - During these circumstances, the "milking action" of the leg musculature, which normally promotes venous return, is impaired, leading to stasis of blood in veins
  - Varicose veins or any condition preventing normal emptying of veins
- A venous thrombosis may partially block venous return in the leg, making leg *swell*

© 2007 Jones and Bartlett Publishers

Venous Thrombosis / Pulmonary Embolus

- However, the *major complication* is related to *detachment* of the *clot* from the wall of the vein
- It may break loose, forming an *embolus* that is carried up the *inferior vena cava* into the *right side of the heart* and from there to the *pulmonary artery*
- The clinical manifestations of a pulmonary embolism depend on the *size* of the embolus and *where* it lodges in the pulmonary artery
- A *large* pulmonary embolism that completely blocks the main pulmonary artery or its major branches *obstructs* the *blood flow* to the *lungs*

© 2007 Jones and Bartlett Publishers

Venous Thrombosis / Pulmonary Embolus

- *Lungs* are *not infarcted* due to blood still flowing into lungs from the *bronchial arteries*, which arise from the descending aorta and interconnect with the pulmonary arteries by means of collateral channels

Subsequent events

1. *Right side* of heart becomes *distended* (because blood cannot be expelled into lungs)
2. The *pulmonary artery* becomes *overdistended* with blood, and its *pressure rises*
3. The *left ventricle* is *unable to pump* adequate volume of blood to *brain* and other *vital organs*
4. The systemic *blood pressure falls*, and patient may go into *shock*

© 2007 Jones and Bartlett Publishers

Venous Thrombosis / Pulmonary Embolus

- Clinically, a patient with a *large* pulmonary embolus becomes very *short of breath* and the *skin* and *mucous membranes* assume a *bluish* discoloration (*cyanosis*) because of an *inadequate oxygenation* of blood

  (*Remember* that the blood is oxygenated when it passes through the lungs)

- *Small pulmonary emboli* may pass through the main pulmonary arteries and become *impacted* in the *peripheral branches*, usually in the arteries supplying the lower lobes of the lungs
- Frequently, the segment of the lung supplied by the obstructed pulmonary artery undergoes necrosis, resulting in a *pulmonary infarct*

© 2007 Jones and Bartlett Publishers

Venous Thrombosis / Pulmonary Embolus

- Clinically, if the patient's lungs become *infarcted*, he or she experiences *difficulty* in *breathing (dyspnea)*, *pleuritic pain*, *cough*, and *expectoration* of *bloody sputum*
- Sometimes, thrombi form in the pelvic veins as a result of a *bacterial infection* in adjacent pelvic organs, as may occur *following* a *uterine infection*
- The *bacteria* may spread to *infect* the venous *thrombi* as well
- If an infected thrombus breaks loose and causes a pulmonary infarct, the bacteria transported invades the infarcted tissues, which breaks down to form a *lung abscess*
- The infected embolus is called a *septic embolus*

© 2007 Jones and Bartlett Publishers

Diagnosis and Treatment of Pulmonary Embolism

Clinical Manifestations
- Unexplained dyspnea, cough or pleuritic chest pain in a predisposed patient

Tests/Procedures
- Chest x-rays: determine if embolus has caused infarct
- Radioisotope lung scans: detects abnormal pulmonary blood flow caused by embolus
- Pulmonary angiogram or computed tomography (CT) scan: required for a definite diagnosis of pulmonary embolism

© 2007 Jones and Bartlett Publishers

Diagnosis and Treatment of Pulmonary Embolism

Treatment
- General *supportive* care
- Anticoagulants: Heparin initially, followed by Coumadin type anticoagulants
- *Surgical* removal of embolus
- *Or dissolve* the embolus with *thrombolytic drugs* (clot dissolving agents), if there has been a *massive embolus*

© 2007 Jones and Bartlett Publishers

Arterial Thrombosis

- In *arterial* thrombosis, *stasis* is *not* a factor because blood flow is rapid and intravascular pressure is high
- The *main cause* of arterial thrombosis is *injury to vessel wall*, secondary to *arteriosclerosis*
- The *arteriosclerotic deposits* cause ulceration and roughening of the lining of the artery, and *thrombi form* on the roughened area
- *Blockage* of a *coronary artery* causes *infarction* of the heart, leading to a *heart attack*
- If a *major artery* supplying the *leg* is *occluded*, the extremity undergoes *necrosis*, leading to *gangrene*

© 2007 Jones and Bartlett Publishers

Arterial Thrombosis

- *Occlusion* of an artery to the *brain* causes *infarction* of the brain, leading to "*stroke*"
- *Intracardiac Thrombosis*: thrombus may become *dislodged* and may be *carried into* the *systemic circulation*, resulting in *infarction* of the *spleen, kidneys, brain*, or *other organs*

© 2007 Jones and Bartlett Publishers

Notes

_____
_____
_____
_____
_____
_____
_____
_____
_____
_____
_____
_____
_____
_____
_____
_____
_____
_____
_____
_____
_____
_____
_____
_____
_____
_____
_____
_____
_____
_____
_____
_____
_____

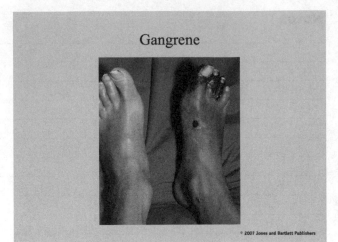

Gangrene

© 2007 Jones and Bartlett Publishers

Thrombosis by Increased Coagulability

It can occur

1. After *injury or operation*, when products of tissue necrosis with thromboplastic activity stimulate the synthesis of many clotting factors, increasing the likelihood of postoperative thrombosis in the leg veins

2. *Estrogen* in *contraceptive pills* stimulate the synthesis of coagulation factors

3. In men with *prostatic carcinoma* treated with estrogen to cause regression of the tumor, which increases the concentration of plasma coagulation factors

© 2007 Jones and Bartlett Publishers

Thrombosis by Increased Coagulability

4. Patients with *advanced cancer* have elevated platelets and high concentration of coagulation factors as a result of the slow release of thromboplastic material into the circulation from the tumor

© 2007 Jones and Bartlett Publishers

Embolism

- *Most emboli* are caused by *blood clots,* but other materials like _fat_, _air_, and _foreign particles_ can cause serious difficulties

Fat embolism

- After severe *bone fracture, fatty* bone marrow and surrounding adipose tissue may be disrupted
- The emulsified fat globules may be *sucked* into the *veins* and *carried* into the *lungs*
- It can lead to *widespread obstruction* of pulmonary *capillaries*

© 2007 Jones and Bartlett Publishers

Embolism

- Some *reach* the *systemic circulation*, eventually *blocking* small vessels in the *brain* and other *organs*

Air Embolism

- Sometimes a large amount of *air* is *sucked* into the circulation after a *chest wound* with injury to the lung
- Also, *air* can be *accidentally injected* into the circulation in attempts at *abortion*
- The *air* is carried by the heart and *accumulates* in the *right heart* chambers, *preventing filling* of the heart by returning venous blood
- As a result, the heart is *unable* to *pump blood* and the individual dies rapidly of *circulatory failure*

© 2007 Jones and Bartlett Publishers

Embolism

Foreign Matter Embolism

- Various types of *particulate material* may be injected by *drug abusers*, who crush and dissolve tablets intended for oral use, injecting the material intravenously
- The *material* is usually *trapped* within the small pulmonary blood vessels, producing symptoms of *severe respiratory distress*

© 2007 Jones and Bartlett Publishers

_____
_____
_____
_____
_____
_____
_____
_____
_____
_____
_____
_____
_____
_____
_____
_____
_____
_____
_____
_____
_____
_____
_____
_____
_____
_____
_____
_____
_____
_____
_____
_____
_____
_____
_____
_____
_____

Edema

- *Accumulation* of *fluid* in *interstitial* tissues, first noted in ankles and legs
- It may result from any condition in which the *circulation* of *extracellular fluid* between the capillaries and interstitial tissues become *disturbed*
- *Pitting* edema: edematous tissue is compressed by indenting the tissues with the fingertips, pushing the fluid aside, leaving a *pit* or *indentation* that gradually refills with fluid
- *Hydrothorax*: fluid accumulates in the *pleural* cavity
- *Ascites*: fluid accumulates in the *peritoneal* cavity

© 2007 Jones and Bartlett Publishers

Factors Regulating Flow of Fluids Between Capillaries and Interstitial Tissue

1. *Capillary hydrostatic pressure:* tends to filter fluid from the blood through the capillary endothelium

2. *Capillary permeability:* determines the ease with which the fluid can pass through the capillaries

3. *Osmotic pressure:* exerted by the *proteins* in the blood plasma (called colloid osmotic pressure) which tends to attract fluid from the interstitial space back into the vascular compartment

© 2007 Jones and Bartlett Publishers

Factors Regulating Flow of Fluids Between Capillaries and Interstitial Tissue

- The *osmotic pressure* of plasma depends primarily on the concentration of the plasma *proteins*
- Because the *capillaries* are *relatively impermeable to protein*, the protein tends to draw water from the interstitial fluid into the capillaries and hold it there
- *Osmotic pressure* is the property causing fluid to migrate in the direction of a higher concentration of molecules
4. *Open lymphatic channels:* collect some of the fluid forced out of the capillaries by hydrostatic pressure of the blood and return the fluid to the circulation

© 2007 Jones and Bartlett Publishers

Pathogenesis of Edema

- *Increased capillary permeability*
  - Responsible for swelling of tissues associated with *acute inflammation,* as in a *boil* or a *severe sunburn*
  - Some *systemic diseases* cause generalized increase in capillary permeability, which leads to widespread edema of the subcutaneous tissues

© 2007 Jones and Bartlett Publishers

Pathogenesis of Edema

- *Low plasma proteins*
  - Excess protein loss, as in *malnutrition or starvation*
  - Inadequate protein intake, as in *debilitating diseases* (unable to eat adequately) and with *intestinal diseases* (assimilation of food impaired)
- *Increased hydrostatic pressure,* as seen in
  - *Heart failure*
  - Localized venous obstruction by a *clot*
- *Lymphatic obstruction,* which blocks the pathway by which fluid is returned from the interstitial space into the circulation

© 2007 Jones and Bartlett Publishers

Edema

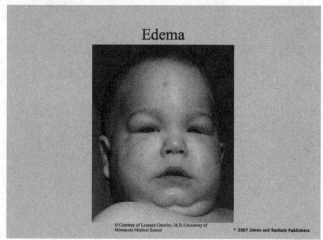

© Courtesy of Leonard Crowley, M.D./University of Minnesota Medical School

© 2007 Jones and Bartlett Publishers

Notes

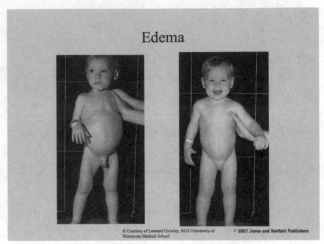

Edema

© Courtesy of Leonard Crowley, M.D./University of Minnesota Medical School   © 2007 Jones and Bartlett Publishers

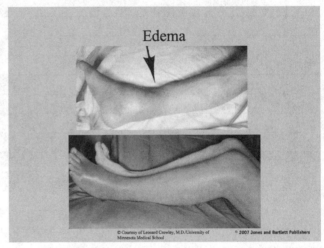

Edema

© Courtesy of Leonard Crowley, M.D./University of Minnesota Medical School   © 2007 Jones and Bartlett Publishers

Chapter Outline

The chapter outline provides you with an organizational guide to the topics and ideas presented in this chapter of the text.

Study Questions

The following questions are provided as a test for comprehension and as a study guide for use with the text chapters. Additional study material is located at http://humandisease.jbpub.com/, which contains useful tools such as an A&P review, animated flashcards, an interactive online glossary, crossword puzzles, and web links.

Key Terms

Define the following terms:

1. Bacterial endocarditis _____

2. Dissecting aneurysm _____

3. Stent _____

4. Atherosclerosis _____

5. Rheumatic fever _____

6. Arteriosclerotic aneurysm _____

7. Angina pectoris _____

8. Myocardial infarction _____

9. Lipoprotein _____

Fill-in-the-Blank

1. The _____ valves are open in systole.

2. The _____ valves are open in diastole.

3. A dissecting aneurysm of the aorta is due to _____.

4. One of the important complications of mitral valve scarring due to rheumatic fever is _____.

5. The _____ stage in the formation of an atheromatous plaque is reversible.

True/False

Tell whether each statement is true or false. If false, explain why the statement is incorrect.

1. A coronary artery narrowed by an atheromatous plaque often can be dilated successfully by coronary angioplasty.

    _____

2. A successfully dilated coronary artery may undergo restenosis, but using a stent to keep the vessel open reduces the incidence of restenosis. _____

    _____

3. Stents coated with drugs that suppress the cell proliferation responsible for the restenosis have not been effective and are not recommended to prevent restenosis. _____

    _____

4. The left anterior descending coronary artery supplies the back wall of the heart. _____

    _____

5. Impulses that cause the heart to beat are initiated in the sinoatrial (SA) node. _____

_____

6. The systolic pressure is a measure of the resistance to blood flow due to constriction of the peripheral arterioles.

_____

7. The rate of flow through arteries varies directly with the radius of the artery. _____

_____

8. The systolic pressure is the highest pressure within the vascular system when blood is ejected from the ventricle during systole. _____

_____

9. A coronary arteriogram (angiogram) may appear normal in some persons with symptoms of coronary artery disease. _____

_____

10. Isolated systolic hypertension (with normal diastolic pressure) occurs primarily in younger persons and is not harmful. _____

_____

11. A small aortic aneurysm (about 5-cm diameter) can usually be detected by a physical examination, and more detailed diagnostic studies are not required. _____

_____

Identify

1. Identify the four major factors that are known to increase the risk of coronary heart disease.

    a. _____

    b. _____

    c. _____

    d. _____

2. Identify five complications of an acute myocardial infarction.

    a. _____

    b. _____

    c. _____

    d. _____

    e. _____

3. The term "acute coronary syndrome" includes three different conditions. What are they?

    a. _____

    b. _____

    c. _____

Matching

Match the item in the left column with its characteristic or property in the right column.

1. ____ Diastolic heart failure

2. ____ Ejection fraction

3. ____ Stroke volume

4. ____ Systolic heart failure

5. ____ Natriuretic peptide

A. A peptide released from stretched cardiac muscle

B. Impaired ejection of blood from ventricle

C. The percentage of the blood in the ventricle that is ejected during systole

D. Impaired ventricular filling

E. The volume of blood ejected from the ventricle during a systolic contraction

Discussion Questions

1. Describe how heart valves function to provide unidirectional flow of blood through the heart. _____

_____

_____

_____

2. Describe what happens if the mitral valve doesn't open properly and what happens if it doesn't close properly.

_____

_____

_____

3. What are the structural changes in the mitral valve that lead to mitral valve prolapse? _____

_____

_____

_____

4. What factors predispose a person to calcific aortic stenosis? _____

_____

_____

_____

5. Describe the conditions that predispose a person to infective endocarditis. _____

_____

_____

_____

6. Which patients should have antibiotic prophylaxis prior to dental procedures or surgical procedures? _____

_____

_____

_____

7. What types of diets lower blood lipids? _____

_____

_____

8. Describe the effect on cardiovascular function resulting from damage to a mitral valve papillary muscle as a result of a myocardial infarction. _____

_____

_____

_____

9. Why are cardiac enzyme tests performed on the blood of patients suspected of having a myocardial infarction?

_____

_____

_____

10. A patient complains of chest pain. Clinical examination, enzyme tests, and electrocardiogram reveal a thrombosis of the left anterior descending coronary artery. How should the patient be treated? _____

_____

_____

_____

11. What methods can be used to reestablish blood flow through a blocked coronary artery? _____

_____

_____

_____

12. Describe the effect of high blood pressure on the heart and vascular system. _____

_____

_____

_____

13. Patients at risk for coronary heart disease frequently take low-dose aspirin tablets daily to reduce the risk of heart attacks. What effect does aspirin have? Why is it used? _____

_____

_____

_____

14. What conditions may lead to cardiac valve scarring? _____

_____

_____

_____

15. What conditions may follow a myocardial infarction? _____

_____

_____

_____

16. What diagnostic measures may assist the clinician in making a diagnosis of acute myocardial infarction? _____

_____

_____

_____

17. What is the cause of an aneurysm of the abdominal aorta that occurs in an older individual? How is it treated?

_____

_____

_____

18. What happens during congestive cardiac failure? _____

_____

_____

_____

19. What conditions may cause mitral insufficiency? _____

_____

_____

_____

20. What is C-reactive protein (CRP)? What does an elevated CRP test indicate? _____

_____

_____

_____

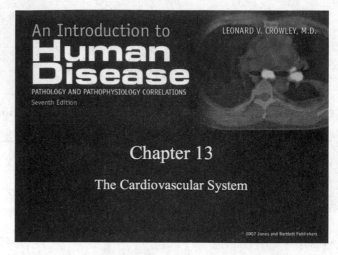

Chapter 13

The Cardiovascular System

Heart Location

Location of Heart

- Enclosed within the *mediastinum*, the medial cavity of the thorax, *extending obliquely* for about 5 inches from the second rib to the fifth intercostal space, rests on the *superior surface of diaphragm*, lies *anterior* to the *vertebral* column and *posterior* to the *sternum*
- Approximately *2/3* of its *mass* lies *left* of the *midsternal* line, the *balance* projecting to the *right,* its broad *flat base* or *posterior* surface is directed toward the *right shoulder*
- Its *apex points* inferior toward the *left* hip

© 2007 Jones and Bartlett Publishers

Heart Coverings, Layers, Chambers

Heart Coverings

- Pericardium (double walled sac)
- Epicardium (visceral layer of pericardium covering myocardium)

Layers of the Heart Wall

- Epicardium, myocardium, and endocardium

Heart has four chambers

- RA (right atrium)
- RV (right ventricle)
- LA (left atrium)
- LV (left ventricle)

© 2007 Jones and Bartlett Publishers

Heart Pumps / Chambers

- Right side of heart is the pulmonary pump
- Left side of heart is the systemic pump

Atria (singular: atrium) are the receiving chambers, thin walled, relatively small

- Blood enters RA via three veins:
1. Superior vena cava (from body regions above diaphragm)
2. Inferior vena cava (from body areas below diaphragm)
3. Coronary sinus (collects blood that drains from myocardium)
- Blood enters LA via four pulmonary veins

© 2007 Jones and Bartlett Publishers

Heart Pumps / Chambers

Ventricles: discharging chambers or actual pumps
- RV: forms most of the heart's anterior surface
- LV: forms or dominates into posterioinferior surface
- Blood enters RV from RA
- Blood enters LV from LA

© 2007 Jones and Bartlett Publishers

Heart Circulation
Pulmonary-Systemic

- *Pulmonary* circulation
  - Right heart circulates blood to lung
- *Systemic* circulation
  - Left heart circulates blood to peripheral tissues
  - *Blood returns* to body *oxygen poor, carbon dioxide rich*
  - It enters the right atrium, passes to right ventricle, which pumps it to lungs via the pulmonary trunk (main pulmonary artery)
  - *Freshly oxygenated blood* leaving the *lungs* is returned to the LA by pulmonary veins and passes to the LV, which pumps it into the aorta, *which supplies oxygenated blood to the rest of body*

© 2007 Jones and Bartlett Publishers

Heart Valves

AV (atrioventricular) valves

- They *prevent back flow* into *atria* when ventricles contract
1. *Tricuspid valve:* has 3 flexible flap, from RA to RV, prevents blood backflow to RA when RV contracts
2. *Bicuspid valve* (*mitral valve*): from LA to LV, prevents blood backflow to LA when LV contracts

Heart Valves

SL (semilunar) valves

- They guard the base of the large arteries issuing from the ventricles (aorta and main pulmonary artery), preventing blood backflow into the ventricles during diastole
1. Aortic valve: from LV to aorta
2. Pulmonary valve: from RV to pulmonary trunk

Coronary Circulation

- It is the fundamental *blood supply* of the *heart*
- It is the *shortest circulation* in the body
- The *myocardium* is *too thick* to make *diffusion* a practical means of *nutrient delivery*
- The *aorta* branches to the *right* coronary arteries and the *left coronary*, which carry *arterial blood* to the *heart* when it is *relaxed*
- *After passing* through the *capillary beds* of the myocardium, the *venous blood* is *collected* by the *cardiac veins*, whose path follow roughly those of the coronary arteries
- These veins *join* together *to form an enlarged vessel called* coronary sinus, which *empties blood into the RA*

Coronary Circulation

- *Remember* that the adult *cardiac* muscle does not proliferate to replace damaged or destroyed muscle fibers
- Most areas of cell death are *repaired* with *noncontractile scar* tissue

Blood Supply to the Heart
- Left coronary artery
  - Anterior descending artery supplies the anterior wall and anterior part of interventricular septum
  - Circumflex artery supplies the lateral wall
- Right coronary artery
  - Supplies the posterior wall and posterior part of interventricular septum

© 2007 Jones and Bartlett Publishers

Coronary Circulation

- In *angina pectoris*, the *thoracic pain* is caused by temporary disproportion between coronary blood flow and oxygen requirement by myocardial muscle, caused by narrowed coronary arteries resulting from arteriosclerosis, stress induced spasm of the coronary arteries
- Far more serious is *prolonged coronary blockage* which can lead to *myocardial infarction (MI)*

© 2007 Jones and Bartlett Publishers

Conduction System of the Heart

- The impulses are initiated by a group of specialized muscle cells called the conduction system of the heart

- They are initiated in the SA (sinoatrial node), in the RA, near the opening of the superior vena cava

- The ability of the cardiac muscle to depolarize and contract is intrinsic (does not depend on the nervous system)

© 2007 Jones and Bartlett Publishers

Notes

_____

_____

_____

_____

_____

_____

_____

_____

_____

_____

_____

_____

_____

_____

_____

_____

_____

_____

_____

_____

_____

_____

_____

_____

_____

_____

_____

_____

_____

_____

_____

_____

_____

_____

Conduction System of the Heart

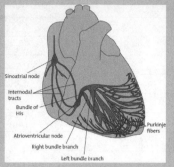

Sinoatrial node
Internodal tracts
Bundle of His
Atrioventricular node
Right bundle branch
Left bundle branch
Purkinje fibers

© 2007 Jones and Bartlett Publishers

Cardiac Cycle

- All the *events* associated with blood flow through the heart *during one complete heart beat*
- That is, *atrial systole* and *diastole* followed by *ventricular systole* and *diastole*
- Systole: contraction period
- Diastole: relaxation period
- Cardiac Output: typically 5 L/minute is amount of blood pumped out by each ventricle

© 2007 Jones and Bartlett Publishers

Blood Pressure

- The blood flow in the arteries is the result of the force of ventricular contraction

- The highest pressure is reached during ventricular contraction (systolic pressure)

- The pressure is the lowest when ventricles are relaxed (diastolic pressure)

© 2007 Jones and Bartlett Publishers

Heart Disease As a Disturbance of Pump Function

Mechanical Pump Abnormality	Comparable Heart Diseases
Faulty pump construction	Congenital heart disease
Faulty unidirectional valves	Valvular heart disease
Dirty or plugged fuel line	Coronary heart disease
Overloaded pump	Hypertensive heart disease
Malfunctioning pump	Primary myocardial disease

© 2007 Jones and Bartlett Publishers

Congenital Heart Disease

Causes
- German measles, Down Syndrome, and other undetermined causes
- *Defective* heart *chamber partitions*
- *Malformed* cardiac *valves*
- *Abnormal communication* between the large vessels and appropriate atrium or ventricle
- Some *congenital abnormalities* can be *corrected surgically*, others are *compatible with life*, and others are *fatal* in the neonatal period
- *Prevention* is to attempt to *protect* the developing fetus from *intrauterine injury*

© 2007 Jones and Bartlett Publishers

Valvular Heart Disease

- Rheumatic Heart Disease: much less frequent than formerly, is a *complication* of *rheumatic fever*
- It is caused by *scarring* of the *heart valves* subsequent to the healing of a rheumatic inflammation
- Primarily affects the *valves* of the *left heart* (mitral and aortic valves)
- Can be largely *prevented* by *treating beta strep infection promptly*
- *Rheumatic fever* is *not* a *bacterial infection* but an immunologic *complication* of infection by the group A beta hemolytic streptococcus
- It is commonly encountered in *children*

© 2007 Jones and Bartlett Publishers

_____

_____

_____

_____

_____

_____

_____

_____

_____

_____

_____

_____

_____

_____

_____

_____

_____

_____

_____

_____

_____

_____

_____

_____

_____

_____

_____

_____

_____

_____

_____

_____

_____

_____

Valvular Heart Disease

- Rheumatic fever is *febrile illness* associated with *inflammation* of connective tissue throughout the body, especially in the *heart* and *joints*
- Nonrheumatic aortic stenosis: can be caused by a *congenital bicuspid aortic valve* abnormality or by *calcified aortic stenosis*
- *Severe aortic stenosis* places a great *strain* on the *left ventricle*, and eventual *heart failure*
- *Aortic stenosis* is *caused* by *degenerative changes* in valve leaflet connective tissue, followed by calcification, which restricts valve mobility

© 2007 Jones and Bartlett Publishers

Valvular Heart Disease

- Recently, studies are demonstrating that *deposits of lipids and macrophages* in the aortic valve leaflets, *similar* to those found in *coronary atherosclerosis*.
- Therefore, it suggests that the *same risk factors* that predispose to coronary artery disease may also predispose to aortic stenosis.
- Mitral valve prolapse
- It is a *common* condition, but only a *few* develop *problems*

© 2007 Jones and Bartlett Publishers

Valvular Heart Disease

- One or more *leaflets* are *enlarged* and redundant, and *prolapse* into the *left atrium* during ventricular systole
- *Antibiotic prophylaxis* prior to *dental work* is recommended *if* condition is *associated* with *mitral regurgitation*
- Serotonin-related heart valve damage
- *High concentrations* of serotonin are found in the blood
- *Serotonin* is produced by *many cells* throughout the body, by some *tumors*, by *drugs* used to treat *migraine*, and by some *drugs* to *suppress appetite* in obesity

© 2007 Jones and Bartlett Publishers

Valvular Heart Disease

- Infective endocarditis
- Usually caused by *bacteria* but also by *other pathogens*, mostly in the valves on the *left side* of the heart
- Divided in two groups
1. Subacute infective endocarditis: caused by organisms of *low virulence*, may be a *complication* of any *valvular heart disease*, and associated with mild symptoms of infection
2. Acute infective endocarditis: *highly virulent* organism, associated with symptoms of a *severe systemic infection*
3. Persons with valvular heart disease should have antibiotic phophylaxis prior to dental or surgical procedures to guard against endocarditis

© 2007 Jones and Bartlett Publishers

Coronary Heart Disease

- Caused by *atherosclerosis* of the *large coronary arteries*, where the *arteries narrow* owing to *accumulation of fatty materials*
- The *lipid deposits*, consisting of neutral fat and cholesterol, *accumulate* in the arteries by *diffusion from the bloodstream*
- Pathogenesis of atherosclerosis
   Endothelial injury
   - Lipids accumulate and precipitate
   - Secondary fibrosis and calcification
   - Formation of atheroma

© 2007 Jones and Bartlett Publishers

Coronary Artery Disease

- The *initial stage* of atherosclerosis is *reversible*, and the *newly formed plaques* are called *unstable plaques*
- The *later stages*, characterized by *crystalization* of *cholesterol* and secondary *degenerative changes*, are *irreversible*
- The plaques which become surrounded by fibrous tissue are called *stable plaques*
- The *vessel* becomes *permanently narrowed*

© 2007 Jones and Bartlett Publishers

Coronary Heart Disease
Risk Factors

- Elevated blood lipids
- High blood pressure
- Cigarette smoking
- Diabetes

Other risk factors that play a less important role

- Obesity accompanied by high blood lipids and elevated blood pressure
- Personality: type A personality, which is aggressive, hard driving, and competitive

© 2007 Jones and Bartlett Publishers

Manifestations of
Coronary Heart Disease

- Also referred to as *Ischemic Heart Disease*
- It is related to a *decrease in blood supply* to the *heart muscle* caused by *narrowing or obstruction* of the coronary arteries
- The *clinical manifestations* are quite *variable*
- Some individuals are *free of symptoms*
- Some experience *chest oppression* that may *radiate into neck or arms*
- The *pain* which is caused by *myocardial ischemia* is called *Angina pectoris*
- Stable angina: pain occurs on exertion, subsides with rest, and is relieved by nitroglycerine

© 2007 Jones and Bartlett Publishers

Manifestations of
Coronary Heart Disease

- Unstable angina: pain occurs more frequently, lasts longer, and are less relieved by nitro
- Prinzmetal's angina: occurs at rest and caused by coronary artery spasm
- A *more severe and prolonged myocardial ischemia* may precipitate an *acute episode*, called a *heart attack*

This *event* may be manifested as either

- A cessation of normal cardiac contractions, called *cardiac arrest*, or
- An actual necrosis of the heart muscle, called *myocardial infarction*

© 2007 Jones and Bartlett Publishers

Myocardial Infarction
Location

- Most often involves left ventricle
  - Anterior wall
    - Left anterior descending artery distribution
  - Lateral wall
    - Circumflex artery distribution
  - Posterior wall
    - Right coronary distribution
  - Massive anterior and lateral wall
    - Main left coronary distribution

© 2007 Jones and Bartlett Publishers

Myocardial Infarction
Triggers

- Any one of four basic mechanisms may trigger a *heart attack* in a *patient* with *coronary heart disease*

1. Sudden *blockage of a coronary artery*, usually caused by a *clot, coronary thrombosis*
2. *Hemorrhage* into an atheromatous plaque, usually caused by *rupture* of a small blood vessel adjacent to the plaque, which enlarges the plaque, further narrowing the lumen of the artery

© 2007 Jones and Bartlett Publishers

Myocardial Infarction
Triggers

3. *Arterial spasm*, which occurs adjacent to atheromatous plaque and precipitates *arterial narrowing or obstruction*
4. *Sudden, greatly increased myocardial oxygen requirements*, caused by *vigorous activity* such as running which abruptly *increases cardiac output*, which in turn *raises myocardial oxygen consumption*

© 2007 Jones and Bartlett Publishers

Myocardial Infarction
Complications

1. Arrhythmias: disturbances of cardiac rhythm, most serious is ventricular fibrillation, which leads to cessation of circulation
2. Heart failure: ventricles may be badly damaged, unable to maintain normal cardiac function, and heart fails
3. Intracardial thrombi: may be carried to systemic circulation, causing infarction to brain, kidneys, spleen

© 2007 Jones and Bartlett Publishers

Myocardial Infarction
Complications

4. Pericarditis: infarct extends to the epicardial surface, which leads to accumulation of fluid and inflammatory cells in the pericardial sac
5. Cardiac rupture: a perforation may occur through the necrotic muscle, permits blood to leak into the pericardial sac, compressing the heart; ventricles cannot fill in diastole, causing cardiac tamponade
6. Papillary muscle dysfunction: the papillary muscle becomes infarcted, unable to contract normally, causing the mitral valve to prolapse slightly into the LA, and causing mitral insufficiency

© 2007 Jones and Bartlett Publishers

Myocardial Infarction
Complications

7. Ventricular aneurysm: late complication, an outward bulging of the healing infarct during ventricular systole. Aneurysm sac fills with blood rather than being ejected to the aorta and cardiac output is reduced.
- Survival
  - Depends on size, patient's age, complications, other diseases
  - Mortality rates vary from 6% with small infarcts that do not develop heart failure to more than 50% with large infarcts that develop severe heart failure

© 2007 Jones and Bartlett Publishers

Myocardial Infarction
Complications

Major *causes* of *death* following an *MI*
1. Fatal arrhythmia
2. Heart failure
3. Cardiac rupture with cardiac tamponade

- 90% of <u>hospitalized</u> patients survive

© 2007 Jones and Bartlett Publishers

Myocardial Infarction
Diagnosis

- Diagnosis
  - <u>Medical history</u>: may at times be inconclusive because severe angina may be similar to the pain of MI
  - <u>Physical examination</u>: will usually not be abnormal unless patient exhibits evidence of shock, heart failure, etc.
  - <u>Laboratory data</u>: physician must rely on these
    - Electrocardiogram: measures the transmission of electrical impulses associated with cardiac contraction, indicating the location and size of infarct

© 2007 Jones and Bartlett Publishers

Myocardial Infarction
Diagnosis

- Enzyme tests: heart muscle is rich in enzymes and proteins that regulate its activities, that leak from the necrotic cells into circulation when muscle becomes infarcted
- Most importantly
1. Troponin T and troponin I (proteins concerned with muscle contractions)
2. Creatine kinase (heart muscle enzyme)
3. Lactic dehydrogenase (heart muscle enzyme)
4. Myoglobin (muscle protein)

© 2007 Jones and Bartlett Publishers

Myocardial Infarction: Treatment

- Treatment
  - Thrombolytic therapy: very effective but the clot may not be dissolved completely and some patients are not suitable because of bleeding problems; angioplasty is favored to restore coronary blood flow
  - Bed rest advancing to graded activity, after as much myocardium as possible has been salvaged
  - Antiarrhythmia drugs: to decrease the irritability of the heart muscle
  - Cardiac pacemaker: if complete heart block develops

© 2007 Jones and Bartlett Publishers

Myocardial Infarction: Treatment

- Anticoagulant drugs: to reduce the coagulability of blood, decreasing the likelihood of thrombus and emboli
- Beta-blockers: reduce myocardial irritability, often given to patients after recovering from MI
- Aspirin: small amount to inhibit platelet function, therefore making them less likely to adhere to roughened atheromatous plaques that can initiate a thrombosis

© 2007 Jones and Bartlett Publishers

Myocardial Infarction: Treatment

Factors controlled or eliminated
1. Cessation of smoking
2. Control of hypertension
3. An anticoronary diet- low cholesterol and fat
4. Weight reduction
5. Graduated exercise program

Surgical treatment: myocardial revascularization procedures
- Bypass surgery: bypasses the obstructions in the coronary arteries usually by means of segments of saphenous veins obtained from the patient's legs

© 2007 Jones and Bartlett Publishers

Myocardial Infarction: Treatment

- <u>Coronary angioplasty</u>: dilates areas of narrowing within coronary arteries, rather than bypassing them (major surgery)
- A guided catheter introduced through skin and into a large artery in the arm or leg threaded under fluoroscopic control into the narrowed coronary artery, and positioned at the site of narrowing. Then a balloon catheter is inflated under very high pressure, which smashes the plaque and pushes it into the arterial wall, enlarging the lumen of the artery

© 2007 Jones and Bartlett Publishers

Coronary Artery Disease (CAD)

- *Cocaine*-induced arrhythmias and myocardial infarcts: the heart beats faster and more forcefully, increasing myocardial oxygen requirements
- *Blood lipids* and CAD
  - *Triglyceride*: derived from ingested *fat* as well as from *carbohydrates and sugar*
  - *Cholesterol*: derived from ingested *cholesterol* and dietary *fat*; *saturated fat* (found in meats and dairy products) *raises* blood cholesterol; *unsaturated fats* (found in fish, poultry, and most vegetable oils) tends to *lower* cholesterol

© 2007 Jones and Bartlett Publishers

Coronary Artery Disease

- *Cholesterol* is *carried* in the *blood* plasma combined with proteins and other lipids as complexes called, *lipoproteins*
1. *LDL* (low density lipoprotein, "*bad cholesterol*") carries cholesterol from the bloodstream to the cells
2. *HDL* (high density lipoprotein, "*good cholesterol*") removes cholesterol from the cells, carrying it to the liver for excretion in the bile

Factors associated with *raising HDL* levels
1. Regular exercise
2. Cessation of smoking
3. Modest regular alcohol intake.

© 2007 Jones and Bartlett Publishers

Coronary Artery Disease

- *Homocysteine* and CAD: Vitamin B and folic acid are necessary to metabolize homocysteine; elevated homocysteine blood levels is a risk factor for atherosclerosis comparable to high lipids, smoking and hypertension;homocysteine levels are higher in men than in premenopausal women but increase in menopausal women
- *Chlamydia pneumoniae* and CAD: *Chlamydia pneumoniae* has been isolated in plaques, which may contribute to arterial intimal damage

© 2007 Jones and Bartlett Publishers

Hypertension

- *Results from* excessive vasoconstriction of small arterioles throughout the body, which raises the diastolic blood pressure, high peripheral resistance forces the heart to increase the force of ventricular contraction in order to supply blood to the tissues, which produces a compensatory increase in the systolic pressure
  - Cardiac effects: *heart* is enlarged
  - Vascular effects: *vessels* wear out prematurely, accelerates atherosclerosis
  - Renal effects: narrowing of renal arterioles decreases blood supply to *kidneys*

© 2007 Jones and Bartlett Publishers

Primary Myocardial Disease

- There are two types
1. Myocarditis: *inflammation heart muscle*, mostly caused in U.S. by *viruses*; onset abrupt, may lead to acute heart failure
2. Cardiomyopathy
   - *Dilated* cardiomyopathy: enlargement of heart and dilatation of its chambers, pimping action of ventricles impaired, leading to chronic heart failure, cause uncertain and no treatment
   - *Hypertrophic* cardiomyopathy: hereditary, transmitted as a dominant trait, marked hypertrophy of heart muscle, chambers do not dilate readily in diastole

© 2007 Jones and Bartlett Publishers

Notes

_____

_____

_____

_____

_____

_____

_____

_____

_____

_____

_____

_____

_____

_____

_____

_____

_____

_____

_____

_____

_____

_____

_____

_____

_____

_____

_____

_____

_____

_____

_____

_____

_____

_____

_____

Heart Failure

- *Occurs* when the *heart* is *no longer able to pump* adequate amounts of blood to the tissues. Usually develops slowly (chronic heart failure) with congestion of the tissues, term used is <u>congestive heart failure</u>
- The mechanisms leading to heart failure
  - *Forward failure*: insufficient blood flow to the tissues, inadequate renal blood flow resulting in salt and water kidney retention leads to increased blood volume and rise in venous pressure

© 2007 Jones and Bartlett Publishers

Heart Failure

- *Backward failure:* causes "back up" of blood within the veins draining back to the heart, leads to increased venous pressure, congestion of viscera, and edema
- *Both* forward and *backward failure are present to* some degree in patients with heart failure

<u>Treatment</u>
1. Diuretic drugs: promote *excretion* of excess *salt and water* by kidneys
2. Digitalis: *increase* the efficiency of *ventricular contractions*

© 2007 Jones and Bartlett Publishers

Heart Failure: Treatment

3. ACE inhibitors: *block* an enzyme called *angiotensin converting enzyme*, which is involved in a renal regulatory mechanism that promotes retention of salt and water

© 2007 Jones and Bartlett Publishers

Acute Pulmonary Edema

- A *manifestation* of *acute heart failure* that is caused by a temporary disproportion in the output of blood from the ventricles
- If the output of blood from the left ventricle is temporarily reduced more than the one from the right, the right heart will pump blood into the lungs faster than the left heart can deliver the blood to the peripheral tissues, rapidly engorging the lungs with blood and the extravasation of fluid in alveoli occurs, causing the patient to become extremely short of breath

© 2007 Jones and Bartlett Publishers

Aneurysms

- *Dilation* of the *wall* of an artery or an *outpouching* of a portion of the wall
  - *Arteriosclerotic* aneurysm: causes weakening of the vessel wall (most aneurysms are acquired as a result of arteriosclerosis)
  - *Dissecting* aneurysm of aorta: the splitting (dissection) of the media (thick middle layer of aorta) by blood due to degenerative changes that cause layers to loose their cohesiveness and separate

© 2007 Jones and Bartlett Publishers

Diseases of the Veins

Thrombosis: blockage of a vein by clots

Phlebitis: inflammation of a vein

1. Venous thrombosis and *thrombophlebitis*: occur most commonly in leg veins but also elsewhere
2. *Varicose veins* of the lower extremities: dilated, tortuous veins, most often in *leg veins*
3. *Varicose veins* in other locations besides the leg veins

© 2007 Jones and Bartlett Publishers

Chapter Outline

The chapter outline provides you with an organizational guide to the topics and ideas presented in this chapter of the text.

Study Questions

The following questions are provided as a test for comprehension and as a study guide for use with the text chapters. Additional study material is located at http://humandisease.jbpub.com/, which contains useful tools such as an A&P review, animated flashcards, an interactive online glossary, crossword puzzles, and web links.

Key Terms

Define the following terms:

1. Heme _____

2. Globin _____

3. Bilirubin _____

4. Anemia _____

5. Polycythemia _____

6. Hemochromatosis _____

Fill-in-the-Blank

1. The usual survival time of red cells in the circulation is _____.

2. The normal number of reticulocytes in the circulation is approximately _____ percent.

3. _____ is the usual cause of hypochromic, microcytic anemia in a middle-aged man.

4. Some patients have congenital deficiencies of the red cell enzymes that are required to metabolize glucose as a source of energy. These patients often have _____.

5. The disease in which there is an excess of iron in the body is called _____.

6. Infectious mononucleosis is caused by _____.

7. A young red cell is called a _____, and it survives in the circulation about _____ days. Worn-out red cells are destroyed primarily in _____. The hemoglobin is broken down, and its components are recycled.

True/False

1. Tell whether each statement is true or false regarding iron deficiency anemia. If false, explain why the statement is incorrect.

   a. It may result from a bleeding ulcer. _____

   _____

   b. It may result from excessive blood donations. _____

   _____

   c. It may result from a deficiency of vitamins required for efficient blood production. _____

   _____

   d. It may result from excessive menstrual blood loss. _____

   _____

Identification

1. List the five white blood cells in the circulation and indicate their functions.

    a. _____

    b. _____

    c. _____

    d. _____

    e. _____

2. List three laboratory tests that are useful to measure iron stores, iron transport, and iron metabolism.

    a. _____

    b. _____

    c. _____

3. The macrocytic anemia resulting from inability to absorb vitamin B_{12} as a result of atrophy of gastric mucosa is called pernicious anemia. List three other causes of macrocytic anemia caused by inability to absorb or utilize vitamin B_{12}.

    a. _____

    b. _____

    c. _____

4. List four causes of hereditary hemolytic anemia.

    a. _____

    b. _____

    c. _____

    d. _____

5. List two treatments that are suitable for treating a patient with aplastic anemia.

    a. _____

    b. _____

6. List three diseases that are associated with secondary polycythemia.

    a. _____

    b. _____

    c. _____

Discussion Questions

1. Where does bilirubin come from? _____

    _____

    _____

    _____

2. Describe the uptake, transport, utilization, and storage of iron. (*Hint:* see Fig. 14-3.) _____

_____

_____

3. What is the difference between the etiologic and the morphologic classifications of anemia? _____

_____

_____

_____

4. Outline a simple etiologic classification of anemia. _____

_____

_____

_____

5. What are the functions of the spleen? What happens if the spleen is removed? _____

_____

_____

_____

6. What are the clinical manifestations of infectious mononucleosis? How is the disease treated? _____

_____

_____

_____

7. How does primary polycythemia differ from secondary polycythemia? _____

_____

_____

_____

8. What is the difference between polycythemia and thrombocytopenia? _____

_____

_____

_____

9. What is the cause of aplastic anemia? How is it treated? _____

_____

_____

_____

10. What is the difference between aplastic anemia and hemolytic anemia? _____

_____

_____

_____

11. What is hemochromatosis? How is the condition diagnosed? How is it treated? _____

_____

_____

_____

12. What is the lymphatic system? How is it organized? What are the major cells in the lymphatic system? What are the major functions of the lymphatic system? _____

_____

_____

_____

13. List the morphologic features found in aplastic anemia (anemia due to bone marrow failure). _____

_____

_____

_____

14. What conditions are associated with megaloblastic anemia? _____

_____

_____

_____

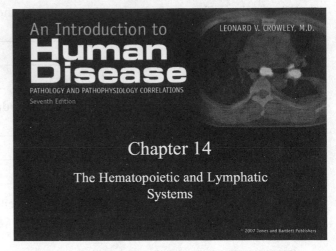

An Introduction to
Human Disease
PATHOLOGY AND PATHOPHYSIOLOGY CORRELATIONS
Seventh Edition

LEONARD V. CROWLEY, M.D.

Chapter 14

The Hematopoietic and Lymphatic Systems

© 2007 Jones and Bartlett Publishers

Composition of Human Blood

Blood

- *Transports* oxygen, nutrients, hormones, leukocytes (white cells), red cells, platelets and antibodies *to tissues* in the *body* and *carbon dioxide* and *other waste products* of cell metabolism *to the excretory organs* of the body
- *Volume* of blood: approximately *5 quarts*, but it *varies* according to *size* of individual
- Almost *half* of the blood consists of *cellular elements* suspended in *plasma* (viscous fluid)

© 2007 Jones and Bartlett Publishers

Composition of Human Blood

- *All blood cells* arise from *precursor cells* within the bone marrow, called *stem cells*
- These undergo *further differentiation* to form *red cells, white cells, and platelets*

The cellular elements are:
- Red cells
- Leukocytes
  - Neutrophils
  - Monocytes
  - Eosinophils
  - Lymphocytes
  - Basophils
- Platelets

© 2007 Jones and Bartlett Publishers

Composition of Human Blood

- Red cells
- Are primarily concerned with transport of *oxygen*
- Most *numerous cells*
- Survival *4 months*
- *Erythroblast* is precursor cell in bone marrow
- *Hemoglobin* is the *oxygen-carrying protein* that is formed by the developing red cell
- Leukocytes
- *Less* numerous
- Different types
- Survival from several hours to several days, *except* for *lymphocytes*

© 2007 Jones and Bartlett Publishers

Composition of Human Blood

- *Lymphocytes* may last for *several years*
- Lymphocytes are *also* produced in the *bone marrow* but are *mainly* produced in the *lymph nodes and spleen*

Types of Leukocytes
1. Neutrophils
- *Most numerous* in *adults*
- Comprise about *70%* of total circulating white cells
- Actively *phagocytic*
- Predominant in *inflammatory* reactions

© 2007 Jones and Bartlett Publishers

Composition of Human Blood: Leukocytes

2. Monocytes
- Actively *phagocytic*
- Increased in certain types of *chronic infection*
3. Eosinophils
- Increase in *allergic* reactions
- Increase in the presence of *animal-parasite infections*
4. Lymphocytes
- *Next* most common in adults
- *Predominant* leukocyte in *children*

© 2007 Jones and Bartlett Publishers

Notes

Composition of Human Blood: Lymphocytes

- Mostly located in the *lymph nodes, the spleen,* and *other lymphoid tissues*
- Take part in both the *cell-mediated* and *humoral* defense reactions

© 2007 Jones and Bartlett Publishers

Composition of Human Blood

Platelets
- Are essential for *blood coagulation*
- Are much *smaller* than leukocytes
- They represent *bits* of the *cytoplasm* of *megakarocytes*, which are the largest precursor cell in the bone marrow
- Have a relatively *short survival*, about 10 days

© 2007 Jones and Bartlett Publishers

Normal Hematopoiesis

Hematopoiesis: the formation and development of blood cells
- The bone marrow replenishes the blood cells
- Substances necessary for hematopoiesis
  - *Protein*
  - *Vitamin B$_{12}$*
  - *Folic acid (one of the vitamin B group)*
  - *Iron*
- *Red cell* production is regulated by the *oxygen* content of the arterial blood
- *White cell* production is not well understood

© 2007 Jones and Bartlett Publishers

Normal Hematopoiesis

Factors that may cause *white cell production*
- Products of *cell necrosis*
- *Hormone* secretion by the adrenals and other endocrine glands

Red cells
- Red cells develop from *erythroblasts*, which are large precursor cells in the bone marrow
- *Hemoglobin,* formed by developing red cells, is a tetramer composed of four different subunits, each one consisting of *heme* and *globin*

© 2007 Jones and Bartlett Publishers

Normal Hematopoiesis

- *Heme* is a porphyrin ring that contains an *iron* atom
- *Globin* forms the *largest* part of the hemoglobin, that forms different *chains* designated by Greek letters such as *alpha, beta, gamma, delta, and epsilon*
- The *heme* and the *globin* are synthesized separately in different locations within the erythoblast
- The *porphyrin ring* is produced by the *mitochondria*; then the iron is inserted to form heme
- The *globin chains* are produced by the *ribosomes*, and are joined to heme to form a hemoglobin unit

© 2007 Jones and Bartlett Publishers

Normal Hematopoiesis

- Finally, the four subunits aggregate to form the complete *hemoglobin tetramer*
- The developing red cell *accumulates* increasing amounts of *hemoglobin* as it matures
- The *nucleus* is *extruded* when *80%* of its total *hemoglobin* has been *synthesized*
- The *cell* is *discharged* from the bone marrow into the circulation, where it completes its *maturation process* within the next *24 hours*
- A newly formed red cell that *lacks a nucleus* but retains some of its organelles can be identified by special strains and is called a reticulocyte
- After about 24 hours, it becomes a mature red cell where it survives in the circulation for about four months.

© 2007 Jones and Bartlett Publishers

Normal Hematopoiesis

- The *worn out red cells* are *removed* in the *spleen*
- The *hemoglobin* is *degraded*
- The *globin chains* are *broken down* and their *products* used to make *other proteins*
- The *iron* is *extracted* and *saved* to make *new hemoglobin*
- The *porphyrin ring* cannot be salvaged and is *excreted* by the *liver* as *bile pigment*

© 2007 Jones and Bartlett Publishers

Regulation of Hematopoiesis

- The *red cell production* is *regulated* by the *oxygen content* of the arterial blood
- A *decreased oxygen* supply *stimulates erythropoiesis*
- The low oxygen tension does *not* act directly on the bone marrow
- It is *mediated* by the *kidneys* which produce *erythropoietin*, which is a hormone-like erythrocyte-stimulating material

© 2007 Jones and Bartlett Publishers

Anemia

A *decrease in red blood cells* or a *subnormal* level of hemoglobin

- Two different methods of classification are used
1. *Etiologic* classification: the *factor* responsible for anemia
2. *Morphologic* classification: *shape* and *appearance* of red cell

© 2007 Jones and Bartlett Publishers

Etiologic Classification
Anemia

1. Inadequate production of red cells
   - *Insufficiency of raw materials*: iron deficiency, Vitamin B$_{12}$ deficiency, folic acid deficiency
   - *Inability to deliver adequate red cells into circulation* because of *marrow damage or destruction* (as in aplastic anemia), or by the *replacement of marrow by foreign* or *abnormal cells* (as in bone marrow replacement anemia)

© 2007 Jones and Bartlett Publishers

Etiologic Classification
Anemia

2. Excessive loss of red cells
   - *External blood loss* (hemorrhage)
   - *Shortened survival of red cells* in circulation, with defective red cells as in hereditary *hemolytic anemia*
   - *Accelerated destruction of cells* as caused by *anti-red antibodies*, or by *mechanical trauma* to circulating red cells

© 2007 Jones and Bartlett Publishers

Morphologic Classification
of Anemia

- *Normocytic* anemia: appearance and size of cells is *normal*
- *Macrocytic* anemia: cells *larger* than normal
- *Microcytic* anemia: cells are *smaller* than normal
- *Hypochromic* anemia: *reduced hemoglobin* content
- *Hypochromic microcytic anemia: smaller* than normal and *reduced hemoglobin* content
- Classification of anemia based on red cell *appearance* is useful since it *suggests the etiology of the anemia.*

© 2007 Jones and Bartlett Publishers

Morphologic Classification
of Anemia

- Iron deficiency anemia = *hypochromic microcytic*
- Vitamin B_{12} or folic acid deficiency anemia = *macrocytic* anemia
- Most other types of anemia = *normocytic*

© 2007 Jones and Bartlett Publishers

Iron-Deficiency Anemia

- *Most common* anemia
- *Hypochromic microcytic* anemia
- Pathogenesis
  - *Inadequate iron intake* in diet, as in *infants* during periods of rapid growth or with *adolescents* subsisting on an inadequate diet
  - *Inadequate reutilization* of iron present in red cells due to *chronic blood loss*

Laboratory Tests
- Serum ferritin
- Serum iron
- Serum iron-binding capacity

© 2007 Jones and Bartlett Publishers

Iron-Deficiency Anemia

The characteristic laboratory profile of iron deficiency anemia is *low serum ferritin* and *serum iron* but a *much higher than normal serum iron-binding protein* with a *much lower than normal percent iron saturation*

Treatment
- Primary focus is to *learn* the *cause* of the anemia
- Then *direct treatment* towards the *cause* rather than the symptoms
- Supplementary *iron*

© 2007 Jones and Bartlett Publishers

Iron-Deficiency Anemia

Examples

- Infant with a history of poor diet
- In adults: a common cause is chronic blood loss from the gastrointestinal tract, as may be caused by a bleeding ulcer or an ulcerated carcinoma of the colon
- In women: excessive menstrual blood loss
- Too frequent blood donations

Vitamin B_{12} and Folic Acid Deficiency Anemia

- *Vitamin B_{12}*: found in meat, liver, and other foods rich in *animal protein*
- *Folic acid*: found in *green leafy vegetables* and other *animal protein foods*
- Both are required not only for normal *hematopoiesis* but also for normal *maturation* of many other types of cells
- The maturation of red cells in the bone marrow is abnormal and is called megaloblastic erythropoiesis
- The mature red cells are *larger* than normal and are called macrocytes; the anemia is called macrocytic anemia

Folic Acid Deficiency Anemia

- Is *relatively common*
- The *body* has very *limited stores*, which rapidly become depleted if not replenished continually
- Pathogenesis
  - *Inadequate diet*: encountered frequently in chronic *alcoholics*
  - *Poor absorption* caused by *intestinal disease*
  - Occasionally occurs in *pregnancy*, which *increases* folic acid *requirements*

Vitamin B$_{12}$ Deficiency
Pernicious Anemia

- <u>Pernicious Anemia</u>- Vitamin B$_{12}$ deficiency macrocytic anemia
  - *Lack* of *intrinsic factor*, not secreted because of gastric mucosal atrophy
  - The atrophy also causes the lack of secretion of acid and digestive enzymes
  - Vitamin B$_{12}$ not absorbed
  - Sometimes develops in *middle aged* and *elderly* individuals
  - Often associated with *autoantibodies* directed against gastric mucosal cells and intrinsic factor

© 2007 Jones and Bartlett Publishers

Other Causes of Vitamin B$_{12}$ Deficiency Anemia

- Following gastric resection to treat ulcer disease or to treat gastric cancer
- Following gastric bypass procedures to treat obesity
- Due to distal small bowel resection or disease (because Vitamin B$_{12}$ is absorbed in the ileum)

Treatment
- Intramuscular administration of Vitamin B$_{12}$

© 2007 Jones and Bartlett Publishers

Bone Marrow Suppression, Damage, or Infiltration

Many conditions can depress bone marrow function
- Anemia of chronic disease, which causes a mild suppression of bone marrow function
- Marrow injured by radiation, anticancer drugs or toxic chemicals; aplastic anemia, which is much more serious, can cause severe bone marrow damage
- A manifestation of an autoimmune disease in which the body's own cytotoxic T lymphocytes attack and destroy the marrow stem cells

© 2007 Jones and Bartlett Publishers

Bone Marrow Suppression, Damage, or Infiltration

- Marrow infiltrated by tumor
- Marrow replaced by fibrous tissue

Treatment depends on cause
- Blood and platelet transfusions
- Immunosuppressive drugs
- Bone marrow transplant in highly selected cases of aplastic anemia

© 2007 Jones and Bartlett Publishers

Hereditary Hemolytic Anemia Classification

- Genetically determined abnormalities of red cells
  1. Abnormally *shaped* cells: most common is hereditary spherocytosis
  2. Abnormal *hemoglobins*: Hemoglobin S (sickle hemoglobin) is an important one; another one is hemoglobin C; both found predominantly in persons of African descent
  3. Defective *hemoglobin synthesis*: in thalassemia, the globulin chains are normal but their synthesis defective; found predominantly in persons of Greek and Italian ancestry; thalassemia minor (mild anemia) and thalassemia major (severe anemia)

© 2007 Jones and Bartlett Publishers

Hereditary Hemolytic Anemia Classification

4. *Red cell enzyme* deficiencies: very common one is deficiency of an enzyme called *glucose-6-phosphatase dehydrogenase*, where the enzyme is unstable and does not function normally

Acquired Hemolytic Anemia
- The *red cells* are *normally* formed but are *unable to survive* normally because they are released into a "*hostile environment*"
- Red cells unable to survive when *antibodies* attack and destroy
- Red cells destroyed by *mechanical trauma*

© 2007 Jones and Bartlett Publishers

Classification of Hereditary Hemolytic Anemias

Diagnostic Evaluation of Anemia

- *History* and *physical examination* may provide important clues
- *Complete blood count* is essential to assess the *degree* of anemia, and for *leukopenia and thrombocytopenia*
- *Blood smear*, to determine if *normocytic, macrocytic,* or *hypochromic microcytic*
- *Reticulocyte count*, to determine the *rate of production* of *new* red cells
- Lab tests to determine iron, B_{12}, folic acid where indicated

© 2007 Jones and Bartlett Publishers

Diagnostic Evaluation of Anemia

- *Bone marrow study:* pernicious anemia, folic acid deficiency anemia, aplastic anemia, and others show *characteristic abnormalities* in the marrow cells
- *Evaluation of blood loss* from gastrointestinal tract through *blood stools* and *x-rays* are performed to localize site of bleeding

© 2007 Jones and Bartlett Publishers

Polycythemia

- Secondary
  - *Compensatory increase in red blood cells* (increased erythropoietin production) as a *response* to low arterial O_2 that may accompany underlying disease, such a emphysema, pulmonary fibrosis; and other conditions that impair the oxygenation of blood; some types of congenital heart disease
- Primary/Polycythemia Vera
  - Is a manifestation of a diffuse hyperplasia of bone marrow of *unknown etiology*, characterized by *overproduction of red cells, white cells, and platelets*; some patients eventually develop granulocytic leukemia

© 2007 Jones and Bartlett Publishers

Polycythemia

Treatment

- Many patients develop *thromboses* due to the increased blood viscosity and elevated platelet count
- Primary Polycythemia: drugs that *suppress* bone marrow overactivity
- Secondary Polycythemia: periodic *removal* of excess blood

© 2007 Jones and Bartlett Publishers

Hemochromatosis

- *Genetic disease*: autosomal recessive trait
- Body becomes *overloaded* with *iron*
- Iron is *absorbed and excreted* with difficulty
- There is an accumulation of iron that leads to *organ damage*, followed by scarring, and permanent derangement of organ function
- The *manifestations* of the disease take years to develop: *tan to brown skin, diabetes, cirrhosis, heart failure*

Treatment

- Repeated *phlebotomies* (withdrawal of blood) until iron stores are depleted and then periodic for life

© 2007 Jones and Bartlett Publishers

Thrombocytopenia

- *Secondary* Thrombocytopenia Purpura
  - Drugs, chemicals damage the bone marrow
  - Bone marrow infiltrated by leukemic cells or metastatic carcinoma
- *Primary* Thrombocytopenia Purpura
  - Associated with antiplatelet autoantibodies
  - The bone marrow produces platelets but are rapidly destroyed
  - Often encountered in children and subsides spontaneously after a short time
  - Tends to be chronic in adults

© 2007 Jones and Bartlett Publishers

The Lymphatic System

- The primary function of the *lymphatic system* is to provide *immunologic defenses* against foreign material by means of *cell-mediated and humoral defense* mechanisms

Lymphatic System

- Lymph nodes: bean-shaped structures that consists of a *mass* of *lymphocytes* supported by a meshwork of reticular fibers in which are scattered *phagocytic cells*
- As the lymph flows through the nodes, the phagocytic cells filter out and destroy the microorganisms and foreign matter that has gotten into the lymphatic channels

© 2007 Jones and Bartlett Publishers

The Lymphatic System

- Spleen: specialized to *filter blood*
- It consists of a compact mass of lymphocytes and a network of sinusoids (capillaries with wide lumens)
- Lymphoid Tissue such as, thymus, tonsils, adenoids, lymphoid aggregates in the intestinal mucosa, respiratory tract, and bone marrow
- Thymus: overlies base of heart; is *large* during *infancy* and *childhood,* undergoes *atrophy* in *adolescence,* and a *remnant* in *adulthood*; plays essential role in *prenatal* development of *lymphoid system*, and in *formation* of the body's *immunologic* defense mechanisms

© 2007 Jones and Bartlett Publishers

Lymphatic System Diseases

- Lymphadenitis: *inflammation* of the lymph nodes
- Infectious Mononucleosis: caused by the *Epstein-Barr* virus; mostly encountered by *young adults*, and is transmitted by close contact, usually *kissing*
- *Neoplasms* affecting the lymph nodes
  - *Metastatic tumors:* arising in the breasts, lung, colon, or other sites
  - *Malignant lymphoma:* two main types are Hodgkin's and Non-Hodgkin's
  - *Lymphocytic leukemia:* derived from lymphoid precursor cells; acute (primitive forms) or chronic (mature cells)

© 2007 Jones and Bartlett Publishers

The Spleen

- *Removes* bacteria or foreign material from the *bloodstream* through *phagocytosis*
- *Manufactures antibodies* that facilitate prompt elimination of pathogenic organisms

Splenectomy

- Reasons
  - *Traumatic injury:* to prevent fatal hemorrhage
  - *Blood diseases:* characterized by excessive destruction of blood cells within the spleen, such as with some types of hereditary hemolytic anemia

© 2007 Jones and Bartlett Publishers

The Spleen

  - *Hodgkin's disease:* occasionally performed before treatment to determine if spleen has been affected by disease
- Effects
  - *Less-efficient* elimination of bacteria
  - *Impaired* production of antibodies
  - *Predisposition* of systemic bloodstream infection

© 2007 Jones and Bartlett Publishers

Chapter Outline

The chapter outline provides you with an organizational guide to the topics and ideas presented in this chapter of the text.

Study Questions

The following questions are provided as a test for comprehension and as a study guide for use with the text chapters. Additional study material is located at http://humandisease.jbpub.com/, which contains useful tools such as an A&P review, animated flashcards, an interactive online glossary, crossword puzzles, and web links.

Key Terms

Define the following terms:

1. Miliary tuberculosis _____

2. Pulmonary fibrosis _____

3. Pneumothorax _____

4. Pulmonary emphysema _____

5. Pneumonia _____

Fill-in-the-Blank

1. Movement of air in and out of the lungs is called _____, and movement of oxygen and carbon dioxide between alveoli and pulmonary capillaries is called _____.

2. Escape of air from the lung associated with collapse of the lung is called a _____.

3. Development of a positive (higher than atmospheric) pressure in the pleural cavity associated with collapse of the lung is called a _____, and this condition is treated by _____.

4. Collapse of part of the lung caused by obstruction of bronchi or bronchioles with absorption of the trapped air into the bloodstream is called _____.

5. The agent that causes severe acute respiratory syndrome (SARS) is _____.

6. Primary atypical pneumonia is caused by _____.

7. The characteristic multinucleated cell associated with the necrosis in tuberculosis is called a _____.

8. The skin test that detects hypersensitivity to the antigens in the tubercle bacillus as an indication of previous exposure to the organism is called the _____ test.

9. Deficiency of surfactant in the lungs of premature infants leads to a condition called _____.

10. The condition characterized by breathing difficulty caused by bronchospasm is called _____.

11. Progressive pulmonary fibrosis caused by inhalation of rock dust is called _____.

12. Pulmonary fibrosis caused by inhalation of asbestos fibers is called _____.

13. The disease caused by exposure to asbestos fibers may predispose a person to development of malignant lung and pleural tumors. The lung tumor is called a _____, and the pleural tumor is called a _____.

14. The disease characterized by chronic bronchitis associated with breakdown of alveolar septa, formation of cystic spaces throughout the lung, and loss of lung elasticity is called _____.

15. The incidence of pulmonary emphysema is _____.

16. _____ is the major factor responsible for the rising incidence of lung carcinoma in women.

17. _____ is a condition characterized by chronic inflammation with dilation of bronchi.

18. Inhalation of a foreign body in the lung may cause _____.

True/False

1. Tell whether each statement is true or false regarding the severe acute respiratory syndrome (SARS). If false, explain why the statement is incorrect.

   a. This highly communicable disease is caused by an unusual coronavirus. _____

   _____

   b. The virus can be transmitted by coughing and sneezing and by the virus-contaminated hands of an infected patient.

   _____

   c. The virus responds to antiviral antibiotics. _____

   _____

   d. The lungs of severely affected SARS patients develop features characteristic of adult respiratory distress syndrome.

   _____

2. Tell whether each statement is true or false regarding the treatment of emphysema by lung volume reduction surgery (LVRS). If false, explain why the statement is incorrect.

   a. LVRS may be suitable for some patients who have emphysema restricted to the upper lobes of the lungs.

   _____

   b. LVRS involves resecting segments of emphysematous upper lobes in an effort to reduce the size of the overinflated lungs so that the less severely affected lower lobes can function more efficiently. _____

   _____

   c. The mortality rate for medically treated patients with emphysema is similar to the mortality rate for surgically treated patients. _____

   _____

   d. Surgical treatment is much more effective than medical treatment in almost all emphysema patients. _____

   _____

3. Tell whether each statement is true or false. If false, explain why the statement is incorrect.

   a. Infants born to mothers with diabetes are at increased risk of developing the neonatal respiratory distress syndrome.

   _____

   b. Infants delivered by cesarean section are at greater risk of neonatal respiratory distress syndrome than are infants delivered vaginally. _____

   _____

   c. Lung volume reduction surgery is a very effective treatment of severe pulmonary emphysema and provides long-term improvement of the disease. _____

   _____

d. Immunocompromised persons who become infected with the tubercle bacillus (*Mycobacterium tuberculosis*) are at a greater risk of developing active progressive pulmonary tuberculosis than are persons with a normal immune system. _____

e. Lung carcinoma is responsible for more deaths in women than breast carcinoma. _____

Identification

1. List three conditions that appear to be related to cigarette smoking.

   a. _____

   b. _____

   c. _____

Discussion Questions

1. How do the lungs function? _____
_____
_____
_____

2. What is the difference between ventilation and gas exchange? _____
_____
_____
_____

3. How is pulmonary function disturbed if the alveolar septa are thickened and scarred? _____
_____
_____
_____

4. How is pneumonia classified? What are its major clinical features? _____
_____
_____
_____

5. How does the tubercle bacillus differ in its staining reaction from other bacteria? _____
_____
_____
_____

6. What factors determine the outcome of a tuberculous infection? _____
_____
_____
_____

7. How does a cavity develop in lungs infected with tuberculosis? Is a person with a tuberculous cavity infectious to other people? _____
_____
_____
_____

8. What type of inflammation is caused by the tubercle bacillus? _____
_____
_____
_____

9. A patient has tuberculosis of the kidney, but no evidence of pulmonary tuberculosis is detected by means of a chest x-ray. How did this happen? _____
_____
_____
_____

10. What is meant by the term "inactive tuberculosis"? Under what circumstances may an old, inactive tuberculous infection become activated? What types of patients are susceptible to reactivation of a tuberculous infection?
_____
_____
_____

11. How does a pneumothorax occur? What is its effect on pulmonary function? _____
_____
_____
_____

12. What factors predispose a person to the development of pulmonary emphysema? How may it be prevented?
_____
_____
_____

13. A 35-year-old man has a pulmonary infiltrate with chills, fever, chest pain, and purulent sputum. What is the most likely diagnosis? _____

_____

_____

_____

14. A postoperative patient with a normal temperature has a pulmonary infiltrate, chest pain, and bloody sputum. What is the most likely diagnosis? _____

_____

_____

_____

15. What is the cause of interstitial pneumonia (primary atypical pneumonia)? _____

_____

_____

_____

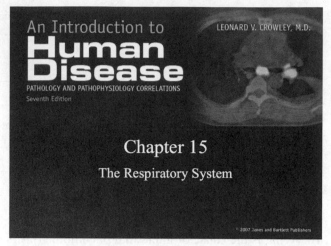

An Introduction to Human Disease
PATHOLOGY AND PATHOPHYSIOLOGY CORRELATIONS
Seventh Edition

LEONARD V. CROWLEY, M.D.

Chapter 15
The Respiratory System

© 2007 Jones and Bartlett Publishers

Respiratory/Circulatory
A Cooperative Effort

- *Oxygen delivery* to the tissues and *waste product removal* requires a *cooperative effort* of the respiratory and circulatory systems
- The *respiratory* system *oxygenates* the blood and *removes* carbon dioxide
- The *circulatory* system *transports* these gases in the bloodstream

© 2007 Jones and Bartlett Publishers

Lung Components

- System of *tubes* to conduct air into and out of the lungs
- Bronchi: largest conducting tube
- Bronchioles (little bronchi): next in size
- Terminal Bronchioles: smallest
- Respiratory Bronchioles: tubes distal to terminal bronchioles; they have alveoli projecting from their walls. Transport air but also participate in gas exchange
- *Alveoli* where oxygen and carbon dioxide exchange between air and pulmonary capillaries
- Lung divided into large segments called *lobes,* each one consisting of *smaller units, lobules*

© 2007 Jones and Bartlett Publishers

Notes

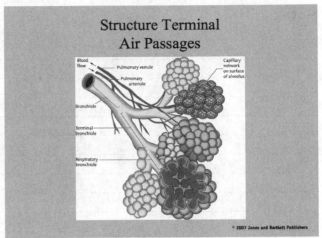

Structure Terminal Air Passages

© 2007 Jones and Bartlett Publishers

Respiration: Function

- *Acinus* or *respiratory unit:* functional unit of the lung
- Respiration has two functions
1. Ventilation
   - Air movement caused by movement of ribs and diaphragm
2. Gas exchange
   - Gases diffuse between blood, tissues, and pulmonary alveoli due to differences in their partial pressures

© 2007 Jones and Bartlett Publishers

Pulmonary Function Tests

- Vital capacity
- One-second forced expiratory volume (FEV_1)
- Arterial PO_2 and PCO_2

© 2007 Jones and Bartlett Publishers

The Pleural Cavity

- *Lungs* are *covered* by a *thin membrane* called *pleura,* which *also extends* over the internal surface of the chest wall
- The *potential space* between the *lungs* and the *chest wall* is called *pleural cavity*
- *Intrapleural pressure* is *less* than the *intrapulmonary* pressure
- The *negative intrapleural pressure* is caused by the tendency of the stretched lung to pull away from the chest wall
- *A release of the vacuum in the* pleural cavity leads to a *collapse of the lung*

© 2007 Jones and Bartlett Publishers

Pneumothorax
Pathogenesis/Manifestations

Pathogenesis
- Lung injury or pulmonary disease that allows air to escape into the pleural space
- Stab wound or penetrating injury to the chest wall
- Spontaneous

Manifestations
- Chest pain
- Shortness of breath
- Air in pleural cavity
- Tension pneumothorax

© 2007 Jones and Bartlett Publishers

Pneumothorax
Treatment

- A chest *tube* is inserted into the *pleural cavity* and left in place until tear in lung heals
    - *Prevents accumulation* of *air* in *pleural cavity*
    - Aids *reexpansion* of lung

© 2007 Jones and Bartlett Publishers

Atelectasis

An incomplete expansion of the lung, a *collapse* of a part of the lung

There are two types

1. *Obstructive* atelectasis: *complete* bronchial obstruction by
   - Mucous secretions, tumor, foreign object
   - Resulting in collapse of the part of the lung supplied by the blocked bronchus
   - Can also develop as a postoperative complication, where because of the pain, the patient does not cough or breathe deeply, accumulating mucous secretions

© 2007 Jones and Bartlett Publishers

Atelectasis

2. *Compression* atelectasis
   - *External* compression on the lung
     - Fluid, air, or blood in the pleural cavity, reducing its volume and preventing lung expansion

© 2007 Jones and Bartlett Publishers

Pneumonia

An *inflammation* of the lung

- The *exudate spreads* unimpeded through the lung
- Filling the *alveoli*
- The affected portions of the lung become relatively solid (*consolidation*)
- At times, the exudate *reaches* the *pleural surface*

© 2007 Jones and Bartlett Publishers

Notes

_____

_____

_____

_____

_____

_____

_____

_____

_____

_____

_____

_____

_____

_____

_____

_____

_____

_____

_____

_____

_____

_____

_____

_____

_____

_____

_____

_____

_____

_____

_____

_____

_____

_____

_____

Pneumonia
Classification

Classification
1. Etiology: most important because it serves as a *guide for treatment*
   - Bacteria, viruses, fungi
2. Anatomic distribution of the inflammatory process—describes *what part of the lung* is involved
   - Lobar: *entire* lung (bacteria, neutrophil infiltration)
   - Bronchopneumonia (bacteria, neutrophil infiltration): *parts* of one or more lobes adjacent to the bronchi

© 2007 Jones and Bartlett Publishers

Pneumonia
Classification

   - Interstitial pneumonia or primary atypical pneumonia (virus or mycoplasma; lymphocyte, monocyte, and plasma cell infiltration): alveolar septa affected
3. *Predisposing factors* that lead to its development
- Any condition associated with *poor lung ventilation and retention of bronchial secretions*
   - Postoperative
   - Aspiration
   - Obstruction

© 2007 Jones and Bartlett Publishers

SARS

- A *highly communicable* serious pulmonary infection, caused by an unusual *coronavirus* that has *spread rapidly* through several *countries* since it was *first identified* in late *2002*
- There are *no effective antiviral drugs* that can influence the course of the disease
- The SARS-associated virus is a unique virus not closely related to other coronaviruses and the *first one* to *cause severe disease* in people
- The virus probably was an *animal virus* that *mutated* and was able to infect humans
- Can be *transmitted* from person to person through *coughing, sneezing, by hands, towels, and other items* contaminated with the virus

© 2007 Jones and Bartlett Publishers

Notes

_____
_____
_____
_____
_____
_____
_____
_____
_____
_____
_____
_____
_____
_____
_____
_____
_____
_____
_____
_____
_____
_____
_____
_____
_____
_____

Pneumocystis Pneumonia

- Humans and many animals harbor this microorganism
- Caused by *protozoan parasite* of low pathogenicity
- Does *not* affect *normal* persons
- *Affects immunocompromised* persons, as in *AIDS*
- Organisms injure the alveoli which leads to exudation of protein-material into alveoli
- The infection is always *very serious* and is often *life-threatening* because of the affected person's inability to inhibit the growth of the parasite

© 2007 Jones and Bartlett Publishers

Tuberculosis

- It is a *special type* of *pneumonia* caused by *Mycobacterium tuberculosis*
- *Because* the tubercle bacillus has a capsule composed of waxes and fatty substances, it is *more resistant to destruction* than others
- Acquired from organisms inhaled in *airborne droplets*
- Organisms *lodge* within pulmonary *alveoli*
- Characteristic *granulomas* are formed
- Sometimes the lung infection *spreads to other parts* such as kidneys, bones, uterus, fallopian tubes, or other sites

© 2007 Jones and Bartlett Publishers

Tuberculosis

- Sometimes the *secondary focus* of infection may *progress* even though the pulmonary infection has healed
- In many cases, the initial infection *does not cause symptoms*

Diagnosis
  - Skin test (*Mantoux*): a positive test reveals *recent* infection
  - chest x-ray: when the *granuloma* is large enough to be detected
  - sputum culture

© 2007 Jones and Bartlett Publishers

Tuberculosis

Treatment

- *Cell-mediated immunity* generally controls the infection
- The *healed granulomas,* however, may contain small numbers of *viable organisms*, and the *infection* may become *reactivated*
- *Not all primary infections respond as favorably*
  - If a *large number* of organisms are inhaled or if the *host is compromised* (body's defenses are inadequate), the inflammation will progress, causing more destruction of lung tissue

© 2007 Jones and Bartlett Publishers

Tuberculosis

- People who have *active progressive* tuberculosis with a *tuberculous cavity* can *infect others* because they can discharge large numbers of tubercle bacilli in the sputum
- *Antibiotics* and *chemotherapeutic* agents are used

© 2007 Jones and Bartlett Publishers

Bronchitis

An *inflammation* of the tracheobronchial mucosa
- *Acute* bronchitis
  - Common and self-limiting
- *Chronic* bronchitis
  - Secondary to chronic irritation by smoking or atmospheric pollution

© 2007 Jones and Bartlett Publishers

Bronchiectasis

The *bronchial walls are weakened* by inflammation and dilate
- Distended bronchi retain secretions
  - Chronic cough
  - Production of large amounts of purulent sputum

© 2007 Jones and Bartlett Publishers

Chronic Obstructive Pulmonary Disease

- *Emphysema* and *chronic bronchitis* occur together so frequently that they are usually considered a *single entity*, designated *COPD*
- The three main anatomic derangements in COPD are
1. Inflammation and narrowing of the terminal bronchioles
2. Dilatation and coalescence of pulmonary air spaces
3. Loss of lung elasticity

© 2007 Jones and Bartlett Publishers

Chronic Obstructive Pulmonary Disease

The chief clinical manifestations of *any* type of chronic pulmonary disease are
- Dyspnea: sensation of *shortness of breath*
- Cyanosis: *blue tinge* of skin and mucous membrane from an excessive amount of *reduced hemoglobin* in the blood

© 2007 Jones and Bartlett Publishers

Chronic Obstructive Pulmonary Disease

Emphysema

- The *air spaces* distal to the terminal bronchioles are *enlarged* and their *walls* are *destroyed*
- The normally *fine alveolar structure of the lung* is *destroyed*
- The *large cystic air spaces form throughout* the lung
- The destructive process usually *begins* in the *upper lobes* but eventually may affect all lobes
- Once *emphysema* has *developed*, the damaged lungs *cannot* be restored to *normal*

© 2007 Jones and Bartlett Publishers

Chronic Obstructive Pulmonary Disease

- However, several measures can be employed to *promote drainage of bronchial secretions, to improve pulmonary ventilation, and to decrease the frequency of superimposed pulmonary infections*

Chronic bronchitis: chronic inflammation of the bronchioles, causing swelling of the bronchial mucosa, reducing the caliber of the bronchi and bronchioles, increasing bronchial secretions

- Derangement of pulmonary structure and function
- *Cigarette smoking* and *atmospheric air pollution* appear to be major factors responsible for *COPD*

© 2007 Jones and Bartlett Publishers

Bronchial Asthma

- *Spasmodic contraction* of smooth muscles in the walls of the *smaller bronchi and bronchioles*
- It causes *shortness of breath* and *wheezing* respiration
- Exerts a *greater effect* on *expiration* than on inspiration
- Attacks are *precipitated by allergens*: inhalation of dust, pollens, animal dander, or other allergens
- Treated with drugs such as *epinephrine or theophylline* that relax bronchospasms and block the release of mediators from mast cells

© 2007 Jones and Bartlett Publishers

Neonate Respiratory Distress Syndrome

- It occurs *soon after birth*
- Due to *inadequate surfactant* in the lungs, which cause the alveoli *not to expand* normally during *inspiration* and tend to *collapse* during *expiration*
- *Predisposed* groups
  - *Premature* infants
  - Infants born by *cesarean* section
  - Infants with *diabetic mothers*

© 2007 Jones and Bartlett Publishers

Adult Respiratory Distress Syndrome

- Pathogenesis
  1. *Conditions that cause shock*, causing fall in blood pressure, and reduced blood flow to lungs
  - The shock may result from any type of severe injury (traumatic shock) or from a serious systemic infection (septic shock)
  2. *Direct lung damage:* caused by aspiration of acid gastric contents, inhalation of irritant or toxic gases, of damage caused by SARS
- Damaged alveolar capillaries *leak* fluid and protein
- Impaired *surfactant* production from damaged alveolar lining cells

© 2007 Jones and Bartlett Publishers

Pulmonary Fibrosis

- May be caused by lungs continually exposed to injurious substances such as *irritant gases* discharged into the atmosphere and many kinds of *airborne organic* and *inorganic particles*
- *Fibrous thickening* of alveolar septa make the *lungs* increasingly *rigid*, *restricting* normal *respiratory* excursions
- Causes progressive respiratory disability *similar* to that in *emphysema*
- *Collagen diseases*- may *lead* to pulmonary fibrosis

© 2007 Jones and Bartlett Publishers

Pulmonary Fibrosis

- Pneumoconoisis: lung injury produced by *inhalation* of *injurious dust* or *other particulate material*
- The best known are
  - *Silicosis*: a type of progressive nodular pulmonary fibrosis caused by inhalation of *rock dust*
  - *Asbestosis*: a diffuse pulmonary fibrosis caused by inhalation of *asbestos* fibers
  - Inhalation of *coal dust, cotton fibers*, *certain types of fungus spores*, and many other substances attending *certain occupations* also may cause pulmonary fibrosis

© 2007 Jones and Bartlett Publishers

Lung Carcinoma

- Usually *smoking-related* neoplasm
- Common malignant tumor in both *men and women*
- *Mortality* from lung cancer in *women exceeds breast cancer*
- *Arises* from mucosa of bronchi and bronchioles

© 2007 Jones and Bartlett Publishers

Lung Carcinoma Classification

- Because the neoplasm of lung cancer usually arises from the bronchial mucosa, the term *bronchogenic carcinoma,* is often used

Classification
- Squamous cell carcinoma: very common
- Adenocarcinoma: very common
- Large cell carcinoma: large, bizarre epithelial cells
- Small cell carcinoma: very poor prognosis

© 2007 Jones and Bartlett Publishers

Notes

_____

_____

_____

_____

_____

_____

_____

_____

_____

_____

Lung Carcinoma

- Because of the rich lymphatic and vascular network in the lung, the *neoplasm* readily gains *access to lymphatic channels* and *pulmonary blood vessels* and soon *spreads* to regional lymph nodes and distant sites

- *Treatment* usually consists of *surgical resection* of one or more lobes of the lung

- *Radiation* and anticancer *chemotherapy* rather than surgery are used to treat small cell carcinoma and tumors that are *too far advanced* for surgical resection

Chapter Outline

The chapter outline provides you with an organizational guide to the topics and ideas presented in this chapter of the text.

Structure and Physiology of the Breast
Examination of the Breasts
    Mammograms
Abnormalities of Breast Development
    Accessory Breasts and Nipples
    Unequal Development of the Breasts
    Breast Hypertrophy
    Gynecomastia
Benign Cystic Change in the Breast
Fibroadenoma
Carcinoma of the Breast
    Breast Carcinoma Risk Related to Hormone Treatment
    Breast Carcinoma Susceptibility Genes
    Classification of Breast Carcinoma
    Evolution of Breast Carcinoma
    Clinical Manifestations
    Treatment
Sarcoma of the Breast
A Lump in the Breast as a Diagnostic Problem

Study Questions

The following questions are provided as a test for comprehension and as a study guide for use with the text chapters. Additional study material is located at http://humandisease.jbpub.com/, which contains useful tools such as an A&P review, animated flashcards, an interactive online glossary, crossword puzzles, and web links.

Key Terms

Define the following terms:

1. Mammogram _____

2. Gynecomastia _____

3. Axilla _____

4. Estrogen _____

5. Progestin _____

6. Mastectomy _____

7. Tamoxifen _____

8. Adjuvant chemotherapy _____

9. Aromatase inhibitor drugs _____

Fill-in-the-Blank

1. Persons with mutations of the tumor suppressor genes *BRCA1* or *BRCA2* have a greatly increased risk of not only breast carcinoma but also _____ carcinoma.

2. A well-circumscribed benign tumor occurring in the breast of a young woman is called a _____.

3. Breast enlargement in the male breast is called _____.

4. Following treatment of an invasive breast carcinoma, most patients are also treated with drugs or hormones. This type of treatment is called _____.

5. When examining axillary lymph nodes from patients with breast carcinoma, it is possible to identify and examine the first lymph node that receives lymphatic drainage from the axilla. This node is called a _____.

True/False

Tell whether each statement is true or false. If false, explain why the statement is incorrect.

1. A mutation of either the *BRCA1* or *BRCA2* gene increases the long-term risk of both breast and ovarian carcinoma.

_____

2. Long-term treatment of postmenopausal patients with estrogen and progestin increases the risk of breast carcinoma.

_____

3. When treating breast carcinoma, the long-term results of total mastectomy with axillary lymph node dissection are much better than the results of segmental mastectomy or lumpectomy followed by radiation therapy. _____

_____

4. An estrogen receptor-positive breast carcinoma has a better prognosis than a breast carcinoma lacking hormone receptors. _____

_____

5. The prognosis of a breast carcinoma in which the *HER-2* gene is amplified is much better than that of a breast carcinoma lacking an amplified *HER-2* gene. _____

_____

6. An axillary lymph node containing metastatic carcinoma is called a sentinel lymph node. _____

_____

7. An estrogen receptor-negative breast carcinoma is usually treated with the drug tamoxifen. _____

_____

8. Adjuvant therapy for most patients with breast carcinoma usually consists of hormonal therapy and/or chemotherapy.

_____

Identify

1. What are the three common conditions that cause a lump in the breast?

   a. _____

   b. _____

   c. _____

2. Name three laboratory tests that are performed on breast carcinoma tissue to assess prognosis and guide treatment.

   a. _____

   b. _____

   c. _____

Discussion Questions

1. Describe the methods used to treat breast carcinoma surgically. _____

_____

_____

_____

2. How can benign breast conditions be distinguished from breast cancer? _____

_____

_____

_____

3. What are the applications and limitations of a mammogram? _____

_____

_____

_____

4. What factors predispose a person to breast carcinoma? _____
_____
_____
_____

5. What is the role of heredity in regard to breast carcinoma? _____
_____
_____
_____

6. A 67-year-old woman has a lump in the breast. Which diagnostic procedures will assist the physician in determining the nature of the lump? _____
_____
_____
_____

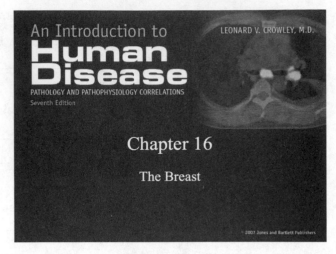

Breast Structure

- Composed of twenty *lobes* of *glandular* tissue
- Each lobe consists of a *cluster of glands* (lobules)
- Lobules are *connected* by series of *branching ducts*
- *Branching ducts* converge to form *ducts* that extend to the *nipple*
- *Suspensory ligaments fix* the breast to the chest wall
- Breasts have an *abundant blood supply* and *lymphatic drainage*

© 2007 Jones and Bartlett Publishers

Breast Structure

- Breasts are *modified sweat glands* that have become *specialized to secrete milk*
- In *puberty* they *enlarge* in response to *estrogen and progesterone*
- *Postpubertal changes* include *proliferation* of *glandular* and *fibrous tissue* and *accumulation* of *adipose* tissue
- *Variations* in *breast size* depend on *amount* of *fat* and *fibrous* tissue *rather* than on amount of *glandular* tissue
- Breasts are *extremely responsive to hormonal stimulation* (during menstrual cycle, pregnancy, lactation and menopause)

© 2007 Jones and Bartlett Publishers

Breast Examination

- *Clinical* examination
  - Inspection, palpation, examination of axillary tissues, first with arms at the sides, then arms are elevated and lowered, and finally with hands on hips, begun at the periphery, all parts of breast palpated in a clockwise direction, and finally the tissues under the nipples are examined
- *Mammogram*
  - May identify lesions *not* detected on clinical examination; recommendations are for a baseline at age 35–40, followed by annually or biannually up to age 50, followed by annually thereafter

Breast Examination

- The *mammogram* is *most useful* for examining the breasts of *postmenopausal* women because they contain *more fat* and less glandular tissue than the breasts of younger women.
- A *dense tumor* in a *postmenopausal breast contrasts sharply* with the *less-dense fatty* tissue
- In contrast, a *younger* woman's breast appear *much denser* because they contain much more *glandular and fibrous* tissue

Normal Mammogram

Abnormalities in Breast Development

- *Accessory breasts and nipples:* most commonly found in the *armpits* or on the lower chest *below* and *medial* to the normal *breasts*
- *Unequal development:* fully developed breasts are usually *similar* in *size* but *not identical,* and sometimes *one fails to develop* as much as its counterpart
- Breast *hypertrophy:* sometimes at *puberty,* one or both breasts *over-respond* to *hormonal* stimulation; the hypertrophy is caused by *overgrowth* of *fibrous* tissue, *not* glandular or fat
- *Gynecomastia:* due to a *temporary imbalance* of *female and male hormones* (increase in estrogen), a distinct *nodule of tissue* develops *under* the *nipple* of the *male* breast

© 2007 Jones and Bartlett Publishers

Abnormalities in Breast Development

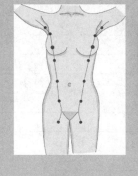
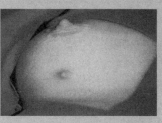

© Courtesy of Leonard Crowley, M.D./University of Minnesota Medical School

© 2007 Jones and Bartlett Publishers

Benign Cystic Breast Disease

- It is a very *common benign* condition also called *fibrocystic disease*
- They are focal areas of *proliferation* of *glandular* and *fibrous* tissue
- It is an *irregular cyclic response* of the breasts to *hormones* during *phases of the menstrual cycle*
- *Ultrasound* examination is *very helpful* in *distinguishing* a *cystic* from a *solid* mass in the breast
- *Treatment*
  - *Aspiration* of cyst
  - *Surgical* excision if no aspirate

© 2007 Jones and Bartlett Publishers

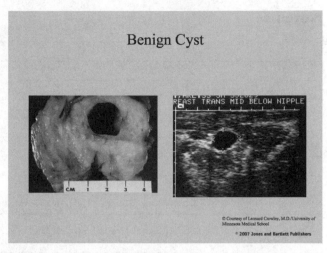

Benign Cyst

© Courtesy of Leonard Crowley, M.D./University of
Minnesota Medical School

© 2007 Jones and Bartlett Publishers

Fibroadenoma

- *Benign*
- Well-circumscribed *tumor* of *glands* and *fibrous* tissue
- Common in *young* women
- *Surgically* excised

© 2007 Jones and Bartlett Publishers

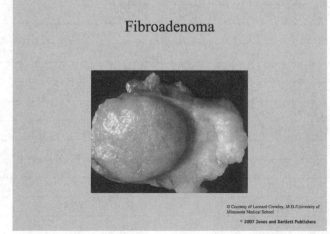

Fibroadenoma

© Courtesy of Leonard Crowley, M.D./University of
Minnesota Medical School

© 2007 Jones and Bartlett Publishers

Breast Carcinoma

- *Risk* factors
  - Some *familial* tendency
  - *Hormonal* factors
  - Birth of *first* child *after age 30*
  - *Early* menarche (first menstrual period)
  - *Late* menopause (cessation of menstrual periods)
  - It *occurs in both sexes* but it is *rare* in *men,* whose breasts are *not* subject to stimulation by *ovarian hormones*
- *Hormones* have been used for many years to treat *menopausal* symptoms

© 2007 Jones and Bartlett Publishers

Breast Carcinoma

- Combined *hormone* therapy (estrogen-progestin) *increases* the *density* of the *breast tissue, complicating* the interpretation of *mammograms*
- *Risk* related to *hormone* treatment
  - Long-term *estrogen-progestin* use
    - *Significantly* increases risk breast carcinoma
  - Long-term use of *estrogen without progestin*
    - *Slightly* increases risk breast carcinoma

© 2007 Jones and Bartlett Publishers

Breast Carcinoma

- Susceptibility *genes*
  - Mutant *BRCA1* gene (*worst* prognosis)
    - *Increases breast* and *ovarian* carcinoma risk (20–40% ovarian)
  - Mutant *BRCA2* gene (*better* prognosis)
    - Similar *high breast* carcinoma risk but *lower ovarian* carcinoma risk (10–20% ovarian)

© 2007 Jones and Bartlett Publishers

Classification of Breast Carcinoma

1. *Site* of *origin*
   - Epithelium of ducts = ductal carcinomas *(90%)*
   - Lobules = lobular carcinomas (the rest)
   - Initially, a carcinoma remains confined within the duct or lobule, called *non-infiltrating* or *in situ*
   - Eventually it breaks through and extends toward the adjacent breast tissue, *invasive*
2. *Presence* or *absence* of *invasion*
3. Degree of *differentiation* of tumor cells

© 2007 Jones and Bartlett Publishers

Evolution of Breast Carcinoma

- A carcinoma can be identified by *mammogram* up to *two years before* detection by *breast exam*
- Initially *in situ* but eventually becomes *invasive*
- Metastasizes to *axillary lymph nodes*
- *Spreads* throughout *body* if untreated
- Early diagnosis allows prompt treatment and improves the cure rate

© 2007 Jones and Bartlett Publishers

Clinical Manifestations Breast Carcinoma

- *Lump* in the breast
- *Nipple* or *skin* may be *retracted*
- Skin *edema* (*orange peel sign*)
- Tumor infiltrates breast and becomes *fixed* to *chest wall*
- *Metastasis*

© 2007 Jones and Bartlett Publishers

Notes

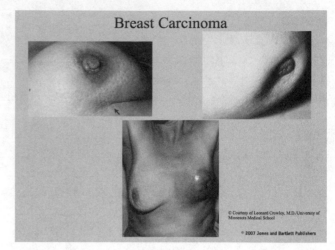

Breast Carcinoma

© Courtesy of Leonard Crowley, M.D./University of
Minnesota Medical School

© 2007 Jones and Bartlett Publishers

Treatment of
Breast Carcinoma

- Both methods achieve the *same* long-term effects
1. *Modified radical mastectomy, also called total* mastectomy with *axillary lymph node dissection*: resecting the entire breast along with the *axillary tissue* but *leaving* the *pectoral muscles* overlying the chest wall
2. *Partial mastectomy / lumpectomy* with *lymph node dissection* and *radiotherapy*: removing only *part of* the *breast* with the *tumor* or only the *tumor* along with a small amount of *adjacent breast tissue*

© 2007 Jones and Bartlett Publishers

Treatment of
Breast Carcinoma

3. Administration of *adjuvant therapy*: an attempt to eradicate any tumor cells that may have *spread* beyond the breast

3a. *Anticancer* drugs (*adjuvant chemotherapy*)

3b. *Antiestrogen* drugs (*adjuvant hormonal therapy*)

Whichever method of treatment selected, part of the tumor obtained surgically is *tested* to

- Detect the *presence of estrogen* and *progesterone receptors*
- Detect the *amplification* of a *gene* called *HER-2*

© 2007 Jones and Bartlett Publishers

Treatment of Breast Carcinoma

Determination of hormone receptor status of tumor has two purposes

1. Prognosis: tumors with hormone receptors are better differentiated, with a more favorable clinical course

2. Guide for treatment: tumors with hormone receptors respond to anti-estrogen adjuvant therapy

© 2007 Jones and Bartlett Publishers

Breast Sarcoma

- *Rare* in comparison to breast carcinoma
- Arises from *fibrous* tissue or *blood vessels*
- *Large bulky* tumor
- May *metastasize widely*
- Treatment is by *surgical resection* of the involved breast

© 2007 Jones and Bartlett Publishers

Breast Sarcoma

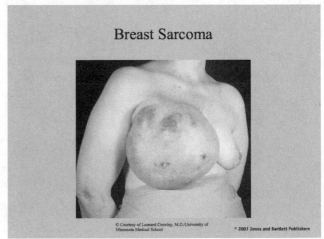

© Courtesy of Leonard Crowley, M.D./University of Minnesota Medical School

© 2007 Jones and Bartlett Publishers

_____

_____

_____

_____

_____

_____

_____

_____

_____

_____

Breast Lump

- Diagnostic *possibilities*
  1. Cystic disease
  2. Fibroadenoma
  3. Carcinoma
- Diagnostic *approach*
  – Clinical evaluation
  – Mammogram
  – Biopsy

© 2007 Jones and Bartlett Publishers

Chapter 17   The Female Reproductive System

2000Chapter 17

Chapter Outline

The chapter outline provides you with an organizational guide to the topics and ideas presented in this chapter of the text.

Infections of the Female Genital Tract
    Vaginitis
    Cervicitis
    Salpingitis and Pelvic Inflammatory Disease
    Condylomas of the Genital Tract
Endometriosis
Cervical Polyps
Cervical Dysplasia and Cervical Carcinoma
    Diagnosis and Treatment
Endometrial Hyperplasia, Polyps, and Carcinoma
Uterine Myomas
Irregular Uterine Bleeding
    Dysfunctional Uterine Bleeding
    Other Causes of Uterine Bleeding
    Diagnosis and Treatment
Dysmenorrhea
Cysts and Tumors of the Ovary
Diseases of the Vulva
    Vulvar Dystrophy
    Carcinoma of the Vulva
Toxic Shock Syndrome
Contraception
Effects of Prenatal Exposure to Diethylstilbestrol (DES)

The Female Reproductive System

263

Study Questions

The following questions are provided as a test for comprehension and as a study guide for use with the text chapters. Additional study material is located at http://humandisease.jbpub.com/, which contains useful tools such as an A&P review, animated flashcards, an interactive online glossary, crossword puzzles, and web links.

Key Terms

Define the following terms:

1. Endometriosis _____

2. Toxic shock syndrome _____

3. Dysfunctional uterine bleeding _____

4. Dysmenorrhea _____

Fill-in-the-Blank

1. Warty overgrowths of genital tract squamous epithelium are caused by _____
   and are called _____.

2. Abnormal, disorderly proliferation of cervical squamous epithelium is called _____.

3. A common benign uterine tumor is called a _____.

4. Cramp-like abdominal discomfort related to menstruation is called _____.

5. The cell that gives rise to a benign cystic ovarian teratoma (dermoid cyst) is _____.

6. An estrogen-producing tumor arising from the follicular cells (granulosa cells) lining an ovarian follicle is called a
   _____.

7. The organism responsible for toxic shock syndrome is _____.

8. The condition in which endometrium is found in locations outside the endometrial lining of the uterus is called
   _____.

True/False

1. Tell whether each statement is true or false regarding estrogen–progestin contraceptive pills. If false, explain why the statement is incorrect.

   a. These pills prevent ovulation. _____
   _____

   b. They may predispose a woman to tubal pregnancies. _____
   _____

   c. They may promote development of endometriosis. _____
   _____

   d. They may lead to thromboembolic complications in susceptible individuals. _____
   _____

   e. The risk of pill-related complications is lower in cigarette smokers. _____
   _____

2. Tell whether each statement is true or false regarding human papillomavirus (HPV). If false, explain why the statement is incorrect.

   a. Only a few types of HPV can infect the cervix. _____

   _____

   b. Most HPV types are carcinogenic (cancer causing). _____

   _____

   c. Most HPV infections cannot be eradicated by the body's immune defenses and become chronic. _____

   _____

   d. Testing cervical material obtained by a Pap smear for HPV may be a useful supplementary test when atypical cells are identified in the Pap smear. _____

   _____

3. Tell whether each statement related to fertilization and implantation of a fertilized ovum is true or false. If false, explain why the statement is incorrect.

   a. Sperm can survive in a woman's genital tract for 5–6 days after sexual intercourse and are still able to fertilize an ovum. _____

   _____

   b. Unprotected sexual intercourse several days before ovulation can result in a pregnancy. _____

   _____

   c. It takes about a week for a fertilized ovum to travel through the fallopian tube and implant in the endometrium.

   _____

   d. Postcoital (after intercourse) contraception (the "morning after pill") is unlikely to prevent conception unless taken within 3 hours after intercourse. _____

   _____

Identify

1. Identify the organisms responsible for the three common causes of vaginitis.

   a. _____

   b. _____

   c. _____

2. A woman consults her physician because of irregular uterine bleeding. Identify five possible causes of uterine bleeding.

   a. _____

   b. _____

   c. _____

   d. _____

   e. _____

Discussion Questions

1. A woman has a human papillomavirus (HPV) infection of her cervical epithelium. What factors influence her risk of developing cervical dysplasia or in situ carcinoma? _____
_____
_____
_____

2. If a woman is 65 years old and has irregular uterine bleeding, what is the likely cause of the bleeding? _____
_____
_____
_____

3. What are the clinical features of toxic shock syndrome in a menstruating woman? _____
_____
_____
_____

4. Describe how contraceptive pills function to prevent pregnancy. _____
_____
_____
_____

5. What are the manifestations and complications of endometriosis? _____
_____
_____
_____

6. What parts of the female genital tract may be involved in gonorrheal infection? _____
_____
_____
_____

7. How does gonorrhea lead to sterility? _____
_____
_____
_____

8. What is the difference between in situ and invasive cervical carcinoma? How is the Pap smear used in the diagnosis of carcinoma? _____

_____

_____

_____

9. Explain whether the following conditions may predispose susceptible individuals to toxic shock syndrome.

   a. Use of tampons _____

_____

   b. Use of a vaginal (contraceptive) diaphragm _____

_____

   c. Use of contraceptive sponges _____

_____

   d. Use of an IUD _____

_____

   e. Use of contraceptive foam and condoms _____

_____

10. A patient has dysmenorrhea and endometriosis is suspected. What diagnostic procedures are helpful in establishing a diagnosis of this condition? _____

_____

_____

_____

11. A 62-year-old woman has irregular vaginal bleeding. What conditions could account for this condition? _____

_____

_____

_____

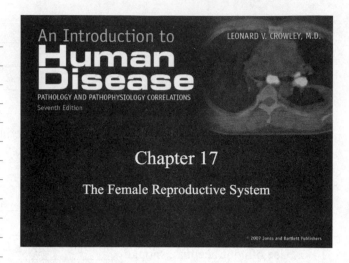

Chapter 17

The Female Reproductive System

An Introduction to
Human Disease
PATHOLOGY AND PATHOPHYSIOLOGY CORRELATIONS
Seventh Edition

LEONARD V. CROWLEY, M.D.

© 2007 Jones and Bartlett Publishers

Infections of the Female Genital Tract

- Infections of the genital tract are *common*
- Frequently involved are the *vagina,* the *cervix,* and the *fallopian tubes*
- Vaginitis: common; causes vaginal discharge, itching, and irritation
- Cervicitis: common in *women* who have *had children*; causes *few symptoms* and is of *little* clinical importance
- Salpingitis / PID (also called *pelvic inflammatory disease*): an inflammation of the *fallopian tubes*, along with *ovaries* at times; most cases are *secondary* to the spread of cervical *gonorrheal or chlamydial* infection

© 2007 Jones and Bartlett Publishers

Infections of the Female Genital Tract

- Salpingitis predisposes to *ectopic pregnancy* (implantation of the *ovum* in the *fallopian tube rather* than in the *endometrial* cavity)
- Condylomas: *venereal* warts, benign tumorlike overgrowths of squamous epithelium, spread by sexual contact

© 2007 Jones and Bartlett Publishers

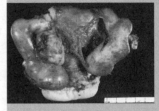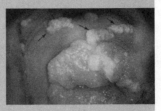

Pelvic Inflammatory Disease
(PID) and Condylomas

© Courtesy of Leonard Crowley, M.D./University of
Minnesota Medical School

© 2007 Jones and Bartlett Publishers

Endometriosis

- *Deposits* of endometrium *outside* its normal location, encountered in the walls of the *uterus*, in the *ovary* or elsewhere in the *pelvis*, in the *appendix*, or in the *rectum*
- *Ectopic endometrium* responds to *hormonal* stimuli, therefore undergoes *cyclic menstrual* desquamation and regeneration
- *Secondary scarring* may obstruct *fallopian tubes*
- Diagnosis: *visualizing* the ectopic deposits within the pelvis with a *laparascope*
- Treatment: Synthetic *hormones, birth control* pills, and *drugs* that *suppress* output of *gonadotropins* from the pituitary gland

© 2007 Jones and Bartlett Publishers

Endometriosis

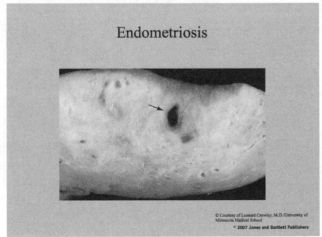

© Courtesy of Leonard Crowley, M.D./University of
Minnesota Medical School

© 2007 Jones and Bartlett Publishers

Cervical Polyps / Dysplasia

Polyps
- *Benign,* arise from the *cervix*
- Usually *small* but may be *quite large*
- Erosion of tip may cause *bleeding*
- *Surgical* removal

Dysplasia
- *Mild* dysplasia
  - Result of cervical *inflammation*
  - Regresses *spontaneously*
- *Severe* dysplasia
  - May progress to *in situ* carcinoma
  - May progress to *invasive carcinoma*

© 2007 Jones and Bartlett Publishers

Cervical Intraepithelial Neoplasia (CIN)

• Most physicians regard cervical dysplasia and in situ carcinoma as very closely related, constituting different stages in a progressive spectrum of epithelial abnormalities, classifying them under the general term, *cervical intra-epithelial neoplasia (CIN)*

It is graded
  - Grade I: *Mild* dysplasia
  - Grade II: *Moderate* dysplasia
  - Grade III: *Severe* dysplasia

© 2007 Jones and Bartlett Publishers

Cervical Intraepithelial Neoplasia (CIN)

In situ *carcinoma*

  - Persons infected with some types of Human Papilloma Virus (*HPV*), the same virus that causes condylomas, are at risk of developing *cervical dysplasia* and *cervical carcinoma*

© 2007 Jones and Bartlett Publishers

HPV

- There are more than *eighty* types of HPV
- About *forty* types can infect the *genital tract*
- Only about *eight* types (called high-risk types) are considered to be *carcinogenic*
- *HPV testing* of cervical material obtained during a regular *Pap* test can be helpful when the cytologic changes in the Pap are *inconclusive*

© 2007 Jones and Bartlett Publishers

Diagnosis and Treatment
Dysplasia and Carcinoma

- *Pap smear* shows abnormal cells
- *Colposcopy* localizes abnormalities: a *binocular magnifying* instrument, performed when *Pap* test is *abnormal*
- *Biopsies* establish diagnosis: will lead/guide the *treatment*

Treatment

- *Dysplasia* and *in situ carcinoma*
  - cryocautery (freezing)
  - *surgical* excision of abnormal area
  - *hysterectomy* (removal of uterus)

© 2007 Jones and Bartlett Publishers

Diagnosis and Treatment
Dysplasia and Carcinoma

- *Invasive* carcinoma
  - *radiation*
  - *radical hysterectomy* (resection of uterus, fallopian tubes, ovaries, and adjacent tissues)

© 2007 Jones and Bartlett Publishers

Benign Endometrial Disorders

- Benign endometrial *hyperplasia*
  - Associated with irregular uterine *bleeding*
- Benign endometrial *polyps*
  - May bleed if *tip eroded*
- Endometrial *adenocarcinoma*
  - Related to prolonged endometrial stimulation by *estrogen*

© 2007 Jones and Bartlett Publishers

Benign Endometrial Disorders

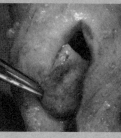

© Courtesy of Leonard Crowley, M.D./University of Minnesota Medical School

© 2007 Jones and Bartlett Publishers

Uterine Myomas

- Benign *smooth muscle* tumors
- Occur in approximately *30%* of women *over 30 years* of age
- May cause irregular *uterine bleeding*, and symptoms related to pressure on bladder and rectum

© 2007 Jones and Bartlett Publishers

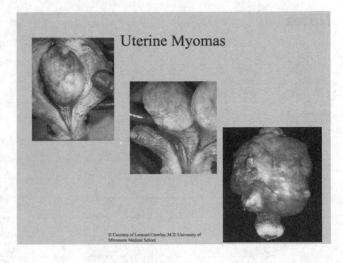

Uterine Myomas

© Courtesy of Leonard Crowley, M.D./University of
Minnesota Medical School

Irregular Uterine Bleeding

- Dysfunctional *uterine bleeding*
  - *Failure in *ovulation (anovulatory cycle)*
- *Other* causes of *uterine bleeding*
  - Benign endometrial *hyperplasia*
  - Endometrial and cervical *polyps*
  - Uterine *myomas*
  - Uterine *carcinoma*

Dysmenorrhea: *painful menstruations*

Two types

1. Primary
2. Secondary

© 2007 Jones and Bartlett Publishers

Dysmenorrhea

1. *Primary*
- Pelvic organs are *normal*
- Most *common* type
- Pain is crampy, caused by *protaglandins*
- Begins just *prior* to menstruation
- Lasts for *one or two days* after onset of *menstrual flow*
- Menstrual periods are *painless* for the first two years after menarche because the cycles are *anovulatory (no ovulation)*
- *Dysmenorrhea* occurs when *ovulatory cycles begin*

© 2007 Jones and Bartlett Publishers

Notes

Dysmenorrhea

2. *Secondary*
   – Result of various *diseases* of the pelvic organs, such as *endometriosis*
   Treatment
   • *Aspirin*
   • Other *anti-inflammatory drugs*
   • *Oral contraceptive pills*

© 2007 Jones and Bartlett Publishers

Ovarian and Endometrial Cysts

They are *benign*
• *Ovarian cysts*
– Arise from ovarian follicles or corpora lutea
– Are common
– Not large
– Regress spontaneously
• Endometrial *cysts*
– Endometrial deposits in ovary filled with *old blood and debris*

© 2007 Jones and Bartlett Publishers

Dermoid Cysts

• *Benign cystic teratoma (dermoid cyst)*
   – Arise from *unfertilized ova* that undergo *neoplastic* change
   – Often contain skin, hair, teeth, bone, parts of gastrointestinal tract, thyroid, and other tissues growing in a jumbled fashion
• *Malignant teratoma*
   – Very *rare*

© 2007 Jones and Bartlett Publishers

Ovarian Tumors

- Cystadenoma
- Cystadenocarcinoma
- Fibroma
- Granulosa-theca cell tumor
- Male hormone-producing tumors

© 2007 Jones and Bartlett Publishers

Benign Cystic Ovarian Tumors

© Courtesy of Leonard Crowley, M.D./University of Minnesota Medical School

© 2007 Jones and Bartlett Publishers

Diseases of the Vulva

- Vulvar *dystrophy*
  - Irregular *white patches* on vulvar skin
  - May *progress* to *carcinoma*
- *Carcinoma* of the vulva
  - Found in *pre-* and *post-menopausal* women

© 2007 Jones and Bartlett Publishers

Vulva Carcinoma

© Courtesy of Leonard Crowley, M.D./University of Minnesota Medical School

© 2007 Jones and Bartlett Publishers

Toxic Shock Syndrome

- Estimated *10-15 cases per 100,000* menstrual age women per year
- *Toxin-producing staphylococcus* grow in vagina
- Use of *tampons* promotes development
- There is *no way to counteract* or neutralize the toxin

© 2007 Jones and Bartlett Publishers

Contraception

- *Natural* family planning
- *Artificial* contraception
  - Diaphragms
  - Condoms
  - Contraceptive pills
  - Intrauterine contraceptive devices (IUDs)

© 2007 Jones and Bartlett Publishers

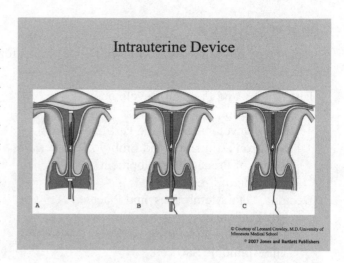

Intrauterine Device

A   B   C

© Courtesy of Leonard Crowley, M.D./University of
Minnesota Medical School

© 2007 Jones and Bartlett Publishers

Prenatal Exposure to Diethylstilbestrol (DES)

- Nonsteroidal estrogens used from *1946–1970* to treat mothers who were *prone* to *spontaneous abortion*
- Cause developmental *abnormalities* in *genital* tracts of female offspring
  - Benign lesions
  - Malignant lesions

© 2007 Jones and Bartlett Publishers

Chapter 18 Prenatal Development and Diseases Associated with Pregnancy

Chapter Outline

The chapter outline provides you with an organizational guide to the topics and ideas presented in this chapter of the text.

Hemolytic Disease of the Newborn (Erythroblastosis Fetalis)
Changes in Hemoglobin and Bilirubin After Delivery
Rh Hemolytic Disease
Diagnosis of Hemolytic Disease in the Newborn Infant
Treatment of Hemolytic Disease
Fluorescent Light Therapy for Hyperbilirubinemia
Intrauterine Fetal Transfusion
Prevention of Rh Hemolytic Disease with Rh Immune Globulin
ABO Hemolytic Disease

Study Questions

The following questions are provided as a test for comprehension and as a study guide for use with the text chapters. Additional study material is located at http://humandisease.jbpub.com/, which contains useful tools such as an A&P review, animated flashcards, an interactive online glossary, crossword puzzles, and web links.

Key Terms

Define the following terms:

1. Amniotic fluid _____

2. Gestational trophoblast disease _____

3. Placenta _____

4. Rh immune globulin _____

Fill-in-the-Blank

1. In a woman with a regular 28-day menstrual cycle, ovulation normally occurs on day _____.

2. If the egg is fertilized, its implantation occurs _____ days after fertilization occurs.

3. During the _____ period, the developing organism is most vulnerable to injury from drugs, maternal infections, or other factors that disturb prenatal development.

4. The outer sac surrounding the embryo is called the _____, and the finger-like processes projecting from the sac are called _____.

5. In the placenta, the blood circulating through the villi is blood pumped into the placenta by the _____, and the blood flowing around the villi is blood pumped into the placenta by _____.

6. An excess of amnionic fluid is called _____.

7. A reduced volume of amnionic fluid is called _____. This condition may be caused by _____.

8. The condition in which the placenta attaches to the lower part of the uterus and covers the cervix is called _____. This condition is usually treated by _____.

9. Identical twins are formed by separation of the inner cell mass during the early stages of prenatal development. If the separation is incomplete, the result is _____.

10. If the placental circulations of identical twins are interconnected, one twin may become anemic, and the other twin will have an excessive amount of blood. This condition is called _____.

11. The placenta produces two steroid hormones, called _____ and _____. It also produces two protein hormones, called _____ and _____.

12. In the usual case of hemolytic disease caused by Rh incompatibility, the Rh (D) type of the father is _____. The infant's Rh type is _____, and the mother's Rh type is _____.

True/False

Tell whether each statement is true or false. If false, explain why the statement is incorrect.

1. Two Rh-negative parents may have an Rh-positive infant. _____

   _____

2. An Rh-negative infant may be born to two Rh-positive parents. _____

   _____

3. Rh immune globulin is sometimes administered to Rh-negative mothers during pregnancy. _____

   _____

4. Rh hemolytic disease usually occurs in firstborn infants and is usually less severe in subsequent pregnancies.

   _____

5. Tell whether each statement is true or false regarding hydatidiform mole. If false, explain why the statement is incorrect.

   a. It occurs less frequently in U.S. and Canadian women than in women living in Asia. _____

      _____

   b. Incomplete removal of a hydatidiform mole may be followed by development of a choriocarcinoma. _____

      _____

   c. A woman who has had a mole evacuated by curettage may attempt another pregnancy as soon as her normal menstrual periods resume after the curettage. _____

      _____

   d. Some moles may exhibit aggressive behavior and invade the uterine wall. _____

      _____

6. Tell whether each statement is true or false regarding Rh immune globulin. If false, explain why the statement is incorrect.

   a. Its administration will usually prevent sensitization of an Rh-negative mother who has given birth to an Rh-positive infant. _____

      _____

   b. Its administration will usually prevent ABO hemolytic disease in group O mothers who have given birth to group A or B infants. _____

      _____

   c. Its administration will reduce the concentration of preexisting Rh antibodies in an Rh-negative mother who has previously been sensitized to the Rh antigen. _____

      _____

   d. It is never given to Rh-positive infants born to Rh-negative mothers. _____

      _____

7. Tell whether each of the following statements is true or false. If false, explain why the statement is incorrect.

a. Choriocarcinoma developing as a complication of a hydatidiform mole is very aggressive and has a very poor prognosis despite appropriate chemotherapy treatment.

_____

_____

b. Most cases of neonatal hemolytic disease result from an Rh-incompatible pregnancy (mother Rh negative; father and fetus Rh positive).

_____

_____

c. ABO hemolytic disease occurs less frequently than does Rh hemolytic disease and is more difficult to treat.

_____

_____

d. Most case of ABO hemolytic disease occur in group O infants born to group A mothers.

_____

_____

e. A high concentration of unconjugated bilirubin in the blood of a newborn infant with neonatal hemolytic disease is hazardous and may cause permanent damage to the infant's nervous system._____

_____

f. Giving immune globulin containing a high concentration of Rh antibodies to an Rh-negative mother who has given birth to an Rh-positive infant greatly reduces the likelihood that the mother will develop Rh antibodies that will complicate future pregnancies in which the infant is Rh-positive.

_____

_____

g. Transfer of fetal Rh-positive red cells into the circulation of an Rh-negative mother usually occurs when the placenta separates and is expelled after delivery. _____

_____

Identify

1. Prenatal development is divided into three separate periods:

a. _____

b. _____

c. _____

2. List the two conditions that may lead to the excess amniotic fluid.

a. _____

b. _____

3. The term "gestational trophoblast disease" includes what three conditions?

a. _____

b. _____

c. _____

Discussion Questions

1. In what part of the genital tract does fertilization of the egg occur? _____

_____

_____

_____

2. Briefly describe how gestational trophoblast disease is treated and how the patient should be managed after the condition is treated. _____

_____

_____

_____

3. Normally, maternal and fetal blood do not intermix in the placenta when the intact placenta remains within the uterus. How does this situation change when the placenta separates from the uterus after the baby has been delivered?

_____

_____

_____

4. Postpartum administration of Rh immune globulin to an Rh-negative woman who has given birth to an Rh-positive infant is recommended and given routinely to such patients. What is the purpose of the injection, and why is it effective? _____

_____

_____

_____

5. Can two Rh (D)-negative parents have an Rh-positive baby? Why or why not? _____

_____

_____

_____

6. Can two Rh (D)-positive parents have an Rh-negative baby? Why or why not? _____

_____

_____

_____

7. Describe how ABO hemolytic disease differs from Rh hemolytic disease. _____

_____

_____

_____

8. Why do spontaneous abortions occur? _____

_____

_____

_____

9. What are the consequences of prolonged retention of a dead fetus within the uterine cavity? _____

_____

_____

_____

10. What is an ectopic pregnancy? What factors predispose a woman to development of an ectopic pregnancy in the fallopian tube? What are the consequences of a tubal pregnancy? _____

_____

_____

_____

11. What conditions are associated with ectopic pregnancies? _____

_____

_____

_____

12. Who should receive the Rh immune globulin injection? When is it given? Why is it given? How does it work?

_____

_____

_____

Notes

An Introduction to
Human
Disease
PATHOLOGY AND PATHOPHYSIOLOGY CORRELATIONS
Seventh Edition

LEONARD V. CROWLEY, M.D.

Chapter 18

Prenatal Development and
Diseases Associated
with Pregnancy

© 2007 Jones and Bartlett Publishers

Fertilization

- Union of *sperm and ovum* occurs in *fallopian tube*
- *Sperm* can *travel* by their *own propulsive efforts* but also *passively transported* by *rhythmic contractions* of *uterine muscles* that aspirate them upward into the uterus and fallopian tubes
- The *ovum* is *expelled* from the *follicle* at *ovulation*
- *Fertilization* is possible *when sperm are present in fallopian tubes when egg is expelled at ovulation*
- The *first cell division* is completed about *thirty hours after fertilization*
- *Sperm penetration* causes *zona pellucida* to become *impermeable* to penetration of *other sperm*

© 2007 Jones and Bartlett Publishers

Early Development of Fertilized Ovum

- *Zygote* develops into a small ball of cells
- Fluid accumulates to form *blastocyst*
- Blastocyst begins to *differentiate*
- *Implantation* of blastocyst into endometrium by end of *first* week
- *Amnionic sac and yolk sac* form
- Small germ disk and yolk sac project into *chorionic* cavity
- *Organ systems* begin to form, and *embryo* becomes *cylindrical* by *fourth* week

© 2007 Jones and Bartlett Publishers

In Vitro Fertilization and Embryo Transfer

- Some women *ovulate normally* but are *infertile* because their *fallopian tubes* are *obstructed* by *scarring* that *cannot* be *corrected surgically* or because both *fallopian tubes* have been *removed* as a consequence of *previous ectopic* pregnancies
- It is sometimes possible to *fertilize the patient's ovum*, allowing it to *develop outside* her body, and then *implant* the *embryo* in her *uterus*
- *Follicle* is *aspirated* by *laparoscopy*
- *Ovum* is *fertilized* and allowed to develop to 8-cell or 16-cell stage
- *Fertilized ovum* introduced into the *uterus*

© 2007 Jones and Bartlett Publishers

Chorionic Vesicle

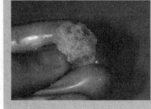 

© Courtesy of Leonard Crowley, M.D./University of Minnesota Medical School

© 2007 Jones and Bartlett Publishers

Stages of Prenatal Development

Three Stages

1. *Pre-embryonic* period
- First three weeks after fertilization, the blastocyst becomes implanted and the inner mass cell differentiates into the three germ layers that will eventually form specific tissues within the embryo

2. *Embry*onic period
- From 3rd through 7th week, the developing organism begins to assume a human shape and is called an embryo; all the organ systems are formed, a very critical period of development

© 2007 Jones and Bartlett Publishers

Stages of Prenatal Development

3. Fetal period
• From 8th week to delivery, the term *fetus* is now applied; it grows and becomes larger and heavier, but there are no major changes in its basic structure comparable to those in the embryonic period

© 2007 Jones and Bartlett Publishers

Stages of Prenatal Development

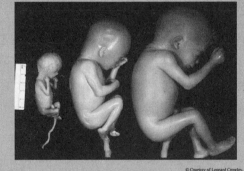

© Courtesy of Leonard Crowley, M.D./University of Minnesota Medical School.
© 2007 Jones and Bartlett Publishers

Stages of Prenatal Development

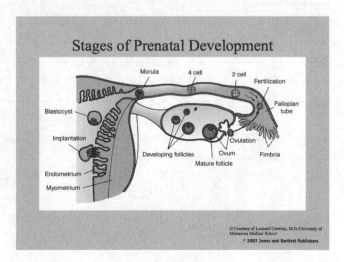

© Courtesy of Leonard Crowley, M.D./University of Minnesota Medical School.
© 2007 Jones and Bartlett Publishers

Duration of Pregnancy

- *Period of gestation* is the total duration of pregnancy from fertilization to delivery
- It is approximately *38 weeks* when dated from the *time of ovulation*
- Usually it is calculated from the *beginning* of the *last menstrual period* (date of ovulation *not* known)
- Expressed in *this way*, the duration of pregnancy is *40 weeks* (the first day of the calculation is *two weeks* before the date of *conception*)
- May be expressed as *280 days*

Duration of Pregnancy

- May be expressed as *ten lunar (28-day) months*
- Or as *nine calendar* (31-day) months
- The nine calendar months are sometimes divided into *three* periods called *trimesters*

Decidua

- Endometrium of pregnancy: decidua
  - Decidua basalis
    - Under the chorionic vesicle
  - Decidua capsularis
    - Over the chorionic vesicle
  - Decidua parietalis
    - Lines the rest of the uterus

Chorion

- Chorion laeve
  - Superficial smooth chorion
- Chorion frondosum
  - Bushy chorion

© 2007 Jones and Bartlett Publishers

Fetal Membranes

- *Amnionic* sac
  - Enclosed within chorion
- *Yolk* sac
  - Forms intestinal tract and other structures

© 2007 Jones and Bartlett Publishers

Relation of Fetus to Decidua, Fetal Membranes, and Chorion

© Courtesy of Leonard Crowley, M.D./University of Minnesota Medical School

© 2007 Jones and Bartlett Publishers

Placenta

- The placenta has a *dual circulation* of *blood*
- The arrangement of the two circulations brings the *maternal and fetal blood into close approximation*
- In this way *oxygen and nutrients* can be *exchanged* between the maternal and fetal circulation
- But there is *no actual intermixing* of maternal and fetal blood

© 2007 Jones and Bartlett Publishers

Placenta

- *Double* circulation of blood
  - *Fetoplacental* circulation
  - *Uteroplacental* circulation
- *Endocrine* function
  Synthesizes
  - steroid hormones: *estrogen and progesterone*
  - protein hormones: *HPL (human placental lactogen)* and *HCG (human chorionic gonadotropin)*

© 2007 Jones and Bartlett Publishers

Amnionic Fluid

- Produced by *filtration and by excretion*, its *quantity varies* with the *stage of pregnancy*
- There are *conditions* where the *volume* of amniotic fluid is *altered* (increased or reduced)
- *Polyhydramnios*: volume of amniotic fluid markedly *increased*
  - *Fetus unable* to *swallow* fluid
  - Fluid *swallowed* but *not absorbed*
- *Oligohydramnios*: volume of amniotic fluid markedly *decreased*
  - Fetal *kidneys* fail to develop
  - Congenital *obstruction of urethra*

© 2007 Jones and Bartlett Publishers

Notes

Spontaneous Abortion

- *10-20%* of all pregnancies end up in spontaneous abortion ("miscarriages")
- *Early* abortion
  - *Chromosome* abnormalities or maldevelopment of embryo
- *Late* abortion
  - Partial *detachment* of *placenta*
  - *Obstruction* of *blood supply* through *cord*

© 2007 Jones and Bartlett Publishers

Spontaneous Abortion

© Courtesy of Leonard Crowley, M.D./University of Minnesota Medical School   © 2007 Jones and Bartlett Publishers

Ectopic Pregnancy

- *Ectopic pregnancy* is the development of the *embryo outside* its normal cavity within the *uterine cavity*
- *Most* occur in the *fallopian tubes*
- *Predisposing factors*
  - Previous *infection* of fallopian tubes
  - *Failure* of normal muscular *contractions* of tubal wall
- Consequences
  - *Rupture* of fallopian tube
  - Potentially *life-threatening* to mother

© 2007 Jones and Bartlett Publishers

Ectopic Pregnancy

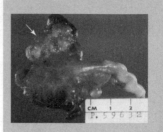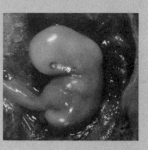

© Courtesy of Leonard Crowley, M.D./University of
Minnesota Medical School

© 2007 Jones and Bartlett Publishers

Pregnancy Failure
Artificial Contraception

- Failure of *contraceptive* pills
  - *Exposure* to estrogen and progestin compounds may induce *congenital abnormalities*
- Failure of *intrauterine* device
  - IUD predisposes pregnant uterus to *infection*

© 2007 Jones and Bartlett Publishers

Abnormal Attachment of
Umbilical Cord/Placenta

- Velamentous insertion of *umbilical cord*
  - Cord attaches to fetal membranes rather than to placenta
- *Normally,* the *placenta attaches high* on the anterior or posterior uterine wall
- If it attaches to the *lower* part, it may *cover* the *cervix*, called *placenta previa*
- *Placenta previa*
  - *Central* placenta previa
  - *Partial* placenta previa

© 2007 Jones and Bartlett Publishers

Velamentous Insertion
Umbilical Cord
Types of Placenta Previa

© Courtesy of Leonard Crowley, M.D./University of Minnesota Medical School   © 2007 Jones and Bartlett Publishers

Twins

- *Fraternal* twins
  - *Two separate* ova fertilized by *two different sperm*
- *Identical* twins
  - *Single* fertilized ovum *splits*
- *Twin transfusion* syndrome
  - One twin *polycythemic*
  - One twin *anemic*
- *Vanishing* twin
  - Twin *dies* and is completely *absorbed*
- *Blighted* twin
  - Twin *dies* and *persists* as *degenerated fetus*

© 2007 Jones and Bartlett Publishers

Gestational Trophoblast Disease

- *Hydatidiform* mole
  - Chorionic villi become cystic structures
- *Invasive* mole
  - Trophoblastic tissue may invade uterine wall
- *Choriocarcinoma*
  - Behaves like *malignant* tumor

© 2007 Jones and Bartlett Publishers

Erythroblastosis Fetalis

- Results from *sensitization* of the *mother* to blood group *antigen* in the red cells of the *infant*
- *Mother* forms *antibody* that crosses the placenta and *damages* the *infant's red cells*
- Variable severity
  - *Hydrops fetalis*
  - *Severe* hemolytic process
  - *Less intense* hemolytic process
  - *Mild* disease

© 2007 Jones and Bartlett Publishers

Fetal Hydrops

© Courtesy of Leonard Crowley, M.D./University of Minnesota Medical School   © 2007 Jones and Bartlett Publishers

Rh Hemolytic Disease

- Rh-*negative* mother and Rh-*positive* infant
- Mother *sensitized* to *"foreign" antigen* in infant's cells
- *Antibody* crosses placenta into infant's blood

Treatment

- Exchange *transfusion*
- *Fluorescent light* therapy for hyperbilirubinemia
- Intrauterine fetal *transfusion*

© 2007 Jones and Bartlett Publishers

ABO
Hemolytic Disease

- *Fetal A or B antigens* stimulate maternal *ABO antibodies*
- *Mild* hemolytic disease
- May be encountered in *first* pregnancy

© 2007 Jones and Bartlett Publishers

Chapter Outline

The chapter outline provides you with an organizational guide to the topics and ideas presented in this chapter of the text.

Structure and Function of the Urinary System
    The Kidneys
    The Ureters
    The Bladder and Urethra
Function of the Kidneys
    The Nephron
    Renal Regulation of Blood Pressure and Blood Volume
    Requirements for Normal Renal Function
Developmental Disturbances
Glomerulonephritis
    Immune-Complex Glomerulonephritis
    Anti-GBM Glomerulonephritis
Nephrotic Syndrome
Arteriolar Nephrosclerosis
Diabetic Nephropathy
Infections of the Urinary Tract
    Cystitis
    Pyelonephritis
    Vesicoureteral Reflux and Infection
Calculi
Foreign Bodies
Obstruction
Renal Tubular Injury
Renal Cysts
    Solitary Cysts
    Multiple Cysts
Tumors of the Urinary Tract
    Renal Cortical Tumors
    Transitional Cell Tumors
    Nephroblastoma (Wilms' Tumor)
Diagnostic Evaluation of Kidney and Urinary Tract Disease
    Urinalysis
    Clearance Tests
    Additional Techniques
Renal Failure (Uremia)
    Hemodialysis
    Renal Transplantation

Study Questions

The following questions are provided as a test for comprehension and as a study guide for use with the text chapters. Additional study material is located at http://humandisease.jbpub.com/, which contains useful tools such as an A&P review, animated flashcards, an interactive online glossary, crossword puzzles, and web links.

Key Terms

Define the following terms:

1. Diabetic nephropathy _____

2. Urea _____

3. Uremia _____

4. Glomerulonephritis _____

5. Pyelonephritis _____

6. Nephritic syndrome _____

7. Nephrosclerosis _____

Fill-in-the-Blank

1. The enzyme released by juxtaglomerular cells is called _____, which converts a protein called_____ into _____. The converted protein then is converted by ACE into _____, which is a powerful vasoconstrictor and also stimulates the adrenal cortex to release a hormone called _____.

2. Glomerulonephritis results from an immunologic reaction within the glomeruli and is divided into two main types, which are called _____ and _____.

3. An infection of the bladder is called _____, and an infection of the kidney is called _____.

4. Dilatation of the renal pelvis, calyces, and ureter resulting from obstruction to outflow of urine is called

   _____.

5. A kidney stone is called a _____.

6. The hereditary kidney disease characterized by formation of multiple progressively enlarging renal cysts that gradually destroy the function of the kidneys is called _____.

7. Two methods of renal dialysis are called _____ and _____.

8. Malignant tumors occur in the kidneys and bladder. The malignant kidney tumor occurring in older adults is called _____. The malignant kidney tumor occurring in infants and young children is called _____. The malignant bladder tumor is called _____.

9. The laboratory test that is likely to show abnormal results in a patient with acute glomerulonephritis is

   _____.

True/False

Tell whether each statement is true or false. If false, explain why the statement is incorrect.

1. Blood and urine clearance tests measure the ability of the kidneys to remove ("clear") waste products from the blood and excrete the products in the urine. _____

_____

2. Diabetic nephropathy is characterized by nodular and diffuse thickening of glomerular basement membranes as well as by marked thickening and narrowing of glomerular arterioles (arteriolonephrosclerosis). _____

_____

3. Tell whether each statement is true or false regarding acute poststreptococcal glomerulonephritis. If false, explain why the statement is incorrect.

   a. It is induced by antigen–antibody complexes filtered from the blood that accumulate within the walls of the glomerular capillaries. _____

   _____

   b. It results from bacterial infection of the glomeruli. _____

   _____

   c. It usually causes a nephrotic syndrome. _____

   _____

   d. It is caused by damage done by enzymes released from leukocytes that accumulate within the glomeruli.

   _____

4. Tell whether each statement is true or false regarding the nephrotic syndrome. If false, explain why the statement is incorrect.

   a. The liver fails to produce plasma protein. _____

   _____

   b. Protein is lost in the urine more rapidly than it can be produced by the body. _____

   _____

   c. The nephrotic syndrome is usually associated with normal concentration of plasma protein and normal plasma osmotic pressure. _____

   _____

   d. It may result from any type of glomerular disease that allows large amounts of protein to escape in the urine.

   _____

   e. It usually is caused by a bacterial infection of the kidney. _____

   _____

   f. It may result from renal tubular disease. _____

   _____

5. Tell whether each statement is true or false regarding the renin–angiotensin–aldosterone syndrome. If false, explain why the statement is incorrect.

   a. Renin is secreted by cells of the juxtaglomerular apparatus in response to high blood sodium concentration, higher than normal blood pressure, or higher than normal blood volume. _____

   _____

   b. Renin converts angiotensinogen to angiotensin I. _____

   _____

   c. Angiotensin-converting enzyme (ACE) converts angiotensin I to angiotensin II. _____

   _____

   d. Angiotensin II stimulates aldosterone release and arteriolar vasoconstriction. _____

   _____

6. Tell whether each statement is true or false regarding congenital polycystic kidney disease. If false, explain why the statement is incorrect.

   a. It is transmitted as mendelian dominant trait. _____

   _____

   b. Manifestations occur in late childhood or adolescence. _____

   _____

   c. Progressively enlarging cysts slowly destroy kidney function. _____

   _____

   d. Affected kidneys become greatly enlarged. _____

   _____

7. Tell whether each statement is true or false regarding bladder carcinoma. If false, explain why the statement is incorrect.

   a. The bladder tumor arises from transitional epithelium of the urinary bladder. _____

   _____

   b. Hematuria (blood in urine) may be the first manifestation of the bladder tumor. _____

   _____

   c. The tumor usually is poorly differentiated and rapidly growing and has a very poor prognosis. _____

   _____

   d. Diagnosis of a tumor is made by cystoscopy and biopsy. _____

   _____

Matching

Match the item in the left column with its characteristic or property in the right column.

1. _____ Polycystic kidney disease   A. Kidney infection

2. _____ Gout   B. Mendelian dominant trait

3. _____ Pyelonephritis   C. Nodular and diffuse basement membrane thickening

4. _____ IgA nephropathy   D. Urate crystals plug tubules

5. _____ Diabetes   E. Immune complexes in mesangial cells

Identify

1. Identify three conditions that predispose a person to urinary tract infection.

   a. _____

   b. _____

   c. _____

2. Identify three features characteristic of the nephrotic syndrome.

   a. _____

   b. _____

   c. _____

Discussion Questions

1. What is the relationship between glomerulonephritis and beta streptococcal infection? _____

   _____

   _____

   _____

2. What is the difference between the nephrotic syndrome and nephrosclerosis? _____

   _____

   _____

   _____

3. Why does edema occur in a patient with nephrosis? _____

   _____

   _____

   _____

4. What are the common causes of urinary tract obstruction? What are its effects on the kidneys and lower urinary tract?

   _____

   _____

   _____

5. What conditions predispose a person to kidney stones? _____

_____

_____

6. Describe the conditions that may lead to renal tubular necrosis. What are its clinical manifestations? _____

_____

_____

_____

7. What is the significance of an elevated level of urea in the blood? _____

_____

_____

_____

8. What are the manifestations of uremia? How is it treated by the physician? _____

_____

_____

_____

9. How is kidney failure treated? _____

_____

_____

_____

10. What methods does the physician use to establish a diagnosis of renal disease? _____

_____

_____

_____

11. What condition(s) may eventually lead to renal failure? _____

_____

_____

_____

12. What adverse effects are caused by a foreign body inserted into the bladder? _____

_____

_____

_____

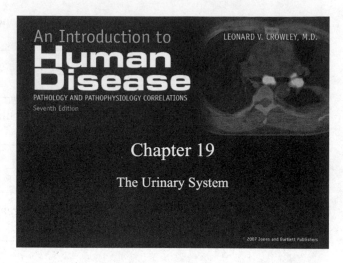

Urinary System

The urinary system

- *Kidneys: produce* urine
- *Excretory duct system:* renal calyces, renal pelves, and ureters, that *transport* the urine
- *Bladder*: urine is *stored*
- *Urethra: conveys* the urine from the bladder for excretion

© 2007 Jones and Bartlett Publishers

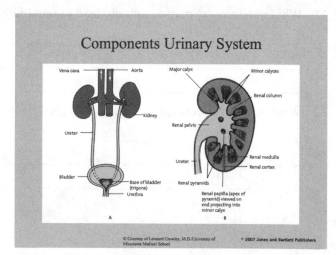

Components Urinary System

© Courtesy of Leonard Crowley, M.D./University of Minnesota Medical School   © 2007 Jones and Bartlett Publishers

Notes

_____
_____
_____
_____
_____
_____
_____
_____
_____
_____
_____
_____
_____
_____
_____
_____
_____
_____
_____
_____
_____
_____
_____
_____
_____
_____
_____
_____
_____
_____
_____
_____
_____

Kidneys

- Are paired, bean-shaped organs located along the *back body* wall *below* the *diaphragm* and *adjacent* to the *vertebral column*
- Are important *excretory organs*, functioning *along with* the *lungs* in excreting the waste products of food metabolism
- Has *three* basic functions
1. Excrete <u>waste products</u> of food metabolism
- *Carbon dioxide and water* are end-products of *carbohydrate and fat metabolism*
- *Urea* and other *acids are end-products of protein metabolism,* that *only* the kidneys can excrete

© 2007 Jones and Bartlett Publishers

Kidneys

2. Regulate <u>mineral and water balance-</u> by excreting minerals and water that have been ingested *in excess* of the body's requirements and conserving them *as required.* (It has been said that the body's *internal environment* is determined *not* by what a person *ingests* but rather by what the *kidneys retain*)
3. <u>Endocrine</u> function: specialized cells in the kidneys elaborate
- A *hormone* called *erythropoietin*, which regulates *red blood* cell production in the bone marrow
- A *humoral* substance called *renin*, which takes part in the regulation of *blood pressure*

© 2007 Jones and Bartlett Publishers

The Nephron

- The basic structural and functional *unit* of the kidney (about one million in each kidney)

Two components

1. Glomerulus
2. Renal tubule

<u>Glomerulus</u>: a tuft of *capillaries* that is supplied by an *afferent glomerular arteriole*, the capillaries then *recombining* into an *efferent glomerular arteriole*, which in turn breaks up into a network of capillaries which *supply the renal tubule*

© 2007 Jones and Bartlett Publishers

The Nephron

2. <u>Renal tubule:</u> reabsorbs most of filtrate; secretes unwanted components into tubular fluid; regulates water balance

• For a nephron to function normally, the following conditions must be satisfied:

1. Free flow of blood through the glomerular capillaries (glomerulus)

2. *Glomerular filter* must function normally (restricting passage of blood cells and protein)

3. *Renal tubules* must selectively *reabsorb* important substances from the filtrate and *excrete* other constituents into the filtrate

Kidney
Bowman's Capsule

• The histologic structure of the glomerulus and related structures is illustrated schematically in Figure 19-2

Glomerulus
Bowman's Capsule

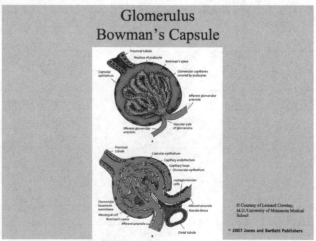

© Courtesy of Leonard Crowley, M.D./University of Minnesota Medical School

Renal Regulation
Blood Pressure / Blood Volume

- <u>Renin:</u> an enzyme that *interacts* with a blood protein, *angiotensinogen*
- *Splits off* a short peptide fragment, *angiotensin I*
- Angiotensin I is converted to *angiotensin II* by *angiotensin converting enzyme* (*ACE*) as blood flows through the *lungs*
- Angiotensin II is a powerful *vasoconstrictor*, that *raises blood pressure*, by causing the peripheral arteriole to *constrict*
- Angiotensin II stimulates the *adrenal cortex* to secrete a steroid hormone, *aldosterone,* which increases *reabsorption* of *sodium chloride* and *water* by kidneys

© 2007 Jones and Bartlett Publishers

Renal Regulation
Blood Pressure / Blood Volume

As A Result

- *Blood Pressure* rises: more fluid within the vascular system
- *Volume* is increased: greater volume of salt and water

Thus:

The system is *self-regulating*

- *renin secretion declines*
- as *blood pressure, volume, and sodium* concentration are restored to *normal*

© 2007 Jones and Bartlett Publishers

Developmental Abnormalities

- Sometimes the developmental process is disturbed and three congenital abnormalities result
1. *Renal agenesis: failure* of one or both kidneys to develop
2. *Duplications* of the urinary tract: formation of *extra* ureters and renal pelves
3. *Malposition*: of one or both kidneys, associated with fusion of kidneys

© 2007 Jones and Bartlett Publishers

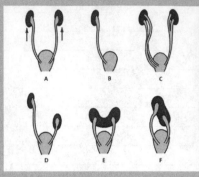

Congenital Abnormalities

© Courtesy of Leonard Crowley, M.D./University of Minnesota Medical School   © 2007 Jones and Bartlett Publishers

Glomerulonephritis

- An *inflammation* of the glomeruli that is caused by *antigen-antibody* reaction within the glomeruli
- The interaction of *antigen and antibody* activates *complement* and liberates *mediators* that *attract leukocytes*
- The leukocytes release destructive lysosomal *enzymes* that cause *injury* to the glomeruli
- The antigen-antibody reaction take place in two ways:
1. Immune-complex glomerulonephritis
2. Antiglomerular basement membrane (anti-GBM) glomerulonephritis

© 2007 Jones and Bartlett Publishers

Nephrotic Syndrome

- Characterized by a *marked loss of protein* in the urine
- *Urinary excretion* of protein is *so great* that the body is *unable to manufacture* protein fast enough and the *concentration* of *protein* in the *blood plasma falls*
- This causes significant *edema* owing to the *low plasma osmotic pressure*

Clinical Manifestations

- Marked leg *edema*
- Ascites (collection *fluid* in *abdominal* cavity)

© 2007 Jones and Bartlett Publishers

Nephrotic Syndrome

- Hydrothorax (*fluid* accumulation in the *pleural* cavities)
- Nephrotic syndrome is produced by a number of *different* types of *renal disease*
- Most *often* occurs in *children*
  - Causes *minimal* glomerular change, *responds well to corticosteroids, complete recovery*
- *Adults*
  - Manifestation of a *more severe* progressive renal disease
  - May result from
  - Glomerulonephritis

© 2007 Jones and Bartlett Publishers

Nephrotic Syndrome

- Diabetes (causing glomerular changes)
- Lupus erythematosus (connective tissue disease)
- Other uncommon types kidney disease

© 2007 Jones and Bartlett Publishers

Arteriolar Nephrosclerosis

- A *complication* of severe *hypertension*
- Renal arterioles undergo *thickening* caused by carrying *blood* at a much *higher pressure* than normal
- The *glomeruli and tubules* undergo secondary *degenerative* changes, which causes *narrowing* of *lumens*, which *reduces blood flow*
- Glomerular *filtration* is *reduced*
- Eventually *kidneys* become *shrunken*
- Patients may *die* of *renal insufficiency*

© 2007 Jones and Bartlett Publishers

Diabetic Nephropathy

- Nodular and diffuse *thickening* of glomerular basement *membranes*
- In some patients, the *protein loss* may lead to *nephrotic syndrome*
- *No specific treatment* that can arrest the progression of disease
- Progressive impairment of renal function that may lead to *renal failure*

© 2007 Jones and Bartlett Publishers

Urinary Tract Infections

- Are common
- Acute or chronic
- Most infections are caused by *gram-negative bacteria*
- Organisms *contaminate perianal* and *genital* areas and *gain access* by ascending the *urethra*

Conditions that *protect*

- *Free* urine *flow*
- *Large* urine *volume*
- Complete *emptying bladder* protect against infection
- *Acid urine* is a *defense* as most bacteria grow poorly in acidic environment

© 2007 Jones and Bartlett Publishers

Urinary Tract Infections

Conditions that *predispose*

- *Any condition* that *impairs free drainage of urine* because stagnation of urine favors multiplication of bacteria
- Injury to mucosa by *kidney stone*, disrupting protective epithelium, bacteria invading deeper tissue
- Introduction of *catheter* that may carry bacteria

© 2007 Jones and Bartlett Publishers

Cystitis

Cystitis
- affects *only* the *bladder*
- more *common* in *women* than men (shorter female urethra)
- *young sexually active women* (sexual intercourse promotes transfer of bacteria from urethra to bladder)
- common in *older men* (enlarged prostate interferes with complete emptying bladder)

Clinical Manifestations
- *Burning pain* on urination
- Desire to *urinate frequently*
- Urine contains *many* bacteria & leukocytes
- Usually *not serious* problem

© 2007 Jones and Bartlett Publishers

Cystitis
Pyelonephritis

- *Responds well* to *antibiotics*
- *However*, *may spread* to upper urinary tract to affect *renal pelvis and kidney*

Pyelonephritis
- *Upper* urinary tract is affected
- *Secondary* to *ascending* infection from the *bladder*, called *ascending pyelonephritis*
- Sometimes it is carried to the *kidneys* through the *bloodstream*, called *hematogenous pyelonephritis*

© 2007 Jones and Bartlett Publishers

Pyelonephritis

- The *clinical manifestations are* the *same* as with an *acute infection*, together with localized pain and tenderness over the affected kidney
- Also *responds well* to *antibiotics*
- Cystitis and pyelonephritis are frequently *associated*
- Some cases become *chronic* and lead to *kidney failure*

© 2007 Jones and Bartlett Publishers

Vesicoureteral Reflux

- *Normally*, effective mechanisms *prevent urine from flowing upward* from the *bladder* into the *ureters* during urination
- Sometimes, however, these *mechanisms* are *defective*
- *Retrograde flow* of urine into *ureters*
- Predisposes to urinary tract *infection*
- Predisposes to *pyelonephritis*

© 2007 Jones and Bartlett Publishers

Predisposing Factors Urinary Calculi

Stones may *form anywhere* in the *urinary tract*
- Predisposing factors
  1. *Increased concentration* of *salts* in urine causes urine to become *saturated*; salts may precipitate to form calculi
  - *Uric acid* in *gout*
  - *Calcium* salts in *hyperparathyroidism*
  2. *Infections* of the urinary tract *reduce* the *solubility* of salts in urine; clusters of *bacteria* serve as sites where urinary *salts* may *crystallize* to form the *stone*

© 2007 Jones and Bartlett Publishers

Predisposing Factors Urinary Calculi

  3. *Urinary tract obstruction* causes *stagnation* of *urine*, where urinary salts precipitate out; stagnation predisposes to *infection,* further increasing stone formation

© 2007 Jones and Bartlett Publishers

Urinary Calculi

- Most calculi are *small* but they may increase in size to form large branching structures that adopt the contour of the pelvis and calyces, called *staghorn calculus*, because they resemble the antlers of the male deer
- *Many small* stones may pass to the *ureters,* these contracting to propel the stone, causing *renal colic*
- *Some* stones become *impacted* in the *ureter* and need to be *removed*

© 2007 Jones and Bartlett Publishers

Urinary Calculi

Treatment
- *Cystoscope* and passing *catheterlike instrument* through cytoscope into ureter, which *snares* and *removes* stones lodged in *distal ureter*
- Shock-wave *lithotripsy*: stones lodged in *proximal ureter* are *broken* into fragments that are excreted in the urine

© 2007 Jones and Bartlett Publishers

Urinary Drainage System Obstruction

- *Causes* of obstruction
  - Enlarged prostate
  - Stricture in urethra
  - Ureteral stricture
  - Calculus
  - Tumor
- Leads to *dilation* of urinary tract proximal to the obstruction
- Causes *compression atrophy* of the kidney

© 2007 Jones and Bartlett Publishers

Renal Tubular Injury

- Pathogenesis
  - *Impaired* renal blood flow
  - *Tubular necrosis* caused by toxic drugs or chemicals
- Clinical manifestation
  - *Acute* renal failure

© 2007 Jones and Bartlett Publishers

Renal Cysts Solitary and Multiple

Solitary cysts
- Very *common*
- *Not* associated with impairment of renal function

Multiple cysts
- *Congenital polycystic kidney* disease: most common cause of *multiple* cysts

© 2007 Jones and Bartlett Publishers

Congenital Polycystic Kidney Disease

- *Mendelian dominant* transmission
- *Cysts enlarge* and *destroy* renal function
- Onset of renal insufficiency in *middle age*
- Suspected by *physical examination* that reveals *greatly enlarged kidneys*

© 2007 Jones and Bartlett Publishers

Renal Cortical Tumors

- *Arise* from epithelium of renal tubules
- *Adenomas* small and asymptomatic
- *Carcinomas* more common

© 2007 Jones and Bartlett Publishers

Transitional Cell Tumors

- *Arise* from transitional epithelium lining urinary tract
- *Most* arise from bladder epithelium
- *Hematuria* is often the first manifestation

© 2007 Jones and Bartlett Publishers

Nephroblastoma (Wilms' Tumor)

- *Uncommon*
- Highly *malignant*
- Affects *infants* and *children*
- *Treatment*
  - Nephrectomy
  - Radiotherapy and anticancer chemotherapy

© 2007 Jones and Bartlett Publishers

Diagnostic Evaluation

- Urinalysis
- Urine culture and sensitivity tests
- Blood chemistry tests
- Clearance tests
- X-ray, ultrasound, cystoscopy
- Renal biopsy

© 2007 Jones and Bartlett Publishers

Renal Failure (Uremia)

- Uremia: the *retention* of excessive *byproducts* of *protein metabolism* (*urea*, etc.) in the blood, and the *toxic* condition produced thereby
- *Acute* renal failure
  - Caused by *tubular necrosis*, which can be caused by impairment of blood flow to the kidneys or by the effects of toxic drugs, *renal function usually returns*
- *Chronic* renal failure
  - Result of progressive, *chronic kidney disease*
  - More than 50% result from *chronic glomerulonephritis*

© 2007 Jones and Bartlett Publishers

Renal Failure (Uremia)

- Congenital polycystic kidney disease
- Nephrosclerosis
- Diabetic nephropathy
  Make Up The Remainder

© 2007 Jones and Bartlett Publishers

Renal Failure

Manifestations

- Weakness, loss of appetite, nausea, vomiting
- Anemia
- Toxic manifestations caused by retained waste products
- Retention of salt and water
- Hypertension

© 2007 Jones and Bartlett Publishers

Hemodialysis

- It *substitutes* for the *functions of the kidneys*, which removes waste products from the patient's blood
- Waste products from the patient's blood diffuse across a semipermeable membrane into a solution (the dialysate) on the other side of the membrane

There are two types

- Extracorporeal (more *common*)
  - Patient's circulation connected to *artificial kidney machine*
- Peritoneal (*less common*)
  - *Patient's own peritoneum* used as dialyzing membrane

© 2007 Jones and Bartlett Publishers

Renal Transplantation

- When kidneys fail, *renal transplantation* may be attempted
- The *kidney* is obtained from a *close relative* or *cadaver donor*
- The *survival* of the *transplant* depends on the *similarity of HLA antigens* between *donor* and *recipient*
- *Only identical twins* will contain *identical HLA antigens* in their tissues
- The *rest* of transplants will invariably contain *foreign HLA antigens* that the patient lacks

© 2007 Jones and Bartlett Publishers

_____

_____

_____

_____

_____

_____

_____

_____

_____

_____

Renal Transplantation

- Consequently, the patient's immunologic defenses will respond to the foreign antigens and attempt to destroy (*reject*) the foreign kidney
- The patient's immune system must be *suppressed by drugs*
- The kidney is placed in the *iliac area*, outside the peritoneal cavity

Prognosis

- More than *90%* of transplanted kidneys survive for *five years* when the *donor's HLA antigens resemble the patient's*
- The *survival rate* of *cadaver transplants* has *improved greatly* in recent years

© 2007 Jones and Bartlett Publishers

Chapter Outline

The chapter outline provides you with an organizational guide to the topics and ideas presented in this chapter of the text.

Study Questions

The following questions are provided as a test for comprehension and as a study guide for use with the text chapters. Additional study material is located at http://humandisease.jbpub.com/, which contains useful tools such as an A&P review, animated flashcards, an interactive online glossary, crossword puzzles, and web links.

Key Terms

Define the following terms:

1. Seminoma _____

2. Prostate-specific antigen _____

Fill-in-the-Blank

1. The infectious agents that are the two main causes of acute urethritis acquired by sexual contact are _____ and _____. These infections are treated by _____.

2. Benign prostatic hyperplasia (BPH) is a common problem in older men. It produces symptoms of _____, resulting from compression of the _____ by the nodules of enlarged prostatic tissue.

3. There are many ways to treat BPH. The surgical procedure is called _____.

4. Prostatic epithelial cells secrete a protein called _____, which also can be detected in the bloodstream. Higher than normal levels are detected in the bloodstream of man with a disease called _____.

5. Testicular carcinomas are uncommon tumors. Many of these tumors produce a hormone called _____ _____ and a protein antigen called _____.

6. Testicular malignant tumors that are composed of many different types of immature tissues are called

   _____.

7. Carcinoma of the penis is an uncommon tumor that almost never occurs in circumcised men. The agent responsible for the carcinoma is _____.

8. The fibrous cord that guides the testis into the scrotum is called the _____.

9. Failure of the proximal end of the tunica vaginalis to close after the testis has entered the scrotum may be complicated by a condition called a/an _____.

True/False

Tell whether each statement is true or false. If false, explain why the statement is incorrect.

1. Most prostate carcinomas arise from the inner group of prostatic glands surrounding the prostatic urethra. _____

   _____

2. Prostate-specific antigen is secreted by prostatic epithelial cells. _____

   _____

3. Most prostate carcinomas are very poorly differentiated, grow rapidly, and have a very poor prognosis. _____

   _____

Matching

Match the disease or condition in the left column with its characteristic features in the right column.

1. ____ Cryptorchidism
2. ____ Hydrocele
3. ____ Varicocele
4. ____ Testicular torsion
5. ____ Prostate hyperplasia

A. Dilated spermatic cord veins
B. Twisted spermatic cord
C. Overgrowth of prostatic tissue
D. Undescended testis
E. Excess fluid in tunica vaginalis

Discussion Questions

1. What are the components of the male reproductive system? _____
_____
_____
_____

2. What methods are available to detect carcinoma of the prostate? _____
_____
_____
_____

3. How is carcinoma of the prostate treated? _____
_____
_____
_____

4. Why do many physicians recommend conservative treatment of prostatic carcinoma in older men with well-differentiated tumors? _____
_____
_____
_____

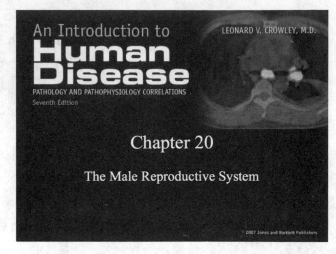

An Introduction to
Human Disease
PATHOLOGY AND PATHOPHYSIOLOGY CORRELATIONS
Seventh Edition

LEONARD V. CROWLEY, M.D.

Chapter 20

The Male Reproductive System

© 2007 Jones and Bartlett Publishers

Male Reproductive System

Components of the male reproductive system
- Penis
- Prostate
- Certain accessory glands
- Testes
- Duct system to transport sperm from testes to urethra
- It begins at the *epididymides*
- It continues as the *two vasa deferentia*
- The two vasa extend upward in the *spermatic cords*

© 2007 Jones and Bartlett Publishers

Male Reproductive System

- They enter the prostatic urethra as the *ejaculatory ducts*
- The urethra is divided into a long *penile urethra* and a short segment transversing the prostate gland, called *prostatic urethra*

© 2007 Jones and Bartlett Publishers

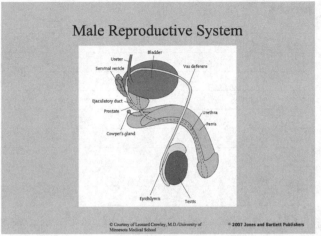

Male Reproductive System

© Courtesy of Leonard Crowley, M.D./University of Minnesota Medical School

© 2007 Jones and Bartlett Publishers

Prostate

- It is a spherical *gland* that surrounds the urethra just below the base of the bladder
- It is composed of numerous branched glands arranged in *two major groups* intermixed with masses of *smooth muscle* and *fibrous* tissue
- The *inner group* of glands *surrounds the urethra* as it passes through the prostate
- The *outer or main group* of glands makes up the *bulk* of prostatic glandular tissue
- The prostate secretes a thin *alkaline* fluid containing a high concentration of an *enzyme* secreted by prostatic epithelial cells

© 2007 Jones and Bartlett Publishers

Prostate

- The prostatic secretions are *discharged* into the urethra during *ejaculation* through very fine ducts that open near the orifices of the ejaculatory ducts
- Secretions *mix* with *sperm* and the *secretions* of the seminal vesicles to form the *seminal fluid*

© 2007 Jones and Bartlett Publishers

Notes

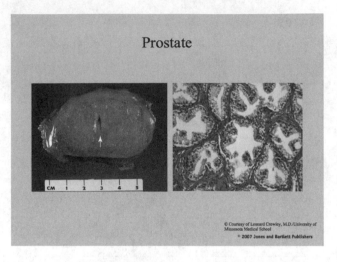

Prostate

© Courtesy of Leonard Crowley, M.D./University of
Minnesota Medical School

© 2007 Jones and Bartlett Publishers

Gonorrhea

- Gonorrhea: a relatively *common* disease
  - *Initially, acute* inflammation of anterior urethra
  - Inflammation may *spread* into posterior *urethra and transport ducts*
  - May also cause an acute inflammation of the *rectal* mucosa
  - Obstruction of vasa may block sperm transport and cause *sterility*

© 2007 Jones and Bartlett Publishers

Nongonococcal Urethritis

- Nongonococcal urethritis
  - Caused by *Chlamydia*
  - Causes an acute urethritis
  - Clinically very *similar* to *gonorrhea*

© 2007 Jones and Bartlett Publishers

Prostatitis

- Acute
  - It develops when an acute *inflammation* of the *bladder or urethra spreads* into the prostate
  - It may follow a *gonococcal* infection of the posterior *urethra*
- Chronic
  - It is a *mild* inflammation
  - Quite *common*
  - Causes *few* symptoms

© 2007 Jones and Bartlett Publishers

Benign Prostatic Hyperplasia

- *Moderate* enlargement of the prostate gland is relatively *common* in *elderly* men
- Usually involves *inner group* of *glands* surrounding the urethra
- *Obstructs* the *outflow* of *urine*
- The prostatic enlargement is *significant only if* it *obstructs* the *neck* of the *bladder*, leading to *incomplete emptying* of the *bladder* or causes *complete urinary tract obstruction*

© 2007 Jones and Bartlett Publishers

Benign Prostatic Hyperplasia

- Complications
  - Cystitis: inflammation of the urinary bladder
  - Pyelonephritis: inflammation of kidneys and pelvis
  - Calculi formation: stones
  - Hydronephrosis: distention of the renal pelvis and calices with urine due to ureter obstruction
- There are *various* medical and surgical *treatments*
- *Transurethral resection* is "gold standard"

© 2007 Jones and Bartlett Publishers

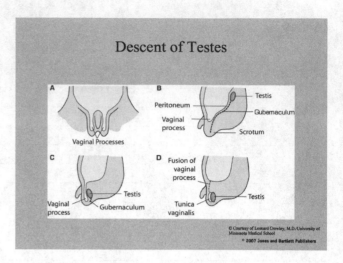

Descent of Testes

A

B
Peritoneum
Vaginal process
Vaginal Processes
Testis
Gubernaculum
Scrotum

C
Vaginal process
Testis
Gubernaculum

D Fusion of vaginal process
Tunica vaginalis
Testis

© Courtesy of Leonard Crowley, M.D./University of Minnesota Medical School

© 2007 Jones and Bartlett Publishers

Carcinoma of the Prostate

Carcinoma of the Prostate
- Usually originates in outer group of glands of the prostate
- Manifestations
  - Early case may be asymptomatic
  - May obstruct bladder neck
  - Infiltration of tissues surrounding prostate
- Metastasizes to bones of spine and pelvis
- The tumor cells often secrete acid phosphatase, as do normal prostatic cells

© 2007 Jones and Bartlett Publishers

Benign Prostatic Hyperplasia

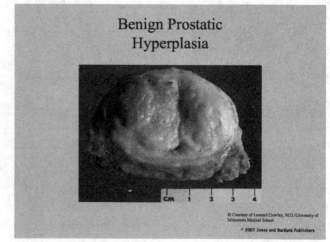

© Courtesy of Leonard Crowley, M.D./University of Minnesota Medical School

© 2007 Jones and Bartlett Publishers

Carcinoma of the Prostate

- The *enzyme leaks* into the *bloodstream*
- Patients with prostatic cancer have *high levels* of this *enzyme* in the blood
- Another substance called *prostate-specific antigen (PSA)* is also secreted
- *Elevated* levels appear in the blood of some patients
- However, it is *not specific* for prostate cancer
- Patients with *prostatic hyperplasia* and other *benign prostatic* diseases also may have *high PSA levels*

© 2007 Jones and Bartlett Publishers

Carcinoma of the Prostate

Diagnosis
- *Rectal exam* identifies irregularity or nodularity on surface of prostate
- *Prostate-specific antigen* and/or *acid phosphatase* test
- Prostate *needle biopsy*

Treatment depends on the *degree* of *differentiation* of the tumor and the extent of the tumor's *advancement*

© 2007 Jones and Bartlett Publishers

Carcinoma Prostate

- *Surgery*
  - Radical prostatectomy: for a *small, localized* tumor; it may *cause impotence* as it disrupts the nerve supply to penis
- Radical prostatectomy *and* radiation: seems to *improve survival*
- In *elderly* men, it is *controversial* to treat with radical surgery and radiation

© 2007 Jones and Bartlett Publishers

Carcinoma of the Prostate

– The tumor grows *slowly*
– It may be *ten* or more years *before it obstructs or metastasizes*
– Treatment may cause significant *disability* and may not significantly improve survival

When it has *metastasized*

– Surgical removal of *testes:* eliminate source of testosterone, which stimulates tumor growth
– Drugs that suppress output of gonadotropic hormones (which inhibit testosterone production)

© 2007 Jones and Bartlett Publishers

Carcinoma of the Prostate

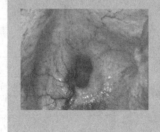 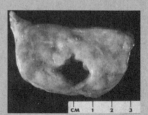

© Courtesy of Leonard Crowley, M.D./University of Minnesota Medical School

© 2007 Jones and Bartlett Publishers

Cryptorchidism

Cause

• *Testis* do *not descend normally* into scrotum
• Usually *retained* in *abdominal cavity*; sometimes in *inguinal canal*
• *Germ cells* require a *lower-than-normal body temperature*
• *Interstitial cells* function normally at *body temperature*

Manifestations

• *Germ cells destroyed* at *higher intra-abdominal temperature*
• *Interstitial cells* function *normally*

© 2007 Jones and Bartlett Publishers

Cryptorchidism

- Undescended testis *more prone* to developing *testicular cancer*

Treatment
- *Surgically* replace testis in scrotum

© 2007 Jones and Bartlett Publishers

Testicular Torsion

Cause
- Abnormal *attachment* of *testis* in *scrotum*
- Predisposes to *rotary twisting* of *testis* and *spermatic cord*
- *Shutting off blood* supply to testis

Manifestations and treatment
- Acute onset of testicular *pain* and *swelling*
- Leads to *hemorrhagic infarction* unless *promptly untwisted*

© 2007 Jones and Bartlett Publishers

Scrotal Abnormalities

Hydrocele
- *Excess fluid* accumulates in *tunica vaginalis*
- *Treated* by *aspiration* or resection of tunica vaginalis

Varicocele
- *Varicose veins* in *spermatic cord*
- Usually left side of scrotum involved
- May *impair fertility*
- *No treatment required unless* varicocele causes discomfort or impairs infertility

© 2007 Jones and Bartlett Publishers

Erectile Dysfunction

Cause

- *Inability to* achieve and maintain a *penile erection*
- Many different causes which *impair blood flow to penis*

Treatment

- *Many* medical and surgical treatments available *depending* on *cause* of dysfunction
- *Phosphodiesterase inhibitor drugs effective* but must be *used* with *caution* because of *possible serious effects*

© 2007 Jones and Bartlett Publishers

Carcinoma of the Testis

- Seminoma
  - Malignant neoplasm of *semen*-producing epithelium
- Malignant teratoma
  - Composed of *many types* of malignant tissues
- Choriocarcinoma
  - *Same* kind of tumor that arises from trophoblastic tissues in the *uterus*

© 2007 Jones and Bartlett Publishers

Carcinoma of the Penis

- *Papilloma virus* may play a role
- Treatment
  - Partial or complete resection of *penis*
  - Removal of *inguinal lymph nodes*

© 2007 Jones and Bartlett Publishers

Notes

_____
_____
_____
_____
_____
_____
_____
_____
_____
_____
_____

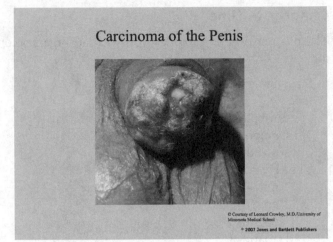

Carcinoma of the Penis

© Courtesy of Leonard Crowley, M.D./University of
Minnesota Medical School

© 2007 Jones and Bartlett Publishers

Chapter Outline

The chapter outline provides you with an organizational guide to the topics and ideas presented in this chapter of the text.

Structure and Function of the Liver
Bile
    Formation and Excretion
    Composition and Properties
Causes and Effects of Liver Injury
Viral Hepatitis
    Clinical Manifestations and Course
    Hepatitis A
    Hepatitis B
    Hepatitis C
    Hepatitis D (Delta Hepatitis)
    Hepatitis E
    Other Hepatitis Viruses
    Hepatitis Among Male Homosexuals
Fatty Liver
Alcoholic Liver Disease
Cirrhosis of the Liver
    Derangements of Liver Structure and Function
    Procedures to Treat Manifestations of Cirrhosis
    Biliary Cirrhosis
Reye's Syndrome
Cholelithiasis
    Factors Affecting the Solubility of Cholesterol in Bile
    Complications of Gallstones
    Treatment of Gallstones
Cholecystitis
Tumors of the Liver and Gallbladder
Jaundice
    Hemolytic Jaundice
    Hepatocellular Jaundice
    Obstructive Jaundice
Biopsy of the Liver

Study Questions

The following questions are provided as a test for comprehension and as a study guide for use with the text chapters. Additional study material is located at http://humandisease.jbpub.com/, which contains useful tools such as an A&P review, animated flashcards, an interactive online glossary, crossword puzzles, and web links.

Key Terms

Define the following terms:

1. Hepatitis _____

2. Bilirubin _____

3. Bile _____

4. Jaundice _____

Fill-in-the-Blank

1. The iron-free pigment derived from breakdown of hemoglobin is called _____.

2. The substance present in bile that may precipitate within the bile to form gallstones is _____.

3. Some persons may have chronic hepatitis but show no symptoms of infection. This condition is called

   _____.

4. The antigen present in the blood of persons infected with hepatitis B is _____.

5. The most frequent cause of chronic hepatitis in the United States is _____.

6. Approximately _____ percent of persons infected with HCV are unable to eliminate the virus and become chronic carriers of the virus.

7. Persons with chronic hepatitis are at risk of two major complications, which are _____ _____ and _____.

8. The two most common causes of cirrhosis are _____ and _____.

9. Two common causes of obstructive biliary cirrhosis are _____ and _____.

10. A child with a viral infection and a fever is given acetaminophen (Tylenol) rather than aspirin to control the fever to avoid the risk of a liver and central nervous system disease called _____.

11. Most gallstones are composed of _____.

True/False

Tell whether each statement is true or false. If false, explain why the statement is incorrect.

1. The infectious particle in the blood of persons with HBV infection is hepatitis B surface antigen. _____

   _____

2. Most HCV-infected persons are unable to eradicate the virus and become chronic carriers of the virus. _____

   _____

3. Many HCV-infected persons are asymptomatic. _____

_____

4. Chronic HCV infection is caused by ingestion of virus-contaminated food or water. _____

_____

5. Primary biliary cirrhosis is caused by chronic HCV infection. _____

_____

6. Primary biliary cirrhosis is an autoimmune disease in which the autoantibody is directed against bile duct epithelial cells. _____

_____

7. Secondary biliary cirrhosis is caused by longstanding obstruction of large extrahepatic bile ducts. _____

_____

Identify

1. Construct a table comparing the major features of the three main types of hepatitis. (*Hint:* see Table 21-1.)

Characteristic	Hepatitis A	Hepatitis B	Hepatitis C

2. Alcoholic liver disease can be divided into three states of progressively increasing severity:

a. _____

b. _____

c. _____

Discussion Questions

1. What are some of the main functions of the liver? _____

_____

_____

_____

2. How does the blood supply to the liver differ from the blood supply to other organs? _____

_____

_____

_____

3. Why does severe liver disease cause disturbances in blood clotting? _____

_____

_____

4. What is the difference between hemoglobin and bilirubin? How does conjugated bilirubin differ from unconjugated bilirubin? _____

_____

_____

_____

5. What is the difference between bilirubin and bile? What role does bile play in digestion? _____

_____

_____

_____

6. Describe the major structural changes and physiological derangements in patients with cirrhosis. What conditions are associated with cirrhosis? _____

_____

_____

_____

7. Why is the pressure in the portal vein elevated in patients with cirrhosis? _____

_____

_____

_____

8. Why do patients with cirrhosis often accumulate a fluid within their peritoneal cavity that is called ascites?

_____

_____

9. Why do patients with cirrhosis often develop varicose veins in their esophagus? _____

_____

_____

_____

10. In patients with cirrhosis, laboratory tests that measure the amounts of proteins concerned with the coagulation of the blood are frequently abnormal. Why? _____

_____

_____

_____

11. What is jaundice? How is jaundice classified? Under what circumstances do gallstones cause jaundice? _____

_____

_____

_____

12. What is hepatitis B virus (HBV) infection? How is it transmitted? What populations are at risk? How can it be prevented? _____

_____

_____

_____

13. What is fatty liver? With what other conditions is it associated? _____

_____

_____

_____

14. What is cholelithiasis? With what other conditions is it associated? _____

_____

_____

_____

15. What conditions may lead to hepatic cirrhosis? _____

_____

_____

_____

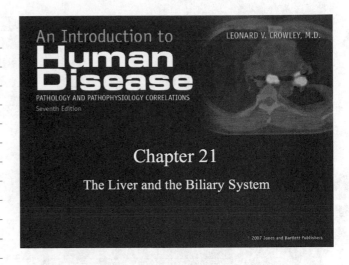

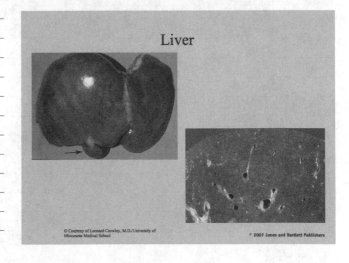

Notes

_____
_____
_____
_____
_____
_____
_____
_____
_____
_____
_____
_____
_____
_____
_____
_____
_____
_____
_____
_____
_____
_____
_____
_____
_____
_____
_____
_____
_____
_____
_____
_____
_____
_____

Liver Structure

- Has a *double* blood supply
1. By the *portal* vein: *three quarters* of blood, drains the spleen and GI tract, *rich* in *nutrients* absorbed from intestines, *low* in *oxygen*
2. By the *hepatic* artery: rest of blood, *high* in *oxygen*, *low* in *nutrients*
- Both bloods *mix* in the liver
- Eventually *collected* into the right and left *hepatic veins*
- They *drain* into the *inferior vena cava*

© 2007 Jones and Bartlett Publishers

Liver Structure
Bile

- Branches of *hepatic artery* and portal vein travel together with a bile duct branch within the liver, called *portal tracts*

Bile
- *Bile pigment* is a product of the *breakdown of red blood cells* in the reticuloendothelial system (mononuclear phagocyte system)
- The *worn-out erythrocytes* are *broken down*
- The *iron* from hemoglobin is *reused*
- The iron-free *heme pigment* is the *bilirubin,* which is excreted in the bile

© 2007 Jones and Bartlett Publishers

Liver Structure
Bile

- *Small* quantities of *bile* pigment are *continually present in blood*
- When *blood passes through liver,* bilirubin is removed
- This *excretion* is accomplished by *conjugation* which is *combining* the *bilirubin* with *glucuronic acid*
- *Bile* is an aqueous solution containing various dissolved *substances*
  1. Conjugated *bilirubin*
  2. Bile salts: *major* constituent of bile, are *derivatives* of *cholesterol* and *amino acids*

© 2007 Jones and Bartlett Publishers

Liver Structure
Bile

3. Lecithin: lipid that also functions as a *detergent*
4. Cholesterol: a lipid, a sterol
5. Water
6. Minerals

- Bile is *secreted continually*
- Concentrated and stored in the *gallbladder*
- During *digestion* the *gallbladder contracts*, squirting *bile* into the *duodenum*
- Bile does *not* contain *digestive enzymes* but *acts* as a *biologic detergent*
- Bile salts *emulsify fat*
- Bile salts function as *detergents*

© 2007 Jones and Bartlett Publishers

Biliary Duct System

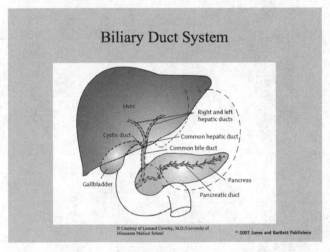

© Courtesy of Leonard Crowley, M.D./University of Minnesota Medical School

© 2007 Jones and Bartlett Publishers

Manifestations and Types of Liver Injury

- Manifestations
  - Cell necrosis
  - Fatty change
  - Mixed necrosis and fatty change

© 2007 Jones and Bartlett Publishers

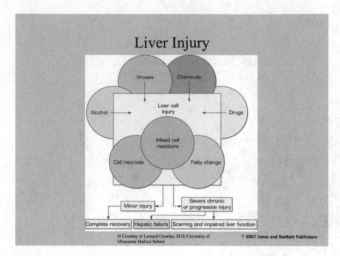

Liver Injury

© Courtesy of Leonard Crowley, M.D./University of Minnesota Medical School

© 2007 Jones and Bartlett Publishers

Manifestations and Types
Liver Injury

- Hepatitis: *inflammation* of the liver
- *Viral* hepatitis: caused by *virus*
- *Alcoholic* liver disease or *alcoholic hepatitis*

© 2007 Jones and Bartlett Publishers

Hepatitis A

- Virus is *excreted* through the *nose* and *throat* and in the *stools*

Transmission

- *Person-to-person* contact
- *Fecal* contamination of *food or water*
- *Self-limiting* disease with *no carriers* and *no chronic liver disease*
- Prevention *after exposure* with *gamma globulin*
- *Immunization* available

© 2007 Jones and Bartlett Publishers

Notes

Hepatitis B

Transmission
- *Blood or body fluids*
- *10%* become *carriers* and may develop *chronic liver disease*
- Prevention *after exposure* with *hepatitis B immune globulin*
- *Immunization* available

© 2007 Jones and Bartlett Publishers

Hepatitis C

Transmission
- *Blood and body fluids*
- 75% become *carriers* and many develop *chronic liver disease*
- *No* prevention of disease *after exposure*
- *No immunization* available

© 2007 Jones and Bartlett Publishers

Hepatitis D
(Delta Hepatitis)

- *Only infects* persons with acute or chronic *HBV infection*
- Delta virus is unable to produce its own virus coat and uses HBsAg produced by HBV
- Most U.S. cases from *sharing needles*

© 2007 Jones and Bartlett Publishers

Hepatitis E

Transmission
- *Oral-fecal*
- *No* prevention of disease *after exposure*
- *No immunization* available

© 2007 Jones and Bartlett Publishers

Hepatitis Outcomes

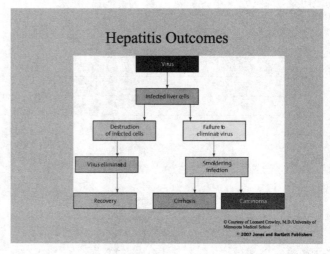

© Courtesy of Leonard Crowley, M.D./University of Minnesota Medical School

© 2007 Jones and Bartlett Publishers

Alcoholic Liver Disease

- The *severity* depends not only on the *amount* of *alcohol* consumed but also *for how long* a time
- Alcoholic Liver Disease refers to a group of structural and functional changes in the liver resulting from excessive alcohol consumption
- Divided in three stages of progression
  - Alcoholic fatty liver: mildest form
  - Alcoholic hepatitis: causes degenerative changes and necrosis of liver cells
  - Alcoholic cirrhosis: most advanced, diffuse scarring, disturbed liver function

© 2007 Jones and Bartlett Publishers

_____
_____
_____
_____
_____
_____
_____
_____
_____
_____
_____
_____
_____
_____
_____
_____
_____
_____
_____
_____
_____
_____
_____
_____
_____
_____
_____
_____
_____
_____
_____
_____

Cirrhosis

- *Diffuse scarring* of the liver from any cause
  - *Alcoholic* liver disease
  - *Chronic* hepatitis
  - An episode of severe liver *necrosis*
  - Other *drugs* and *chemicals*
  - Longstanding *bile duct obstruction*
  Manifestations
- Liver *failure*
- Liver *unable* to *inactivate estrogen* in *males*
  - Testicular atrophy, loss of sex drive, breast hypertrophy

© 2007 Jones and Bartlett Publishers

Treatment of Cirrhosis

- Portal hypertension
  - Ascites, collateral circulation formation
  Surgical Procedures
- *Portal-systemic anastomoses* to control *varices*
  - Splenorenal shunt
  - Portacaval shunt
- *Transjugular intrahepatic portosystemic shunt (TIPS)*

© 2007 Jones and Bartlett Publishers

Surgical Procedures to Treat Cirrhosis

© Courtesy of Leonard Crowley, M.D./University of Minnesota Medical School
© 2007 Jones and Bartlett Publishers

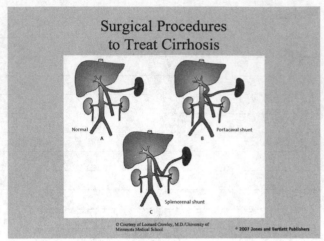

Surgical Procedures
to Treat Cirrhosis

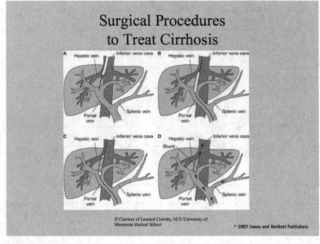

Surgical Procedures
to Treat Cirrhosis

Biliary Cirrhosis

- *Primary*
  - *Autoimmune* disease
- *Secondary*
  - *Obstruction* of large extrahepatic *bile ducts*
    - *Gallstone, carcinoma* in head of *pancreas, cancer* arising from *common bile duct*

Reye's Syndrome

- Probably related to the combined effect of *viral* illness and *acetylsalicylic acid* (aspirin)
- Affects *infants* and *children*
- Characteristics
  - Accumulation of *fat* within the *liver*
  - *Swelling* of the *brain* with neurologic dysfunction

© 2007 Jones and Bartlett Publishers

Cholelithiasis

- The formation of *stones* in the *gallbladder*
- Incidence
  - *Higher* in *women* than men
  - Higher in *women* who have *borne several children*
  - *Twice* as *high* in women who use *contraceptive pills*
  - Higher in *obese* women

© 2007 Jones and Bartlett Publishers

Cholelithiasis

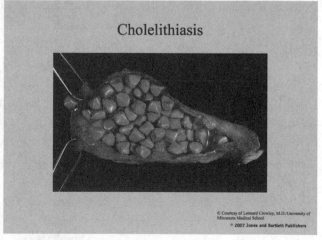

© Courtesy of Leonard Crowley, M.D./University of Minnesota Medical School
© 2007 Jones and Bartlett Publishers

Cholecystitis

- *Inflammation* of gallbladder
- Chronic *infection is* common
- *Gallstones* may *predispose* to cholecystitis
- *Impaction* of a *stone* in the *neck* of the *gallbladder* may precipitate *acute cholecystitis*

© 2007 Jones and Bartlett Publishers

Cholecystitis

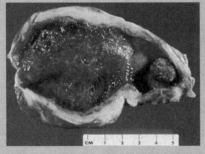

© Courtesy of Leonard Crowley, M.D./University of Minnesota Medical School

© 2007 Jones and Bartlett Publishers

Liver Tumors

- *Benign adenomas*: in women taking *contraceptive pills*
- *Primary carcinoma*: *uncommon* in *U.S.* and Canada but *common* in *Asia* and *Africa* (related to high incidence *HBV* carriers)
- *HBV* carriers have a *high risk* to develop *liver disease* and also *primary liver carcinoma*
- *Metastatic* carcinoma: common in *developed* countries
  - *Spread* from primary sites such as *GI tract, lung, breast*
  - The *tumor cells* are *carried* in the *blood delivered* to the *liver* by the *hepatic artery*

© 2007 Jones and Bartlett Publishers

Metastatic Carcinoma

© Courtesy of Leonard Crowley, M.D./University of
Minnesota Medical School

© 2007 Jones and Bartlett Publishers

Jaundice

- A *yellow discoloration* of the *skin* and *sclera*
- Results from *accumulation* of *bile* pigment in the tissues and body fluids

Causes of Accumulation

1. *Hemolytic* jaundice: accelerated breakdown of red cells
2. *Hepatocellular* jaundice: liver severely damaged, impairing the conjugation of bilirubin
3. *Obstructive* jaundice: bile duct is obstructed, preventing delivery of bile into duodenum

© 2007 Jones and Bartlett Publishers

Liver Biopsy

- Indicated when the *cause* of the *liver disease* is *undetermined* or to evaluate extent of liver cell damage in persons with chronic hepatitis
- Needle inserted through skin *directly* into liver
  - Provides specific *diagnosis*
  - Provides *basis* for *treatment*

© 2007 Jones and Bartlett Publishers

Chapter Outline

The chapter outline provides you with an organizational guide to the topics and ideas presented in this chapter of the text.

Structure and Function of the Pancreas
Pancreatitis
    Acute Pancreatitis
    Chronic Pancreatitis
Cystic Fibrosis of the Pancreas
Diabetes Mellitus
    Type 1 Diabetes Mellitus
    Type 2 Diabetes Mellitus
    Mature-Onset Diabetes in Young Persons
    Actions of Insulin
    Fat Metabolism and Formation of Ketone Bodies
    Biochemical Disturbances in Diabetes
    Monitoring and Control of Diabetes
    Treatment of Diabetes
    Complications of Diabetes
    Other Causes of Hyperglycemia
Hypoglycemia
Tumors of the Pancreas

Study Questions

The following questions are provided as a test for comprehension and as a study guide for use with the text chapters. Additional study material is located at http://humandisease.jbpub.com/, which contains useful tools such as an A&P review, animated flashcards, an interactive online glossary, crossword puzzles, and web links.

Key Terms

Define the following terms:

1. Ketone bodies _____

2. Ketosis _____

3. Diabetes _____

Fill-in-the-Blanks

1. After each of these diabetes-related conditions, mark *type 1* if the condition affects only persons with type 1 diabetes; mark *type 2* if the condition affects only persons with type 2 diabetes; mark *both* if the condition affects both type 1 and type 2 diabetics.

   a. Insulin essential to control the diabetes _____

   b. An autoimmune disease _____

   c. Responds to oral drugs that lower blood glucose _____

   d. May lead to blindness _____

   e. May lead to hyperosmolar hyperglycemic nonketotic coma _____

   f. Proper diet and weight reduction may control disease _____

   g. May lead to ketoacidosis _____

   h. May damage kidneys if poorly controlled _____

   i. Poor control associated with higher than normal glycosylated hemoglobin test _____

Identify

1. Identify two factors that predispose a person to pancreatitis.

   a. _____

   b. _____

2. Construct a table comparing the major characteristics of the two major types of diabetes with respect to age of onset, body build, major complications, response to insulin, and response to oral antidiabetic drugs.

Characteristic Features	Type 1 Diabetes	Type 2 Diabetes

3. Identify six complications of poorly controlled diabetes.

a. _____

b. _____

c. _____

d. _____

e. _____

f. _____

Discussion Questions

1. Describe the major abnormalities in the pancreas of persons with cystic fibrosis of the pancreas. _____

_____

_____

_____

2. Describe the major abnormalities in the lungs of persons with cystic fibrosis of the pancreas. _____

_____

_____

_____

3. What are ketone bodies, and why are they elevated in persons with poorly controlled type 1 diabetes? _____

_____

_____

_____

4. Why do some persons with type 2 diabetes develop diabetic coma even though they do not have ketosis? _____

_____

_____

_____

5. Which of the following descriptors applies to cystic fibrosis of the pancreas.

a. Transmitted as mendelian dominant trait _____

_____

b. Red cells sickle under low oxygen tension _____

_____

c. Characterized by secretion of thin, watery mucus _____

_____

d. Pancreas secretes excessive digestive enzymes that may digest the pancreas _____

_____

e. Frequently complicated by symptoms of chronic pulmonary disease _____

_____

6. A 27-year-old woman has insulin-dependent diabetes. What abnormalities would be expected in this condition?

_____

_____

_____

Notes

_____

_____

_____

_____

_____

_____

_____

_____

_____

_____

_____

_____

_____

_____

_____

_____

_____

_____

_____

_____

_____

An Introduction to
Human Disease
PATHOLOGY AND PATHOPHYSIOLOGY CORRELATIONS
Seventh Edition

LEONARD V. CROWLEY, M.D.

Chapter 22

The Pancreas and Diabetes Mellitus

© 2007 Jones and Bartlett Publishers

Pancreas

The pancreas is *two glands* in one
- Digestive gland
- Endocrine gland

Digestive Gland

The *exocrine* tissue of the pancreas, which is concerned solely with *digestion*, secretes *alkaline* pancreatic *juice* rich in *digestive enzymes* into the *duodenum* through the pancreatic *duct* to aid digestion

© 2007 Jones and Bartlett Publishers

Pancreas

Endocrine Gland

The *endocrine* tissue of the pancreas consists of multiple *small clusters of cells* scattered throughout the gland called the *pancreatic islets* or *Islets of Langerhans* which discharge secretions *directly* into the bloodstream

- *Each islet* is composed of several different types of cells, the *main* ones being
- Alpha cells
- Beta cells
- Delta cells

© 2007 Jones and Bartlett Publishers

Pancreas

- Islet *Alpha* cells
- secrete *glucagon*
- *raises* blood glucose
- Islet *Beta* cells
- secrete *insulin*
- *lowers* blood glucose
- Islet *Delta* cells
- secrete *somatostatin*
- *inhibits* secretion of glucagon and insulin

© 2007 Jones and Bartlett Publishers

Acute Pancreatitis

Pathogenesis

- *Escape* of *pancreatic juice* from the ducts into the substance of the *pancreas*
- Pancreatic digestive *enzymes* in the juice cause *destruction* of pancreatic *tissue* and severe *hemorrhage*
- Involves the *active secretion* of *pancreatic juice* while the pancreatic *duct* is *obstructed* at its entrance into the duodenum
- *Build-up increases pressure* within the duct system, causing ducts to *rupture*

© 2007 Jones and Bartlett Publishers

_____
_____
_____
_____
_____
_____
_____
_____
_____
_____
_____
_____
_____
_____
_____
_____
_____
_____
_____
_____
_____
_____
_____
_____
_____
_____
_____
_____
_____
_____
_____
_____
_____
_____
_____
_____
_____
_____
_____
_____
_____
_____
_____
_____

Predisposing Factors
Pancreatitis

Gallbladder disease/gallbladder *stones*

- *Common bile duct* and *common pancreatic duct* enter the *duodenum* through a common *channel*, the *ampulla of Vater*
- If *stone* becomes *impacted* in *ampulla*, it can *obstruct* pancreatic *duct,* precipitate *pancreatitis*

Excessive alcohol consumption

- Potent *stimulus* of pancreatic *secretions*
- Induces *edema* and *spasm* of pancreatic *sphincter* in the ampulla of Vater
- These combined lead to high intraductal *pressure,* duct *necrosis,* and *escape* of pancreatic juice

© 2007 Jones and Bartlett Publishers

Pancreatitis: Acute / Chronic

Clinical Manifestations
Acute Pancreatitis
- – Severe *abdominal pain*
- – Seriously ill
- – *High mortality* rate

Chronic Pancreatitis
- – *Repeated episodes* of mild inflammation of pancreas
- – Leading to *progressive destruction* of pancreatic tissue

© 2007 Jones and Bartlett Publishers

Cystic Fibrosis

- Relatively *common*
- *Serious hereditary* disease, autosomal recessive trait
- *Abnormal gene* from a *mutation* of a *normal* gene called *CF gene*, on long arm of *chromosome 7*
- Manifests in *infancy and childhood*
- Incidence *rare* in *blacks* and *other* races
- Incidence in *whites 1 in 3,000*
- *Mortality,* more than *50%* die before age *32*

Pathogenesis
- *Defective transport* across cell membrane of *chloride, sodium,* and the water molecules in which they are dissolved

© 2007 Jones and Bartlett Publishers

Cystic Fibrosis

- *Electrolyte and water secretion* is *deficient* in the mucus secreted by the pancreas, bile ducts, respiratory tract, and other secretory cells
- The *mucus* becomes abnormally *thick*, precipitates, and *forms dense plugs* that *obstruct* the pancreatic ducts, bronchi, bronchioles, and bile ducts
- Function of *sweat glands* is *abnormal*, unable to conserve sodium and chloride, excessive *high salt sweat concentration, diagnostic sweat test*

© 2007 Jones and Bartlett Publishers

Diabetes Mellitus
Two Types

- Very common and important *metabolic* disease

There are *two major groups*, depending on *cause*

1. *Type 1 Diabetes*; cause is insulin deficiency
2. *Type 2 Diabetes*; typically an *adult*-onset diabetes; *cause is inadequate response to insulin*; becoming more common in children.

- Manifestation is *elevated glucose* levels in blood called *hyperglycemia*

© 2007 Jones and Bartlett Publishers

Type 1
Diabetes Mellitus

- Occurs primarily in *children* and *young adults*
- As a result of damage to pancreatic islets, leading to *reduction or absence* of *insulin secretion*
- Often *follows* a *viral* infection that *destroys* the pancreatic *islets*
- *Abnormal immune* response may play part in causing disease as these patients have *autoantibodies* directed against their own cells
- May develop a *complication* called *diabetic ketosis*
- There is a *hereditary predisposition*

© 2007 Jones and Bartlett Publishers

Type 2 Diabetes Mellitus

- It is by far the *more common* type
- *More complex* metabolic disease
- Occurs in *older, overweight* or obese adults; becoming more common in overweight/obese younger people
- Insulin *secretion* is *normal or increased*
- *Tissues* are insensitive or have *impaired response* to *insulin*
- *Cause* is *not completely understood* but *weight reduction restores insulin responsiveness*
- *Islet function* is *not completely normal* as pancreas is *not* able to *increase insulin output* to *compensate* for the *insulin resistance*

© 2007 Jones and Bartlett Publishers

Type 2 Diabetes Mellitus

- May develop a *complication* called *hyperosmolar nonketotic coma* caused by marked *hyperglycemia*
- Is a *hereditary* disease where *genetic factors* play an even *greater* role
- *Children* of parents that have it are at significant *risk* of developing it
- *Incidence* in some populations as high as *40% (example:* Pima Indians of Arizona)

© 2007 Jones and Bartlett Publishers

Metabolic Derangements
Type 1 Diabetes

© Courtesy of Leonard Crowley, M.D./University of Minnesota Medical School

© 2007 Jones and Bartlett Publishers

Complications of Diabetes

1. Increased susceptibility to infection
2. Diabetic coma
3. Ketoacidosis
4. Hyperosmolar coma
5. Arteriosclerosis
6. Blindness
7. Renal failure
8. Peripheral neuritis

© 2007 Jones and Bartlett Publishers

Comparison of Types of Diabetes

TABLE 22-1

Comparison of two major types of diabetes mellitus

	TYPE 1	TYPE 2
Usual age of onset	Childhood Young adulthood	Middle age or later
Body build	Normal	Overweight
Plasma insulin	Absent or low	Normal or high
Complications	Ketoacidosis	Hyperosmolar coma
Response to insulin	Normal	Reduced
Response to oral antidiabetic drugs	Unresponsive	Responsive

© 2007 Jones and Bartlett Publishers

Formation of Ketone Bodies

- In Type 1, fat deposition in adipose tissue is impaired and *body fat* is *metabolized* as a *source of energy*
- It *splits* first into a *fatty acid* and *glycerol*
- Further *chemical reactions* take place
- The *molecules* are *converted* by the *liver* into compounds called *ketone* bodies
- *Ketosis* results when there is an excess *accumulation* of *ketone bodies* in body

© 2007 Jones and Bartlett Publishers

Insulin

- Influences *carbohydrate, protein, and fat* metabolism
- Chief sites of influence are on *liver* cells, *muscle*, and *adipose* tissues (fat)
- Promotes *entrance* of *glucose* into cells
- Favors *utilization* of *glucose* as source of *energy*
- Promotes *storage* of glucose as *glycogen*
- In *adipose* tissue, it favors *conversion* of *glucose* into *fat* (*triglycerides*) and *storage* of newly formed triglyceride within *fat* cells
- Promotes *entry* of *amino acids* into cells and stimulates *protein synthesis*
- The *main stimulus* for *insulin release* is *elevation* of *glucose* in blood, as it occurs *after a meal*

© 2007 Jones and Bartlett Publishers

Hyperglycemia

Hyperglycemia: elevated blood glucose levels

- *Other conditions* may lead to impairment of glucose utilization and *hyperglycemia*, but they are *less common* than *diabetes*
- *Chronic pancreatic disease*: damage or destruction of pancreatic islets
- *Endocrine diseases*: overproduction of pituitary or adrenal hormones (they act to raise blood glucose)
- *Ingestion of different drugs*: as a side effect, glucose utilization is impaired
- *Hereditary disease*: carbohydrate metabolism is disturbed

© 2007 Jones and Bartlett Publishers

Hypoglycemia in Diabetes

- The *pancreas* continually *monitors* the *glucose* and *adjusts* its *output* of *insulin*
- In *type 1 diabetes*, the patient must *adjust* the dose of *insulin* to *match* the amount of *carbohydrate* to *metabolize*
- If there is *insufficient insulin*, the *glucose* is *high*
- If there is *too much* insulin, the *glucose* is *low*, a condition called *hypoglycemia*

Two conditions *predispose* to *hypoglycemia* in a diabetic patient taking insulin

© 2007 Jones and Bartlett Publishers

Hypoglycemia in Diabetes

1. *Skipping a meal:* with reduced intake food, blood glucose falls; *carbohydrate intake is insufficient* in relation to amount *insulin*
2. *Vigorous exercise:* with increased activity, blood glucose falls, there is *increased glucose utilization,* and *relative excess of insulin*
- *Too much insulin* causes a *precipitous drop* in *glucose*, leading to *insulin shock*

© 2007 Jones and Bartlett Publishers

Hypoglycemia in Diabetes

- *Adrenal medulla* responds by discharging *epinephrine (adrenaline)* which *raises* blood *glucose*
- Neurologic manifestations appear if *blood glucose continues to fall*

Other causes of *hypoglycemia*
- *Oral hypoglycemic drugs* in type 2 diabetics
- *Self-administration* of oral hypoglycemic *drugs or insulin* by *emotionally disturbed* person
- Islet cell *tumor*

© 2007 Jones and Bartlett Publishers

Treatment of Diabetes

- *Diet*, where *carbohydrate* intake is controlled
- *Type 1 diabetes* also requires *insulin, dosage* being adjusted to *control* the level of *blood glucose*
- In type 2 diabetes, *weight reduction* and *diet* might be *enough* to manage condition
- *If* patient does *not respond adequately* to diet and exercise regimen, *oral hypoglycemic drugs* that promote *release of insulin* may be necessary

© 2007 Jones and Bartlett Publishers

_____

_____

_____

_____

_____

_____

_____

_____

_____

_____

_____

Tumors of the Pancreas

- Carcinoma of the pancreas
  - Usually develops in head
    - Blocks common bile duct
    - Causes obstructive jaundice
- Islet cell tumors
  - Benign
  - Beta cell tumors produce hyperinsulinism

© 2007 Jones and Bartlett Publishers

Chapter Outline

The chapter outline provides you with an organizational guide to the topics and ideas presented in this chapter of the text.

Study Questions

The following questions are provided as a test for comprehension and as a study guide for use with the text chapters. Additional study material is located at http://humandisease.jbpub.com/, which contains useful tools such as an A&P review, animated flashcards, an interactive online glossary, crossword puzzles, and web links.

Key Terms

Define the following terms:

1. Reflux esophagitis _____

2. Barrett's esophagus _____

Fill-in-the-Blank

1. The inheritance of cleft lip and palate, which is related to interaction of multiple genes and environmental factors, is called a _____ inheritance pattern.

2. Each tooth is formed from a separate tooth bud, and _____ is deposited in the dentine and enamel as the tooth is formed.

3. To prevent staining of the teeth, the antibiotic _____ is not given to pregnant women or to children during the time when the teeth are forming.

4. Masses of bacteria intermixed with bacterial products and proteins from saliva form aggregates called_____ _____ that adhere to the teeth and predispose a person to tooth decay.

5. The substance _____, when added to water supplies and toothpaste, helps prevent tooth decay.

6. Chronic gingivitis complicated by spread of the infection into the space between the teeth and gums to form pockets of pus is called _____.

7. A small superficial ulcer in the oral cavity is called _____.

8. Failure of the lower esophageal sphincter to open properly is called _____.

9. Inability of the lower esophageal sphincter to close properly is called _____. It leads to a condition called _____, which eventually may be complicated by a condition called _____.

10. The metaplastic change in the epithelium of the distal esophagus is called _____. It may predispose a person to the development of _____ in the distal esophagus.

11. An enzyme called _____ is required for the synthesis of prostaglandins, which have many functions. There are _____ forms of the enzyme.

12. Many cases of chronic gastritis appear to be caused by an organism called _____. This organism may also slightly increase the risk of developing two different types of gastric tumors, which are called _____ and _____.

13. If a person has a gastric or duodenal ulcer and is also colonized by an organism called _____, the person is treated not only with antacids but also with _____ to eradicate the organism.

True/False

Tell whether each statement is true or false. If false, explain why the statement is incorrect.

1. Many cases of acute gastritis are caused by nonsteroidal anti-inflammatory drugs (NSAIDs), which act by inhibiting an enzyme (cyclooxygenase) that is required to synthesize prostaglandins. _____
   _____

2. There are two forms of cyclooxygenase (COX). One form (COX-1) promotes the synthesis of prostaglandins that protect the gastric mucosa from the harmful effects of gastric acid. The other form (COX-2) promotes the synthesis of prostaglandins that function as mediators of inflammation. _____
   _____

Matching

Match the abnormalities in the right column with the diseases in the left column.

Disease or Condition

1. ____ Regional enteritis (Crohn's disease)
2. ____ Meckel's diverticulitis
3. ____ Mesenteric artery thrombosis
4. ____ Chronic ulcerative colitis
5. ____ Antibiotic-associated colitis
6. ____ Nontropical sprue
7. ____ Lactose intolerance
8. ____ Irritable bowel syndrome
9. ____ Colon diverticulosis
10. ____ Colon diverticulitis
11. ____ Intussusception
12. ____ Colon volvulus

Abnormality

A. Protrusion of mucosa through weak area in bowel wall
B. Hypersensitivity to wheat protein (gluten)
C. Inflammation of colon diverticula
D. Inflammation and ulceration of colon mucosa
E. Chronic inflammation and scarring of distal ileum
F. Deficiency of lactase enzyme
G. Overgrowth of *Clostridium difficile*
H. Inflammation of congenital small bowel diverticulum
I. Disturbed bowel function without structural changes
J. Rotary twist of sigmoid colon on its mesentery
K. Telescoping of proximal colon into distal colon
L. Extensive necrosis of small bowel and proximal colon

Discussion Questions

1. What are some of the major causes of esophageal obstruction? What symptoms does esophageal obstruction produce?
   _____
   _____
   _____

2. How does acute appendicitis usually develop? What is the pathogenesis of acute appendicitis? _____
   _____
   _____
   _____

3. What is intestinal obstruction? What symptoms does it produce? What are some of the common causes of intestinal obstruction? _____

_____

_____

_____

4. What symptoms and physical findings are likely to be encountered in a patient with a carcinoma of the colon? Why?

_____

_____

_____

5. What conditions predispose a person to chronic diverticulosis of colon? _____

_____

_____

_____

6. As a result of the tumor, what conditions might be encountered in a patient with a small ulcerated carcinoma of the cecum? _____

_____

_____

_____

7. What condition usually results from a complete thrombosis or embolic occlusion of the superior mesenteric artery?

_____

_____

_____

An Introduction to
Human Disease
PATHOLOGY AND PATHOPHYSIOLOGY CORRELATIONS
Seventh Edition

LEONARD V. CROWLEY, M.D.

Chapter 23

The Gastrointestinal Tract

2007 Jones and Bartlett Publishers

Gastrointestinal Tract

- Is concerned with the digestion and absorption of food

Comprising

- the oral cavity and related parts of face
- The esophagus, stomach, small and large intestines, and the anus

© 2007 Jones and Bartlett Publishers

Cleft Lip / Cleft Palate

- *Multifactorial inheritance* pattern
- *Face and palate* formed by coalescence of cell masses
- *Maldevelopment* leads to *defects*
- Cleft *lip*: defect in *upper lip* and *jaw*
- Cleft *palate*: defect in *palate*
- Frequently *occur in combination*
- *Incidence* is one per one thousand births
- They are *corrected surgically* at *different times*

© 2007 Jones and Bartlett Publishers

Abnormalities of Tooth Development

- *Teeth* are specialized structures developed in the tissues of the jaws
- There are *two sets of teeth*, the *temporary or deciduous teeth* (20 teeth) and the *permanent teeth* (32 teeth)
- *Missing teeth* or an *extra teeth* is a relatively *common abnormality*
- *Enamel forms* within the developing teeth at specific times
- If the *antibiotic tetracycline* is administered *during enamel formation*, it *causes permanent yellow-gray to brown discoloration* in the *crowns*

© 2007 Jones and Bartlett Publishers

Abnormalities of Tooth Development

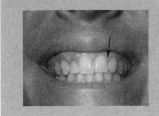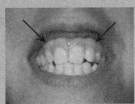

© Courtesy of Leonard Crowley, M.D./University of Minnesota Medical School

© 2007 Jones and Bartlett Publishers

Dental Caries Periodontal Disease

- The *oral cavity* contains a diverse collection of aerobic and anaerobic *bacteria*, which *mix* with *saliva products*, *forming aggregates* called *dental plaque*
- These *adhere* to *teeth* and *predispose* to *tooth decay (caries)*
- The *loss of tooth structure* that results from the combined action of and bacterial action is called a *dental cavity*
- Masses of bacteria and debris accumulating around base of teeth may incite an *inflammation*, affecting the *gums*, called *gingivitis*
- If *inflammation extends* and forms *small pockets of infection* between the teeth and gums, called *periodontal disease*

© 2007 Jones and Bartlett Publishers

Stomatitis

- An inflammation of the oral cavity
1) Caused by irritants
- Alcohol, tobacco, hot or spicy foods
2) Caused by infectious agents
- Herpesvirus, *Candida albicans* fungus, bacteria that cause trench mouth

© 2007 Jones and Bartlett Publishers

Stomatitis

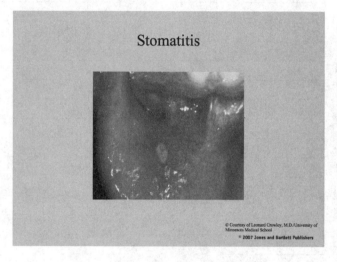

© Courtesy of Leonard Crowley, M.D./University of Minnesota Medical School

© 2007 Jones and Bartlett Publishers

Carcinoma Oral Cavity

- Arises from *squamous* epithelium
  - Lips
  - Cheek
  - Tongue
  - Palate
  - Back of throat

© 2007 Jones and Bartlett Publishers

Notes

_____
_____
_____
_____
_____
_____
_____
_____
_____
_____
_____
_____
_____
_____
_____
_____
_____
_____
_____
_____
_____
_____
_____
_____
_____
_____
_____
_____
_____
_____

Carcinoma
Oral Cavity

© Courtesy of Leonard Crowley, M.D./University of Minnesota Medical School   © 2007 Jones and Bartlett Publishers

---

Esophagus

- The esophagus is a *muscular tube* that extends from the *pharynx* to the *stomach* with *sphincters* at both *upper* and *lower ends*
- The *upper* sphincter relaxes to allow *passage* of *swallowed* food
- The *lower* sphincter, called *cardiac sphincter*, relaxes when the food reaches this point to allow *passage* of food to *stomach*

© 2007 Jones and Bartlett Publishers

Diseases of the Esophagus

1. Failure of *cardiac sphincter* to function properly
2. Tears in lining of *esophagus* from *retching* and *vomiting*
3. Esophageal *obstruction* as a result of *carcinoma, food impaction, or stricture*

Symptoms

- Difficulty swallowing (dysphagia)
- Substernal discomfort or pain
- Inability to swallow (complete obstruction)
- Regurgitation of food into trachea
- Choking and coughing

© 2007 Jones and Bartlett Publishers

Cardiac Sphincter Dysfunction

- Two major disturbances of cardiac sphincter
1. Cardiospasm
   - Cardiac sphincter *fails to open* properly (malfunction of nerve plexus in esophagus)
   - Esophagus becomes *dilated*
2. Incompetent Cardiac Sphincter
   - *Inability* of sphincter to *remain closed* properly
   - *Acid gastric juices leak back* into esophagus

© 2007 Jones and Bartlett Publishers

Cardiac Sphincter Dysfunction

Complications of *Incompetent Cardiac Sphincter*
- Leads to *inflammation*, a condition called *reflux esophagitis*
- The squamous mucosa lining may become *ulcerated* and *scarred*
- Undergoes a change, glandular *metaplasia* of squamous epithelium

© 2007 Jones and Bartlett Publishers

Esophageal Obstruction

Causes
- *Carcinoma*
  - Squamous epithelium
  - Columnar epithelium
- Food *impaction*
- *Stricture*

© 2007 Jones and Bartlett Publishers

Acute Gastritis

- *Inflammation* of *stomach*

Acute

- In most cases *self-limited*, of *short* duration
- May be associated with mucosal *ulceration,* with *bleeding*

  Most are caused by
  - *nonsteroidal anti-inflammatory drugs*: aspirin, ibuprofen, naproxen
  - *alcohol*: a gastric irritant that stimulates gastric acid secretion

Chronic
  - Often associated with *H. pylori (Helicobacter pylori)* colonization of mucosa: the *ammonia* produced by organism damages the gastric mucosa

© 2007 Jones and Bartlett Publishers

Gastritis
H. pylori

- *H. pylori* infection is very *common*
- *Not* all persons that *harbor* the organism *have chronic gastritis*
- The *risk increases* with *age*
- It is *spread person-to-person* in households by close contact and also by *fecal-oral route*
- *Increases* the *risk* of *gastric carcinoma* and *malignant lymphoma* from lymphocytes in the gastric mucosa

© 2007 Jones and Bartlett Publishers

Peptic Ulcer

- Pathogenesis
  - Increased *acid* secretions and *digestive enzymes* erode gastric mucosa
  - *Helicobacter pylori* plays a *role*
- Complications
  - Hemorrhage, perforation, peritonitis, scarring
- Treatment
- *Antacids*- drugs that *block acid secretion* by gastric epithelial cells
- *Antibiotic* therapy if associated with *H. pylori*
- *Surgery* if *medical* therapy *fails*

© 2007 Jones and Bartlett Publishers

Notes

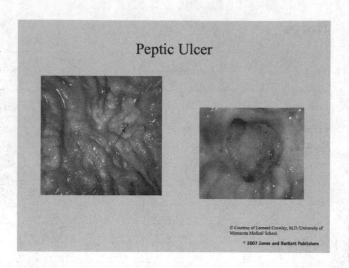

Peptic Ulcer

© Courtesy of Leonard Crawley, M.D./University of
Minnesota Medical School

© 2007 Jones and Bartlett Publishers

Carcinoma of the Stomach

- Manifestations
  - Vague *upper abdominal discomfort*
  - *Iron-deficiency anemia* from chronic blood loss
- Diagnosis with *biopsy* by means of *gastroscopy*
- Long-term *survival* relatively *poor*

© 2007 Jones and Bartlett Publishers

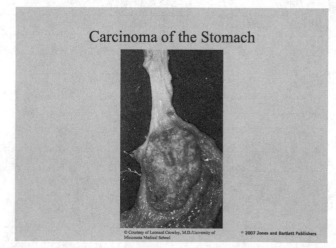

Carcinoma of the Stomach

© Courtesy of Leonard Crawley, M.D./University of
Minnesota Medical School

© 2007 Jones and Bartlett Publishers

Inflammatory Disease Intestines

- Enteritis: *inflammation* of *any part* of *intestinal tract*
- Colitis: *inflammation* of *colon*

Acute enteritis: common, short duration

Chronic enteritis: less common

- There are *two* major types *Chronic enteritis*
    1) *Regional enteritis (Crohn's* disease): distal ileum (*small* bowel)
    2) *Ulcerative colitis: large* intestine (colon) and rectum

Causes are *unknown*

© 2007 Jones and Bartlett Publishers

Complications Chronic Enteritis

- Serious *nutritional* disturbances, chronic *diarrhea* leads to *poor absorption* of *food*
- *Bleeding* excessively of *ulcerated* areas
- *Perforation* of ulcerated areas, leading to *leakage* of *intestinal* contents into *peritoneal* cavity
- Intestinal *obstruction*

© 2007 Jones and Bartlett Publishers

Inflammatory Disease Intestines (Three)

1. *Antibiotic-associated colitis:* broad spectrum antibiotics *destroy* the *normal intestinal flora,* allowing *growth* of the *bacterium*
2. *Appendicitis*: most *common inflammatory* lesion of the *bowel; narrow* caliber of appendix means base can become *plugged* with *fecal* material
3. *Merkel's diverticulum*: a *part* of the epithelium lining may have *acid*-secreting *mucosa*

© 2007 Jones and Bartlett Publishers

Notes

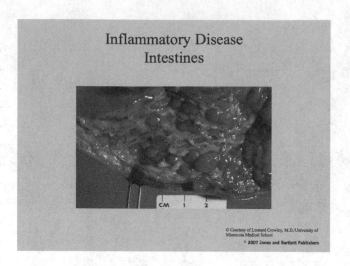

Inflammatory Disease
Intestines

© Courtesy of Leonard Crowley, M.D./University of
Minnesota Medical School
© 2007 Jones and Bartlett Publishers

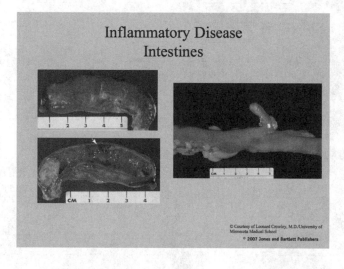

Inflammatory Disease
Intestines

© Courtesy of Leonard Crowley, M.D./University of
Minnesota Medical School
© 2007 Jones and Bartlett Publishers

Chronic Enteritis
Regional Enteritis
(Crohn's Disease)

- *Inflammation* primarily of the *distal ileum*
  - Causes *thickening and scarring* of bowel *wall*
- Inflammation may be *scattered*, leaving normal intervening areas called "*skip areas*"
- *Controlled* by various *drugs* with possible *surgical resection* of affected part of bowel

© 2007 Jones and Bartlett Publishers

Chronic Enteritis
Ulcerative Colitis

- Recurrent chronic *inflammation* of *colon and rectum*
- Treated with *antibiotics* and *corticosteroids* or *surgical resection* of the colon
- Chronic inflammation predisposes to bleeding and perforation of colon
- Predisposes to colon carcinoma

© 2007 Jones and Bartlett Publishers

Disturbances
Bowel Function
(Two)

1. *Lactose* intolerance
   - Adults *unable* to *digest lactose* due to *lactase deficiency*
   - *Unabsorbed lactose raises osmotic pressure* of *bowel contents*

2. *Intolerance* to *wheat protein gluten*
   - Caused by *hypersensitivity* to *wheat protein*
   - Causes *impaired intestinal absorption*

© 2007 Jones and Bartlett Publishers

Irritable Bowel
Syndrome

- Consists of *disturbed* bowel *function without structural* or *biochemical abnormalities*
- Diagnosed by *exclusion*
- Treatment
  - *Reduce emotional tension*
  - *Improve intestinal motility*

© 2007 Jones and Bartlett Publishers

Colon Diverticulosis / Diverticulitis

- *Outpouching* of colonic mucosa through weak areas in wall (*diverticulum*) causing *diverticulosis*
- Chronic *constipation* and *low-residue diet predisposes* to this condition
- Most diverticula are *asymptomatic*, but occasionally problems arise
- *Complications*: inflammation, perforation, and bleeding
- When bits of *fecal material* become *trapped* within the *pouches* and incite *inflammation*, this reaction is called *diverticulitis*

© 2007 Jones and Bartlett Publishers

Diverticulosis Colon

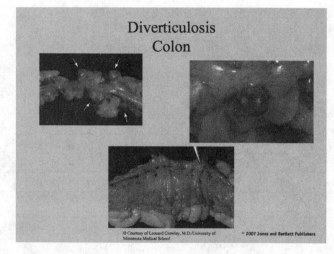

© Courtesy of Leonard Crowley, M.D./University of Minnesota Medical School   © 2007 Jones and Bartlett Publishers

Intestinal Obstructions

- Adhesions
- Hernia
- Tumor
- Volvulus
- Intussusception

© 2007 Jones and Bartlett Publishers

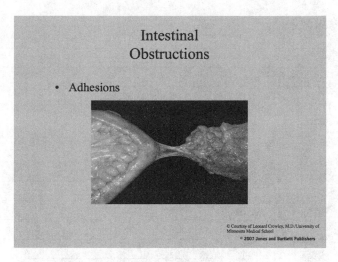

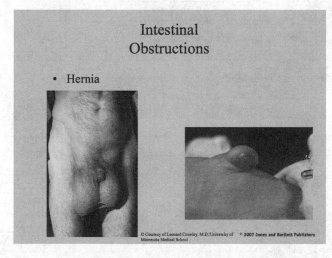

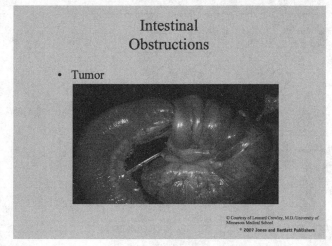

Notes

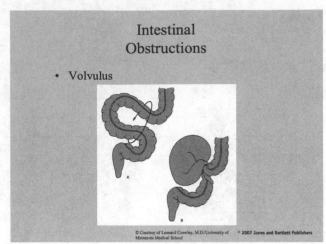

Intestinal Obstructions

- Volvulus

© Courtesy of Leonard Crowley, M.D./University of Minnesota Medical School   © 2007 Jones and Bartlett Publishers

Intestinal Obstructions

- Intussusception

© Courtesy of Leonard Crowley, M.D./University of Minnesota Medical School   © 2007 Jones and Bartlett Publishers

Mesenteric Thrombosis

- The superior mesenteric artery supplies blood to the small bowel and proximal half of colon
- *Obstruction* of the artery causes extensive *bowel infarction*

© 2007 Jones and Bartlett Publishers

Tumors of the Colon

- *Benign* polyps
- *Carcinoma*
  - *Left* half of colon
    - Causes obstruction and symptoms of lower intestinal obstruction
  - *Right* half of colon
    - Does *not* cause obstruction *but symptoms* related to *chronic blood loss*

© 2007 Jones and Bartlett Publishers

Colon Carcinoma

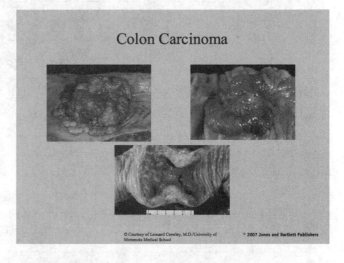

© Courtesy of Leonard Crowley, M.D./University of Minnesota Medical School   © 2007 Jones and Bartlett Publishers

Imperforate Anus

- Two types of *congenitally absent anal opening*
  1. Rectum and anus *formed normally* but *no* anal *orifice*
  2. *Entire* distal rectum *fails to develop*
- Corrected *surgically*

© 2007 Jones and Bartlett Publishers

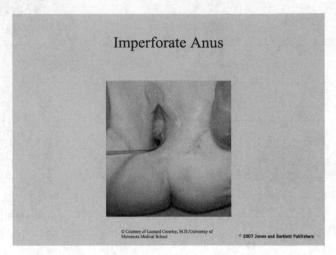

Imperforate Anus

© Courtesy of Leonard Crowley, M.D./University of
Minnesota Medical School

© 2007 Jones and Bartlett Publishers

Hemorrhoids

- *Varicose* veins of hemorrhoidal venous plexus
- *Constipation* and increased *straining predispose* to
  development
    - *Internal*
    - *External*

© 2007 Jones and Bartlett Publishers

Diagnostic Evaluation
GI Disease

- *Endoscopic* procedures
    - *Visualize* and *biopsy* abnormal areas
- *Radiologic* examination
    - Upper gastrointestinal tract – *UGI*
    - Colon – *BE (barium enema)*

© 2007 Jones and Bartlett Publishers

Notes

_____

_____

_____

_____

_____

_____

_____

_____

_____

_____

_____

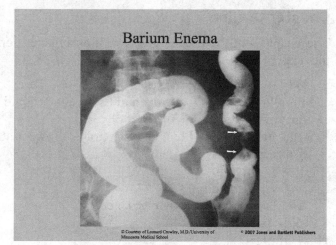

Barium Enema

© Courtesy of Leonard Crowley, M.D./University of Minnesota Medical School

© 2007 Jones and Bartlett Publishers

Chapter Outline

The chapter outline provides you with an organizational guide to the topics and ideas presented in this chapter of the text.

Body Water and Electrolytes
Interrelations of Intracellular and Extracellular Fluid
Units of Concentration of Electrolytes
Regulation of Body Fluid and Electrolyte Concentration
Disturbances of Water Balance
    Dehydration
    Overhydration
Disturbances of Electrolyte Balance
Acid–Base Balance
    Buffers
    Respiratory Control of Carbonic Acid
    Control of Bicarbonate Concentration
    Relation between pH and Ratio of Buffer Components
Disturbances of Acid–Base Balance
    Compensatory Mechanisms Responding to Disturbances in pH
    Metabolic Acidosis
    Respiratory Acidosis
    Metabolic Alkalosis
    Respiratory Alkalosis
    Diagnostic Evaluation of Acid–Base Balance

Study Questions

The following questions are provided as a test for comprehension and as a study guide for use with the text chapters. Additional study material is located at http://humandisease.jbpub.com/, which contains useful tools such as an A&P review, animated flashcards, an interactive online glossary, crossword puzzles, and web links.

Key Terms

Define the following terms:

1. Acidosis _____

2. Alkalosis _____

3. Electrolyte _____

4. pH _____

Fill-in-the-Blank

1. Positively charged ions are called _____, and negatively charged ions are called _____.

2. The units of concentration of electrolytes are expressed as _____.

3. The principal ions in intracellular fluids are _____.

Matching

The numbered column lists several clinical conditions associated with acid–base balance disturbances. The lettered column lists the four types of acid–base disturbances. Match the letter with the clinical condition. There are six conditions but only four acid–base disturbances; thus, some letters are used more than once, and some may not be used at all.

1. _____ Diabetes. Excessive ketone bodies formed.

2. _____ Hyperventilation. Fall in alveolar PCO_2 and blood carbonic acid.

3. _____ Impaired lung function caused by chronic pulmonary disease.

4. _____ Kidney failure. Retention of nonvolatile acids.

5. _____ Excess loss of gastric juice resulting from vomiting.

6. _____ Adrenal corticosteroid excess.

A. Metabolic acidosis

B. Respiratory acidosis

C. Metabolic alkalosis

D. Respiratory alkalosis

Discussion Questions

1. Body fluids are distributed within "compartments" as intracellular fluids and extracellular fluids. The extracellular fluids, in turn, are distributed between the fluid surrounding the cells (interstitial fluid) and that within the blood and lymph vessels (intravascular fluid). Which of these fluid compartments most closely resemble each other in electrolyte composition? _____

_____

_____

_____

2. What percentage of body weight consists of water? _____

_____

_____

3. What factors lead to overhydration of patients? _____

_____

_____

_____

4. What is the effect of prolonged use of diuretics on fluid and electrolyte balance? _____

_____

_____

_____

5. What is the source of the carbonic acid produced by the body? _____

_____

_____

_____

6. What is the source of the ketone bodies produced by the body? _____

_____

_____

_____

7. What is the source of the lactic acid produced by the body? _____

_____

_____

_____

8. What is the normal pH of blood and body fluids? _____

_____

_____

_____

9. What regulatory mechanisms does the body use to maintain the normal body fluid pH? _____

_____

_____

_____

10. How do blood buffers function to maintain normal body fluid pH? _____

_____

_____

11. How do the lungs control the concentration of carbonic acid in the blood? _____

_____

_____

12. How do the kidneys regulate the concentration of bicarbonate in the blood? _____

_____

_____

_____

13. What is the normal ratio of bicarbonate to carbonic acid at the normal pH of blood and body fluids? _____

_____

_____

_____

14. How does the body respond to a disease or condition characterized by an increase in carbonic acid in blood and body fluids? _____

_____

_____

_____

15. How does the body respond when bicarbonate levels fall as a result of buffering of excess acids produced within the body? _____

_____

_____

_____

16. What is metabolic acidosis? _____

_____

_____

_____

17. What are the principal causes of metabolic acidosis? _____

_____

_____

_____

18. What is respiratory alkalosis? _____

_____

_____

19. What are the principal causes of respiratory alkalosis? _____

_____

_____

_____

20. What compensatory mechanisms does the body employ in an attempt to correct the pH change resulting from the respiratory alkalosis? _____

_____

_____

_____

21. Why does excessive use of antacids disturb body pH? _____

_____

_____

_____

22. What effect do excess adrenal corticosteroids have on body pH? What mechanism is responsible for the pH disturbance? What effect do the corticosteroids have on blood electrolytes? _____

_____

_____

_____

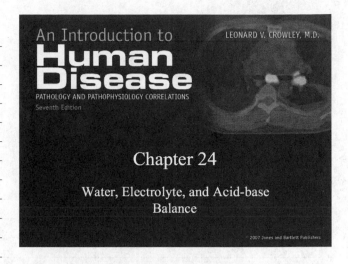

Body Water and Electrolytes

- *Body water* contains dissolved mineral salts (*electrolytes*) that dissociate in solution, yielding
  - *Cations*: *positively* charged ions
  - *Anions*: *negatively* charged ions
  - *Body fluids* are *electrically neutral*, the sum of the cations is always balanced by the sum of the anions
  - In *disease*, the *concentration* of the *ions* may *vary but* the *electrical neutrality* is always *maintained*

© 2007 Jones and Bartlett Publishers

Intracellular / Extracellular Fluid

- *Disturbances* of *body water* are associated with *corresponding change* in *electrolytes*
- If the *electrolyte concentration changes*, there is a *corresponding change* in *body water*
- Conversely, *changes* in *body water* are *associated* with *electrolyte concentration changes*
- The body consists of *70% water*
- *Most* is *intracellular* (inside cells)
- *Rest* is *extracellular* (within interstitial tissues surrounding cells, blood plasma, and lymph)

© 2007 Jones and Bartlett Publishers

Intracellular / Extracellular Fluid

- *Fluids and electrolytes diffuse freely* between the *intravascular* and *interstitial* fluids
- However, the *capillaries* are *impermeable* to *protein*
- Therefore, the *interstitial* fluid contains very *little protein*
- *Intracellular fluids are separated from interstitial fluid by a cell membrane*
  - Freely permeable to water
  - Relatively impermeable to sodium and potassium ions

© 2007 Jones and Bartlett Publishers

Intracellular / Extracellular Fluid

Chief *extracellular* ions
1. Na^+ (sodium)
2. Cl^- (chloride)

Chief in*tracellular* ions
1. K^+ (potassium)
2. PO_4^{3-} (phosphate)

- The *differences* in *concentration* of *ions* on *different sides* of the cell membrane are a result of the *metabolic* activity of the cell
- The amount of *sodium* in the body determines the volume of *extracellular* fluid because this is the chief *extracellular cation*

© 2007 Jones and Bartlett Publishers

Intracellular / Extracellular Fluid

- The amount of the *potassium* in the body determines the volume of the *intracellular* fluid because this is the chief *intracellular cation*
- In dealing with disturbances of electrolytes, the clinician is concerned primarily with *concentrations* of the various *ions* and with the *interrelation* of *positively* and *negatively* charged *ions* with one another *rather* than with the *actual number*

© 2007 Jones and Bartlett Publishers

Regulation of Body Fluid and Electrolyte Concentration

- The amount of *water* and *electrolytes* in the body represents a *balance* between the amounts *ingested* in *food* and *fluids* and the amounts *excreted* in the *urine*, through the *GI* tract, in *perspiration*, and as *water vapor* excreted by the *lungs*
- Disturbances of water balance
  - Dehydration: most *common*, caused by *inadequate water intake* or *excess water loss*, e.g., as a consequence of *diarrhea or vomiting*, *comatose* patients with inadequate water intake

© 2007 Jones and Bartlett Publishers

Regulation of Body Fluid and Electrolyte Concentration

  - Overhydration: *less common*; e.g., patient with *renal* disease that has an *excessive intake* of fluids, *excessive administration* of *IV fluids*

Disturbances of *electrolyte* balance

- The *same conditions* that produce *water imbalance* also *disturb* the *electrolyte* composition
- *Most* result from *depletion* of *body electrolytes*

Conditions that may cause these disturbances

- Vomiting, diarrhea: sodium & potassium depletion

© 2007 Jones and Bartlett Publishers

Regulation of Body Fluid and Electrolyte Concentration

- *Diuretics* administered to patients with *heart* failure, *liver* cirrhosis, *kidney* disease as *diuretics* promote the *excretion* of *salts* and *water* by the kidneys by *impairing* the *reabsorption* of these substances
- Uncontrolled *diabetes*: excessive *loss of water* in urine as a result of the *diuretic effect* of the excreted *glucose*
- *Renal* tubular disease: the regenerating renal tubules *unable* to *conserve electrolytes and water*

© 2007 Jones and Bartlett Publishers

Acid–Base Balance

- The *body produces large amounts* of *acid* in consequence of normal *metabolic* processes, such as the breakdown of proteins and glucose, the oxidation of fat, etc.
- *However,* body fluids remain *slightly alkaline*
- The *pH* is maintained within the narrow range of *7.38 to 7.42*
- *How? Regulatory* mechanisms that *neutralize* and *eliminate* the *acids* as soon as they are produced, *maintaining* the *pH*

Regulatory Mechanisms that Maintain pH: Buffer System

- *Buffer* systems of the blood
- A buffer is anything that cushions a blow or absorbs an impact
- Buffers minimize change in hydrogen ion by converting strong acids and bases into weaker ones

Chemically

- it is a weak acid and its salt
- or a weak base and its salt

Regulatory Mechanisms Buffer System

The major buffer system of the blood

- The *sodium bicarbonate–carbonic acid* system
- The concentration of *carbonic acid* (dissolved carbon dioxide) is controlled by the *lungs*
- The concentration of *bicarbonate* is controlled by the *kidneys*

Regulatory Mechanisms
Buffer System

Respiratory control of *carbonic acid*

- *Carbonic acid* is dissolved as *carbon dioxide* in *plasma*
- *Hyperventilation lowers* the carbon dioxide and carbonic acid in plasma
- *Decreased or inadequate ventilation raises* the carbon dioxide and carbonic acid in plasma

© 2007 Jones and Bartlett Publishers

Regulatory Mechanisms
Buffer System

Control of *bicarbonate concentration*

- *Kidneys* selectively *reabsorb* filtered *bicarbonate* as required by the body
- *Kidneys* can *manufacture bicarbonate* to replace the amounts lost buffering acids from metabolic processes

© 2007 Jones and Bartlett Publishers

Relation Between pH and
Ratio of Buffer Components

In any buffer system

- *The pH* depends on *ratio* of *bicarbonate* to *carbonic acid*
- *Normal* ratio
  - *20* parts *sodium bicarbonate*
  - *1* part *carbonic acid*

© 2007 Jones and Bartlett Publishers

Disturbances in Acid–Base Balance

- *Acidosis*
  - Blood pH shifts to *acid* side
  - May be caused by an *excess* of *carbonic acid*
  - Or by a reduced amount of *bicarbonate*
- *Alkalosis*
  - Blood pH shifts to *base* side
  - May be caused by a *decrease* in *carbonic acid*
  - Or to an *excess* of *bicarbonate*

Classification Acid–Base Disturbances

- These possibilities allow classification of acid-base disturbances into four large categories

The terms

- *Metabolic*: disturbance lies in the *bicarbonate* member of the buffer pair
- *Respiratory*: disturbance lies in the *carbonic acid* member of the buffer pair

1) Metabolic acidosis
  - Amount of acid generated exceeds the body's buffering capacity
  - Concentration of bicarbonate in the plasma falls because it is consumed in neutralizing the excess acid

Classification Acid–Base Disturbances

2) Respiratory acidosis
  - Inefficient excretion of carbon dioxide by lungs
  - Leads to rise in alveolar PCO_2, which increases amount of carbon dioxide

3) Metabolic alkalosis
  - Excess plasma bicarbonate
  - Inefficient compensation
  - Requires simultaneous correction of potassium deficiency

Classification
Acid–Base Disturbances

4) Respiratory alkalosis
- Decrease of carbonic acid caused by hyperventilation
- Relative excess of bicarbonate

© 2007 Jones and Bartlett Publishers

Comparison of Common
Acid–Base Disturbances

TABLE 24-1

Comparison of common acid–base disturbances

DISTURBANCE	PRIMARY ABNORMALITY	COMPENSATION	USUAL CAUSES
Metabolic acidosis	Excess endogenous acid depletes bicarbonate	Hyperventilation lowers PCO_2; kidney excretes more hydrogen ions and forms more bicarbonate	Renal failure; ketosis; overproduction of lactic acid
Respiratory acidosis	Inefficient excretion of carbon dioxide by lungs	Formation of additional bicarbonate by kidneys	Chronic pulmonary disease
Metabolic alkalosis	Excess plasma bicarbonate	None	Loss of gastric juice; chloride depletion; excess corticosteroid hormones; ingestion of excessive bicarbonate or other antacids
Respiratory alkalosis	Hyperventilation lowers PCO_2	Increased excretion of bicarbonate by kidneys	Severe anxiety with hyperventilation; stimulation of respiratory center by drugs; central nervous system disease

© 2007 Jones and Bartlett Publishers

Diagnostic Evaluation
Acid–Base Balance

- Clinical evaluation
- Laboratory studies
  - pH
  - PCO_2
  - Bicarbonate

© 2007 Jones and Bartlett Publishers

Chapter Outline

The chapter outline provides you with an organizational guide to the topics and ideas presented in this chapter of the text.

Endocrine Functions and Dysfunctions
The Pituitary Gland
    Pituitary Hormones
    Physiologic Control of Pituitary Hormone Secretion
    Pituitary Hypofunction
    Overproduction of Growth Hormone
    Overproduction of Prolactin
The Thyroid Gland
    Actions of Thyroid Hormone
    Hyperthyroidism
    Hypothyroidism
    Thyroiditis
    Tumors of the Thyroid
The Parathyroid Glands and Calcium Metabolism
    Hyperparathyroidism
    Hypoparathyroidism
The Adrenal Glands
    The Adrenal Cortex
    Disturbances of Adrenal Cortical Function
The Adrenal Medulla
    Tumors of the Adrenal Medulla
The Pancreatic Islets
The Gonads
Hormone Production by Nonendocrine Tumors
Stress and the Endocrine System
Obesity
    Causes of Obesity
    Health Consequences of Obesity
    Treatment of Obesity

Study Questions

The following questions are provided as a test for comprehension and as a study guide for use with the text chapters. Additional study material is located at http://humandisease.jbpub.com/, which contains useful tools such as an A&P review, animated flashcards, an interactive online glossary, crossword puzzles, and web links.

Key Terms

Define the following terms:

1. Acromegaly _____

2. Amenorrhea _____

3. Goiter _____

4. Cretinism _____

5. Thyroiditis _____

6. Pheochromocytoma _____

7. Myxedema _____

Identify

1. Identify five major complications of obesity.

   a. _____

   b. _____

   c. _____

   d. _____

   e. _____

Matching 1

Match the abnormalities in the right column with the diseases in the left column.

1. ____ Acromegaly

2. ____ Amenorrhea–galactorrhea syndrome

3. ____ Exophthalmic goiter

4. ____ Addison's disease

5. ____ Cushing's disease

6. ____ Cushing's syndrome

7. ____ Cretinism

8. ____ Chronic thyroiditis

9. ____ Hyperparathyroidism

10. ____ Hyperaldosteronism

A. Neonatal hypothyroidism

B. ACTH-producing pituitary tumor

C. Growth hormone-secreting pituitary tumor

D. Administration of excess adrenal corticosteroids

E. Autoantibody-induced thyroid hyperfunction

F. Autoantibody-induced destruction of adrenal cortex

G. Autoantibody-induced destruction of thyroid gland

H. Prolactin-secreting pituitary tumor

I. Hormone-secreting parathyroid tumor

J. Catecholamine-secreting adrenal tumor

11. _____ Pheochromocytoma

12. _____ Morbid obesity

K. Excess food intake

L. Aldosterone-secreting adrenal cortical tumor

Matching 2

Match the disease or condition in the left column with the features of the disease in the right column.

1. _____ Addison's disease

2. _____ Cushing's syndrome

3. _____ Hypertension with high aldosterone

4. _____ Hypertension with high catecholamines

5. _____ Amenorrhea–galactorrhea syndrome

A. Corticosteroid-producing adrenal tumor

B. Pituitary tumor

C. Adrenal medullary tumor

D. Aldosterone-producing adrenal tumor

E. Atrophy or destruction of adrenal glands

Discussion Questions

1. What are the major hormones produced by the anterior lobe of the pituitary gland? What factors regulate secretion of anterior lobe pituitary hormones? (see Fig. 25-1) _____

_____

_____

_____

2. What is the effect of overproduction of growth hormone? _____

_____

_____

_____

3. What factors regulate the rate of production of thyroid hormone? What are the major effects of an abnormal output of thyroid hormone? (see Table 25-1) _____

_____

_____

_____

4. What is the difference between cretinism and myxedema? _____

_____

_____

_____

5. Why does the thyroid gland become enlarged in persons with a nontoxic goiter? _____

_____

_____

_____

6. What is the difference between chronic thyroiditis (Hashimoto's disease) and thyrotoxicosis (Grave's disease)? What are the roles played by autoantibodies in thepathogenesis of these diseases? _____

_____

_____

_____

7. What are the main classes of adrenal cortical hormones, and what are their functions? _____

_____

_____

_____

8. What diseases result from adrenal cortical dysfunction? _____

_____

_____

_____

9. How is parathyroid hormone output regulated? What are the possible effects of parathyroid dysfunction?

_____

_____

_____

10. Describe the "stomach stapling" procedures used to treat morbid obesity. _____

_____

_____

_____

11. A 27-year-old woman has small, diffuse toxic goiter. What manifestations would you expect in this patient?

_____

_____

_____

12. A 25-year-old woman has acromegaly. What manifestations would you expect in this patient? _____

_____

_____

_____

13. A 35-year-old woman has hypothyroidism caused by chronic thyroiditis. What manifestations would you expect in this condition?

_____

_____

_____

14. A 64-year-old man has Addison's disease caused by atrophy of both adrenal glands. What clinical manifestations would you expect in this condition? _____

_____

_____

_____

15. A 46-year-old woman has Cushing's disease associated with hyperplasia of both adrenal glands. What are the manifestations that are often encountered in this condition?

_____

_____

_____

_____

An Introduction to
Human Disease
PATHOLOGY AND PATHOPHYSIOLOGY CORRELATIONS
Seventh Edition

LEONARD V. CROWLEY, M.D.

Chapter 25

Endocrine Glands

© 2007 Jones and Bartlett Publishers

Endocrine Glands

The major endocrine glands:
- *Pituitary*
- *Thyroid*
- *Parathyroid*
- *Adrenal cortex and medulla*
- *Pancreatic islets*
- *Ovaries and testes*
- The amount of hormone synthesized and released into circulation by an endocrine gland may be regulated *directly* or *indirectly* by the *level* of *hormone circulating* or of the substance under hormonal control

© 2007 Jones and Bartlett Publishers

Endocrine Gland Disorders

1. *Hypersecretion* of gland
2. *Insufficient* secretion of gland
- Determination of clinical effects
  - *Degree* of dysfunction
  - *Age* of affected individual
  - *Gender* of affected individual

© 2007 Jones and Bartlett Publishers

Pituitary Gland Structure

- Suspended by stalk from *hypothalamus* at base of brain
  - *Anterior* lobe
  - *Intermediate* lobe
  - *Posterior* lobe

© 2007 Jones and Bartlett Publishers

Pituitary Hormones

- <u>Anterior</u> lobe
  - Growth hormone
  - Prolactin
  - Thyroid-stimulating hormone (TSH)
  - Adrenocorticotrophic hormone (ACTH)
  - Follicle-stimulating hormone (FSH)
  - Luteinizing hormone (LH)

© 2007 Jones and Bartlett Publishers

Pituitary Hormones

<u>Posterior lobe</u>
  - Antidiuretic hormone (ADH)
  - Oxytocin

© 2007 Jones and Bartlett Publishers

Physiologic Control
Pituitary Hormone Secretion

- *Tropic* hormones (regulate other endocrine glands) are *regulated* by *level* of hormone *produced* by *target gland*
- *Prolactin* secretion controlled by *prolactin inhibitory factor*
- *Thyroid stimulating hormone stimulates release* of *prolactin* as well as *thyroid hormones*

Clinical Disturbances
Pituitary *Hypofunction*

- Panhypopituitarism (multiple decrease)
  - Anterior lobe *fails* to *secrete* any hormones
- Pituitary dwarfism: retarded growth and development
  - Deficiency of *growth hormone*
- Diabetes insipidus: *unable* to *absorb water* and *excretes* large amounts of diluted *urine*
  - *Failure* of posterior lobe to *secrete ADH* (antidiuretic hormone) or failure of the kidney to respond to ADH (nephrogenic diabetes insipidus)

Clinical Disturbances
Pituitary Hormone *Overproduction*

- *Growth* hormone *overproduction*
  - Caused by *pituitary adenoma*
  - Causes *gigantism* in *children*
  - Causes *acromegaly* in *adults*
- *Prolactin overproduction*
  - Result of small *pituitary adenoma*
  - Causes *galactorrhea (milk secretion from non-pregnant breasts)* and *amenorrhea (cessation of menstrual periods)*

Notes

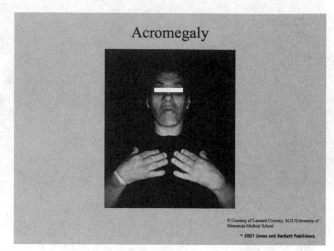

Acromegaly

© Courtesy of Leonard Crowley, M.D./University of Minnesota Medical School

© 2007 Jones and Bartlett Publishers

Thyroid Gland

- *Two* lateral lobes connected by isthmus
- Regulated by <u>TSH</u> (thyroid stimulating hormone)
- Controls rate of *metabolic* processes
- Required for normal *growth and development*

© 2007 Jones and Bartlett Publishers

Thyroid Gland

Hyperthyroidism	Hypothyroidism
Rapid pulse	Slow pulse
Increased metabolism	Decreased metabolism
Hyperactive reflexes	Sluggish reflexes
Emotional lability	Placid and phlegmatic
GI effect: diarrhea	GI effect: constipation
Warm, moist skin	Cold, dry skin

© 2007 Jones and Bartlett Publishers

_____
_____
_____
_____
_____
_____
_____
_____
_____
_____
_____
_____
_____
_____
_____
_____
_____
_____
_____
_____
_____
_____
_____
_____
_____
_____
_____
_____
_____
_____
_____
_____
_____
_____
_____
_____
_____
_____

Nontoxic Goiter

- *Thyroid* gland *enlarges* due to *excessive stimulation* by *TSH*
- *Treat* by supplying *thyroid* hormone
- May need to *remove surgically*

© 2007 Jones and Bartlett Publishers

Toxic Goiter (Graves' Disease)

- Caused by *antithyroid antibody,* which *stimulates* the *gland*
- *Mimics* the *effects* of *TSH* but *not* subject to *control mechanisms*
- Treatment
  - Antithyroid drugs, thyroidectomy, large dose of radioactive iodine

© 2007 Jones and Bartlett Publishers

Toxic Goiter

© Courtesy of Leonard Crowley, M.D./University of Minnesota Medical School

© 2007 Jones and Bartlett Publishers

*Hypo*thyroidism

- Adult
  - *Myxedema* (*hypothyroidism* in *adults*)
  - *Treated* by *thyroid hormone*
- Infant
  - *Cretinism* (*hypothyroidism* in *infants*)
  - *Early diagnosis* and *treatment* required to assume normal development

© 2007 Jones and Bartlett Publishers

Myxedema

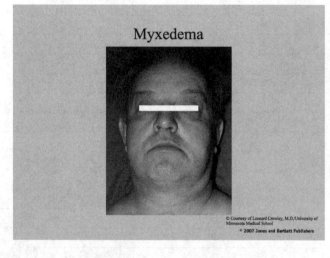

© Courtesy of Leonard Crowley, M.D./University of Minnesota Medical School

© 2007 Jones and Bartlett Publishers

Chronic Thyroiditis
(Hashimoto's Thyroditis)

- *Autoantibody destroys thyroid* tissue
- Often leads to *hypothyroidism*
- Cellular infiltration is the result of an *immunologic reaction* between antigen and antibody

© 2007 Jones and Bartlett Publishers

Notes

_____

Thyroid Tumors

- *Benign* adenoma
- *Carcinoma*
  - Well-differentiated
  - Undifferentiated
  - Medullary

© 2007 Jones and Bartlett Publishers

---

*Para*thyroid Glands
Calcium Metabolism

- *Blood calcium* is in *equilibrium* with *calcium* in the bone
- *Calcium* level is *regulated* by the *parathyroid glands*
  - *Reduced* calcium in blood: tetany (*increases neuromuscular excitability*, causing spasm of skeletal muscle)
  - *Elevated* calcium in blood: *reduces neuromuscular excitability*

© 2007 Jones and Bartlett Publishers

---

*Hyper*parathyroidism

- Usually a result of hormone-secreting *parathyroid adenoma*
- Blood *calcium rises*
- Excessive *calcium withdrawn* from *bone*
- Excessive *calcium excreted* in *urine*
- *Treated* by *removal* of *tumor*

© 2007 Jones and Bartlett Publishers

*Hypo*parathyroidism

- Usually result of *removal* of *parathyroid* glands *during thyroid surgery*
- Blood *calcium falls* precipitously
- Leads to *neuromuscular excitability* and *tetany*
- *Treated* with *high-calcium diet* and supplementary *vitamin D*

© 2007 Jones and Bartlett Publishers

Adrenal Cortex

- Adrenals: paired glands above kidneys (adrenal medulla and adrenal cortex)
- *Hormones* secreted by *adrenal cortex*
  - Glucocorticoids
  - Mineralocorticoids (aldosterone is main one; renin-angiotensin system is main stimulus)
  - Sex hormones
- *Disturbances* produce *abnormalities* in metabolism of *carbohydrates* and *protein*

© 2007 Jones and Bartlett Publishers

Addison's Disease

- It is an *adrenal cortical hypofunction*
- *Deficiency* of *all steroid hormones*
- *Hyperpigmentation* caused by increased ACTH
- *Autoimmune* disorder
- *Treated* by administration of deficient *corticosteroids*

© 2007 Jones and Bartlett Publishers

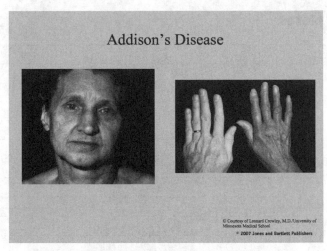

Addison's Disease

© Courtesy of Leonard Crowley, M.D./University of Minnesota Medical School

© 2007 Jones and Bartlett Publishers

Cushing's Disease/Syndrome

- *Excessive production* of *adrenal corticosteroids*
- Caused by several conditions
  - Hormone-producing *pituitary tumor*
  - Hormone-producing *adrenal cortex tumor*
  - *Administration* of large amounts of *corticosteroid*
  - *Other tumors*

© 2007 Jones and Bartlett Publishers

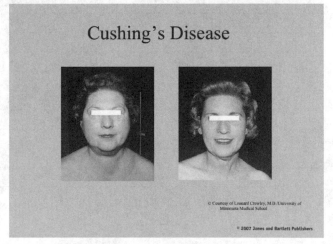

Cushing's Disease

© Courtesy of Leonard Crowley, M.D./University of Minnesota Medical School

© 2007 Jones and Bartlett Publishers

Overproduction of Other Adrenal Cortex Hormones

- Overproduction of *aldosterone*
  - *Aldosterone* secreting *adenoma*
- Overproduction of *adrenal sex hormones*
  - Congenital *adrenal hyperplasia*
  - *Adrenal sex-hormone–producing tumor*

© 2007 Jones and Bartlett Publishers

Adrenal Medulla

- Produces *catecholamines* which *stimulate* the *symphathetic* nervous system
  - Norepinephrine (noradrenaline)
  - Epinephrine (adrenaline)
  - Any emotional stress causes release of these hormones
- *Pheochromocytoma secretes* large amounts of *catecholamines*

© 2007 Jones and Bartlett Publishers

Pancreatic Islets

- Parts of *pancreas* that *function* as an *endocrine* gland
- Produce hormones
  - Insulin (beta cells)
  - Glucagon (alpha cells)
  - Somatostatin (delta cells)

© 2007 Jones and Bartlett Publishers

The Gonads

- Function
  - Production of *germ* cells
  - Production of *sex* hormones: *controlled* by *gonadotrophic hormones* of *pituitary*
- *Tumors* may secrete *hormones*
- Tumors *treated* by *surgical* excision

© 2007 Jones and Bartlett Publishers

Hormone Production Nonendocrine Tumors

- Sometimes *nonendocrine tumors* can *secrete hormones* (called *ectopic* hormones) that are *identical* with *or mimic* the action of true hormones
- Usually *origin* is *malignant* tumors
  - Lung, pancreas, kidneys, connective tissue

© 2007 Jones and Bartlett Publishers

Stress and the Endocrine System

- *Stress: caused* by *injury, surgery, prolonged exposure to cold, vigorous exercise, pain,* or *strong emotional stimulus such as anxiety* or *fear*
- *Acute response* to stress
  - *Fear-fight-flight* reaction
  - *Mediated* by *sympathetic* nervous system and *adrenal medulla*
- *Chronic* response to stress
  - *Predisposes* to *illness*

© 2007 Jones and Bartlett Publishers

Obesity

- Occurs when *caloric intake exceeds* requirements
- Usually NOT result of *endocrine or metabolic disturbance*

Treatment

- Drugs: suppress appetite; combination of fenfluramine and phentermine (fen-phen) has undesirable effects (heart valve damage)
- Ileal bypass
- Gastric bypass
- Vertical-banded gastroplasty

© 2007 Jones and Bartlett Publishers

Obesity-Treating Operations

© Courtesy of Leonard Crowley, M.D./University of Minnesota Medical School

© 2007 Jones and Bartlett Publishers

Chapter Outline

The chapter outline provides you with an organizational guide to the topics and ideas presented in this chapter of the text.

Structure and Function
Development of the Nervous System
Muscle Tone and Voluntary Muscle Contraction
Muscle Paralysis
    Flaccid Paralysis
    Spastic Paralysis
Cerebral Injury
Neural Tube Defects
    Anencephaly
    Spina Bifida
    Prenatal Detection of Neural Tube Defects
Hydrocephalus
Stroke
    Cerebral Thrombosis
    Stroke Caused by Arteriosclerosis of Extracranial Arteries
    Cerebral Hemorrhage
    Manifestations of Stroke
    Rehabilitation of the Stroke Patient
Transient Ischemic Attack
Cerebral Aneurysm
Infections of the Nervous System
    Meningitis Caused by Bacteria and Fungi
    Viral Infections
Creutzfeldt-Jakob Disease
    Mad Cow Disease
Alzheimer's Disease
Multiple Sclerosis
Parkinson's Disease
Huntington's Disease
Degenerative Diseases of Motor Neurons
Tumors of the Nervous System
    Tumors of the Peripheral Nerves
    Tumors of the Brain
    Tumors of the Spinal Cord
Peripheral Nerve Disorders
    Peripheral Nerve Injury
    Polyneuritis (Peripheral Neuritis)
    Guillain Barré Syndrome (Idiopathic Polyneuritis)
Neurologic Manifestations of Human Immunodeficiency Virus Infections
    AIDS Virus Infections of the Nervous System
    Opportunistic Infections of the Nervous System
    AIDS-Related Tumors

Study Questions

The following questions are provided as a test for comprehension and as a study guide for use with the text chapters. Additional study material is located at http://humandisease.jbpub.com/, which contains useful tools such as an A&P review, animated flashcards, an interactive online glossary, crossword puzzles, and web links.

Key Terms

Define the following terms:

1. Upper motor neuron lesion _____

2. Lower motor neuron lesion _____

3. Parkinson's disease _____

4. Meningitis _____

5. Stroke _____

6. Anencephaly _____

Fill-in-the-Blank

1. The frequency of neural tube defects can be reduced significantly by ingestion of the vitamin _____ before conception and during pregnancy.

2. Failure of the cephalic end of the neural tube to close leads to a condition called _____, and failure of the caudal end to close properly leads to a condition called _____.

3. A stroke is a vascular injury to the brain that is classified as either an _____ or a _____.

4. A sac-like protrusion of the lining of a cerebral artery through a defect or weak area in the arterial wall is called a _____. The major complication of this condition is _____, and the treatment of this complication is _____.

5. A brief, temporary episode of neurologic dysfunction, followed by return of normal cerebral functions, is called a _____.

6. Recent onset of marked atrophy and weakness of skeletal muscles that were previously affected by poliomyelitis many years previously but were followed by complete recovery is called _____.

7. Creutzfeldt-Jakob disease is caused by an abnormal form of a protein called a _____. The disease may result either from a spontaneous mutation of a normal gene that codes for a normal protein or from _____.

8. This type of abnormal protein causes a disease in cows called _____, which can be transmitted to humans by _____.

9. A hereditary disease characterized by formation of multiple tumors arising from peripheral nerves is called _____.

10. Multiple sclerosis plaques within the brain can be demonstrated by a procedure called _____.

11. A poorly differentiated astrocytic tumor arising in older adults is called a _____.

12. A malignant brain tumor arising from the cerebellum in children is called a _____.

13. A brain tumor arising from the cerebral meninges is called a _____, and a brain tumor arising from the ependymal lining of the ventricular system is called an _____.

14. Persons with an immunodeficiency disease called _____ are prone to develop lymphomas of the nervous system that respond poorly to treatment.

True/False

Tell whether each statement is true or false. If false, explain why the statement is incorrect.

1. Postpolio syndrome is characterized by late onset of muscle atrophy, weakness, and fatigue many years after recovery from poliomyelitis. _____

_____

2. The abnormal form of the prion protein is identical to the normal form except for the configuration of the abnormal protein (the way the protein is folded). _____

_____

3. Mad cow disease is a type of rabies that causes cows to become aggressive and hostile. _____

_____

4. New-variant Creutzfeldt-Jakob disease is acquired by eating meat from cows infected with abnormal prions.

_____

Identify

1. What are the two principal types of neural tube defects?

   a. _____

   b. _____

2. Identify three neurologic manifestations of HIV infection.

   a. _____

   b. _____

   c. _____

Discussion Questions

1. Briefly describe the organization of the central nervous system. Describe the function and circulation of cerebrospinal fluid. _____

_____

_____

_____

2. Describe how flaccid paralysis differs from spastic paralysis. _____

_____

_____

_____

3. List or describe possible harmful effects of a severe blow to the head. _____
_____
_____
_____

4. Explain how atherosclerosis of a carotid artery can cause a stroke. _____
_____
_____
_____

5. What are the common causes of hydrocephalus? How does a brain tumor cause hydrocephalus? _____
_____
_____
_____

6. List and describe briefly the methods available to detect a neural tube defect in a fetus. _____
_____
_____
_____

7. Describe the two types of shunt procedures used to treat hydrocephalus, distinguishing between them with respect to the site of drainage from the shunt. _____
_____
_____
_____

8. What is a brief episode of neurologic dysfunction that subsides spontaneously in a short time? _____
_____
_____
_____

9. What are the effects of hydrocephalus in a middle-aged adult? _____
_____
_____
_____

10. What is a congenital aneurysm of the circle of Willis? _____
_____
_____
_____

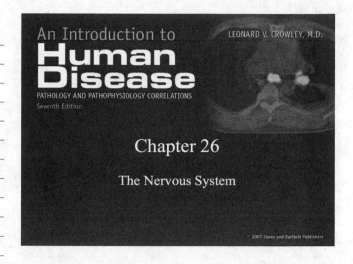

Chapter 26

The Nervous System

Nervous System

The *CNS* (central nervous system)
- *Brain*
- *Spinal cord*

Surrounded by membranes called *meninges*
- Neurons (nerve cells) and neuroglia (supporting cells)
- A sensory nerve or afferent: transmits impulses into the nervous system
- A motor or efferent nerve: transmits impulses from brain or spinal cord to muscle
- The transmission of a nerve impulse is by means of neurotransmitters
- Some important ones: acetylcholine, norepinephrine, dopamine

© 2007 Jones and Bartlett Publishers

Meninges

1. *Dura*: firm, outer
2. *Arachnoid*: middle
- (Subarachnoid space: space between arachnoid and pia) contains
  - CSF (*cerebrospinal fluid*)
  - Strands of arachnoid *connective* tissue
3. *Pia*: thin, inner
  - Adheres to *brain and spinal cord*

© 2007 Jones and Bartlett Publishers

_____

_____

_____

_____

_____

_____

_____

_____

_____

_____

_____

_____

_____

_____

_____

_____

_____

_____

_____

_____

_____

_____

_____

_____

_____

_____

_____

_____

_____

_____

_____

_____

_____

Brain

1. Cerebrum; 2. Brain stem; 3. Cerebellum
Brain is hollow with four *cavities* called *ventricles*
- Tissue of *brain* and *spinal cord*
  - Nerve cells = *neurons*
  - Supporting cells = *neuroglia*
- Arterial blood supply
  - Large vessels enter base of skull
  - Vessels join to form arterial circle at base of brain
- Venous blood
  - Returned from brain into large venous sinuses in dura
  - Sinuses eventually drain into jugular veins

© 2007 Jones and Bartlett Publishers

Development of Nervous System

- Neural plate to neural folds to neural tube
- Forebrain to cerebral hemispheres
- Midbrain
- Hindbrain to pons, medulla, cerebellum
- Mesoderm surrounds neural tube

© 2007 Jones and Bartlett Publishers

Development of Nervous System

© Courtesy of Leonard Crowley, M.D./University of Minnesota Medical School

© 2007 Jones and Bartlett Publishers

Notes

_____

_____

_____

_____

_____

_____

_____

_____

_____

_____

_____

_____

_____

_____

_____

_____

_____

_____

_____

_____

_____

_____

_____

_____

_____

_____

_____

_____

_____

_____

_____

Voluntary Motor Activity

- Controlled by nerve impulses originating in motor neurons in the cerebral cortex
- Pyramidal system controls voluntary motor functions
- Extrapyramidal system regulates muscle groups concerned with automatic functions such as walking

© 2007 Jones and Bartlett Publishers

Muscle Paralysis

- *Flaccid* paralysis
  - Reflex arc responsible for muscle tone interrupted
  - Muscle deprived of innervation, tone lost
- *Spastic* paralysis
  - Reflex arc not disturbed
  - Muscle retains innervation
  - Muscle tone increased

© 2007 Jones and Bartlett Publishers

Cerebral Injury

- Large blood vessels over surface of brain may be torn by force of injury
  - Epidural hemorrhage
  - Subdural hemorrhage
  - Subarachnoid hemorrhage

© 2007 Jones and Bartlett Publishers

Neural Tube Defects

- Anencephaly
- Spina bifida
    - Occult
    - Meningocele
    - Meningomyelocele

© 2007 Jones and Bartlett Publishers

Neural Tube Defects

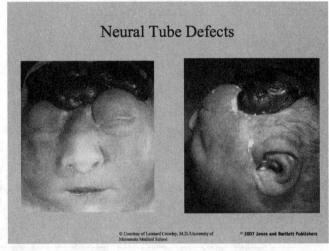

© Courtesy of Leonard Crowley, M.D./University of Minnesota Medical School

© 2007 Jones and Bartlett Publishers

Neural Tube Defects

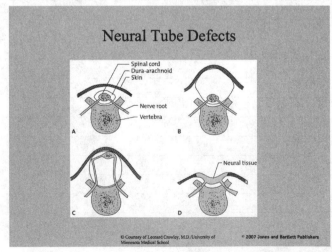

© Courtesy of Leonard Crowley, M.D./University of Minnesota Medical School

© 2007 Jones and Bartlett Publishers

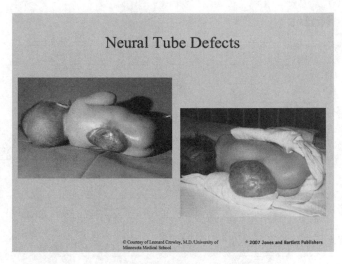

Neural Tube Defects

© Courtesy of Leonard Crowley, M.D./University of Minnesota Medical School   © 2007 Jones and Bartlett Publishers

Hydrocephalus

- Congenital
  - Obstruction of aqueduct
  - Absence of openings in roof of fourth ventricle
- Acquired
  - Obstruction in region of fourth ventricle

© 2007 Jones and Bartlett Publishers

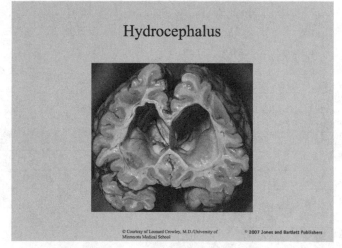

Hydrocephalus

© Courtesy of Leonard Crowley, M.D./University of Minnesota Medical School   © 2007 Jones and Bartlett Publishers

Stroke
Cerebrovascular Accident

- Any injury to brain tissue resulting from disturbance of blood supply to brain
- Encompasses three conditions
  - <u>Cerebral Thrombosis</u>: cause of most strokes; thrombosis of cerebral artery narrowed by arteriosclerosis
  - <u>Cerebral Embolus</u>: occurs less frequently; blockage of a cerebral artery by fragment of blood clot from an arteriosclerotic plaque or from heart; three cardiac conditions predispose to it

© 2007 Jones and Bartlett Publishers

Stroke
Cerebrovascular Accident

1. A mural thrombus formed on wall of left ventricle adjacent to a healing myocardial infarction
2. Thrombus formed on rough surface of of diseased mitral or aortic valve
3. Small thrombus in left atrial appendage (auricle) of a person with atrial fibrillation
   - <u>Cerebral hemorrhage</u>: most serious type of stroke; rupture of a cerebral artery in person with hypertension

© 2007 Jones and Bartlett Publishers

Stroke
Cerebrovascular Accident

- In most cerebral infarcts, no blood leaks into brain; called an *ischemic infarct*
- However, in some cases, a small amount of blood leaks into the damaged brain tissue; called *a hemorrhagic infarct*
- <u>Arteriosclerosis of extracranial arteries</u>: sclerosis of a major artery arising from aorta to supply the brain, before the vessel enters the brain; a commonly affected site is the carotid artery in neck, where arteriosclerotic plaque may narrow the lumen and reduce cerebral blood flow

© 2007 Jones and Bartlett Publishers

Stroke
Cerebrovascular Accident

- In the diagnosis of *extracranial vascular disease*, various procedures are used, such as *cerebral angiogram;* the visualized arteriosclerotic plaques can be remove surgically, called *carotid endarterectomy*
- *Other less invasive* methods are being investigated in selected patients, including the same type of *balloon angioplasty and stent* insertion procedures used to treat coronary artery plaques

© 2007 Jones and Bartlett Publishers

Stroke
Cerebrovascular Accident

- It is possible to distinguish a cerebral infarct from a cerebral hemorrhage by a computed tomography CT scan
- Magnetic resonance imaging (MRI) provides similar information and is equally effective
- Manifestations of all these conditions related to strokes, depend on *location and size*

© 2007 Jones and Bartlett Publishers

Stroke
Cerebrovascular Accident

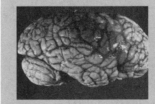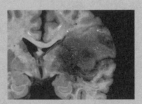

© Courtesy of Leonard Crowley, M.D./University of Minnesota Medical School   © 2007 Jones and Bartlett Publishers

Notes

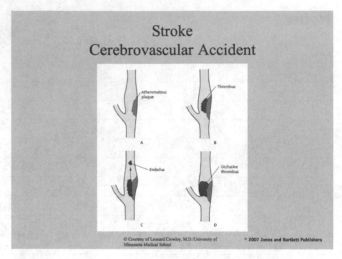

Stroke
Cerebrovascular Accident

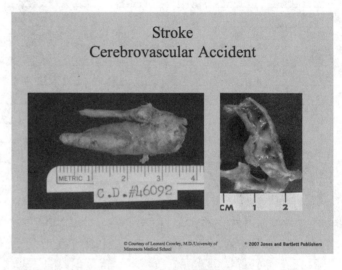

Stroke
Cerebrovascular Accident

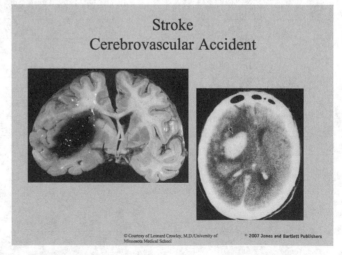

Stroke
Cerebrovascular Accident

Transient Ischemic Attack

- Brief episodes of neurologic function
- Dysfunction result of embolization of material from plaque in the carotid artery
- One-third of patients eventually suffer major stroke

© 2007 Jones and Bartlett Publishers

Cerebral Aneurysm

- Congenital aneurysm of circle of Willis
  - Rupture causes subarachnoid hemorrhage
- Arteriosclerotic aneurysm
  - Cerebral artery dilates and compresses adjacent tissue
  - Rupture very uncommon

© 2007 Jones and Bartlett Publishers

Cerebral Aneurysm

© Courtesy of Leonard Crowley, M.D./University of Minnesota Medical School

© 2007 Jones and Bartlett Publishers

Notes

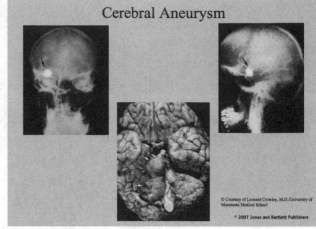

Cerebral Aneurysm

© Courtesy of Leonard Crowley, M.D./University of
Minnesota Medical School

© 2007 Jones and Bartlett Publishers

Infections

Three types:
1. Bacterial
2. Fungal
3. Viral
- Infections affecting *meninges* = *meningitis*
- Infections of *brain tissue* = *encephalitis*
- *If both involved, meningoencephalitis*

© 2007 Jones and Bartlett Publishers

Meningitis Caused by Bacteria and Fungi

- Meningococcus (*Neisseria meningiditis*)
- Pneumococcus (*Streptococcus pneumoniae*)
- *Hemophilus influenzae*

© 2007 Jones and Bartlett Publishers

Viral Infections

- Viruses that affect nervous system
  - Measles, mumps, herpes simplex virus, intestinal and respiratory viruses, cytomegalovirus, poliomyelitis virus, and *arborviruses (important group)*
- Manifestations
  - Systemic infection symptoms
  - Meningeal irritation (meningitis); *aseptic meningitis* is one caused by a *virus*; a suppurative (pus-producing) meningitis is caused by *bacteria*
  - Brain tissue involvement (encephalitis)
  - Spinal fluid abnormalities

© 2007 Jones and Bartlett Publishers

Viral Infections

- Arboviruses: important group responsible for many cases of meningitis and encephalitis
- Viruses infect birds and animals as well as humans and are transmitted by mosquitoes
- Types of encephalitis
1. Western equine encephalitis
2. Eastern equine encephalitis
3. St. Louis encephalitis
4. California encephalitis
5. West Nile virus: a "foreign" virus from Africa, first case identified in 1999 in New York City area

© 2007 Jones and Bartlett Publishers

Creutzfeldt-Jakob Disease

- Caused by small *protein* particle produced as a result of gene mutation
- The normal form of protein is the "*good prion*" designated *PrPc*
- The abnormal form of protein is the "*bad prion*" designated *PrPsc*
- Mad cow disease prion may cause Creutzfeldt-Jakob disease in humans

© 2007 Jones and Bartlett Publishers

Alzheimer's Disease

- Characteristics
  - Progressive mental deterioration
  - Emotional disturbances
- Anatomic and biochemical features
  - Thickening of neuron neurofilaments form neurofibrillary tangles
  - Biochemical abnormalities and brain enzyme deficiencies: acetylcholine and acetylcholine synthesizing enzyme
  - No specific treatment although some drugs may be useful to temporarily improve cerebral function

© 2007 Jones and Bartlett Publishers

Alzheimer's Disease

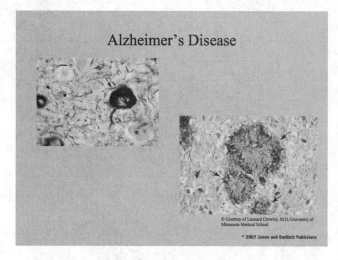

© Courtesy of Leonard Crowley, M.D./University of Minnesota Medical School

© 2007 Jones and Bartlett Publishers

Multiple Sclerosis

- Much evidence indicates that it is an *autoimmune disease*, probably initiated by a *viral infection* in a *genetically predisposed* person
- Manifestations
  - Activated T lymphocytes and monocytes target myelin proteins and destroy myelin insulation

© 2007 Jones and Bartlett Publishers

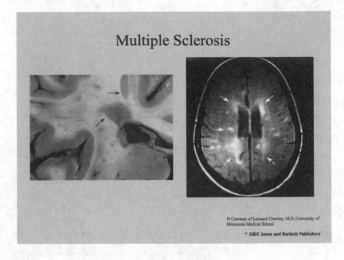

Multiple Sclerosis

© Courtesy of Leonard Crowley, M.D./University of
Minnesota Medical School

© 2007 Jones and Bartlett Publishers

Parkinson's Disease

- Cause of most cases unknown
- Some cases develop subsequent to viral infection of nervous system or toxic drugs
- Manifestations
  - Progressive loss of neurons in <u>substantia nigra</u> of midbrain
  - Rigidity of voluntary muscles
  - Tremor of fingers and extremities
  - Many investigators believe that *embryonic stem cells* are the key to *successful treatment*
  - It may be possible to induce *stem cells* to *differentiate* into *dopamine-producing neurons* which can be used to treat disease

© 2007 Jones and Bartlett Publishers

Huntington's Disease

- An *uncommon* but relatively *well-known* hereditary disease
- Characterized by progressive *mental deterioration* associated with *abnormal jerky and writhing movements*
- *First manifestations* occur between age *30 to 50,* progressing and *usually fatal within 15–20 years*
- Unfortunately there is *no way to arrest progression of disease* but *drugs* are available to *help control some of its manifestations*

© 2007 Jones and Bartlett Publishers

Notes

Degenerative Disease of Motor Neurons

- Caused by degeneration of neurons
- Amyotrophic lateral sclerosis
  - Affects upper and lower motor neurons
  - Flaccid paralysis of muscles
  - Respiratory problems

© 2007 Jones and Bartlett Publishers

Tumors of the Peripheral Nerves

- Arise from Schwann cells
- Neuromas of cranial nerves
- Multiple nerve tumors in *multiple neurofibromatosis*

© 2007 Jones and Bartlett Publishers

Brain Tumors

- Metastatic tumors more common than primary
- Primary tumors
  - Glioma
    - Astrocytoma
    - Glioblastoma multiforme
    - Oligodendroglioma

© 2007 Jones and Bartlett Publishers

Primary Brain Tumors

- Medulloblastoma
- Ependymoma
- Lymphoma
- Meningioma

© 2007 Jones and Bartlett Publishers

Spinal Cord Tumors

- Same type of tumors that arise in brain
- Tumors in spinal vertebrae may extend from vertebrae to compress or invade spinal cord
  - Bone metastasis
  - Multiple myeloma

© 2007 Jones and Bartlett Publishers

Peripheral Nerve Disorders

- Peripheral nerve injury
  - Traumatic injury
  - Nerve entrapment neuropathy
- Polyneuritis
- Guillain Barré syndrome

© 2007 Jones and Bartlett Publishers

Neurologic Manifestations of HIV Infections

- Nervous system infections directly caused by AIDS virus
  - Acute viral meningitis
  - AIDS encephalopathy
  - Polyneuritis

© 2007 Jones and Bartlett Publishers

Neurologic Manifestations of HIV Infections

- Nervous system infections caused by opportunistic pathogens
  - Herpes
  - Cytomegalovirus
  - *Cryptococcus neoformans*
  - *Toxoplasma gondii*

© 2007 Jones and Bartlett Publishers

AIDS-Related Tumors

- Primary tumor metastasis to nervous system
  - Kaposi's sarcoma
  - Lymphoma
- Primary lymphoma of the brain

© 2007 Jones and Bartlett Publishers

Chapter Outline

The chapter outline provides you with an organizational guide to the topics and ideas presented in this chapter of the text.

Study Questions

The following questions are provided as a test for comprehension and as a study guide for use with the text chapters. Additional study material is located at http://humandisease.jbpub.com/, which contains useful tools such as an A&P review, animated flashcards, an interactive online glossary, crossword puzzles, and web links.

Key Terms

Define the following terms:

1. Endochondral bone formation _____

2. Fracture _____

3. Intervertebral disks _____

4. Rheumatoid arthritis _____

Fill-in-the-Blank

1. In a long bone, the thick tubular part is called the _____, and the end is called the _____.

2. The active bone-forming cells are called _____. The mature cells that become incorporated in the bone as it forms are called _____, and the large multinucleated cells that are concerned with bone resorption are called _____.

3. In a movable joint, the ends of the bones forming the joint are covered by _____, and the interior of the joint is lined by _____, which secretes _____ to lubricate the joint.

4. The two types of bone formation are called _____ bone formation and _____ bone formation.

5. The hereditary condition characterized by disturbed endochondral bone formation that leads to a type of dwarfism in which the limbs are disproportionately short in relation to the trunk is called _____.

6. The congenital abnormality characterized by very thin, delicate bones that are easily broken under very minimal stress is called _____.

7. The name of the congenital condition in which the foot is turned inward on the ankle is called _____.

8. The inflammatory change in rheumatoid arthritis involves _____ initially, followed by spread of the inflammatory process over the surface of the joint.

9. A fracture in which the bone is broken into several fragments is called a _____ fracture.

10. A fracture in which the overlying skin is disrupted is called a _____ fracture.

11. The parts of the intervertebral disks are the _____ and the _____.

12. The condition characterized by a lateral curvature of the spine is called _____.

13. A systemic (collagen) disease characterized by inflammation of muscles and overlying skin is called _____
_____.

14. A disease characterized by atrophy of muscles resulting from degeneration of the nerve cells supplying the muscles is called _____.

15. A disease characterized by atrophy and degeneration of muscles caused by abnormalities in the muscle fibers is called _____.

16. The autoimmune disease characterized by muscle weakness that is caused by progressive autoantibody-mediated damage to acetylcholine receptors at the myoneural junction of the muscle fiber is called _____.

17. The two forms of muscular dystrophy are type _____ and type _____. The method of inheritance is _____. Sometimes the muscles of affected patients appear large because the muscle fibers have been replaced by _____.

True/False

Tell whether each statement is true or false. If false, explain why the statement is incorrect.

1. The blood and synovial tissues of rheumatoid arthritis (RA) patients contain an autoantibody directed against the patients' own gamma globulin. _____

_____

2. Immune complexes composed of gamma globulin and autoantibody are deposited in joints of RA patients.

_____

3. Antigen–antibody complexes activate complement and generate an inflammation within the joints in RA patients. _____

_____

4. Lymphocytes and macrophages attracted to the joints by the RA inflammatory process secrete cytokines (tumor necrosis factor) that damages joints. _____

_____

5. Drugs that block the effects of tumor necrosis factor have not been useful or effective in treating RA patients.

_____

Identify

1. Construct a table comparing the three main types of arthritis. (*Hint:* see Table 27-1.)

Characteristics	Rheumatoid Arthritis	Osteoarthritis	Gout

Matching

Match the types of arthritis on the right with each disease characteristic on the left.

1. _____ Affects primarily small bones of hands and feet   A. Osteoarthritis

2. _____ Autoantibodies formed   B. Rheumatoid arthritis

3. _____ Disturbed purine metabolism   C. Gout

4. _____ Major weight-bearing joints involved

5. _____ Fragmentation and degeneration of articular cartilage

6. _____ Destructive cytokines produced by inflammatory cells

7. _____ Uric acid deposit in and around joints

8. _____ May lead to kidney damage

Discussion Questions

1. What is a "slipped disk"? Why does it occur? Why does it sometimes produce pain radiating down the leg? How is it treated? _____

_____

_____

_____

2. Explain whether each of the following descriptors applies to rheumatoid arthritis.

    a. Primarily a degenerative change involving major weight-bearing joints _____

    _____

    b. Deformities result from joint instability caused by destruction of articular surfaces or joints _____

    _____

    c. Associated with autoantibodies _____

    _____

    d. Involves the synovial linings _____

    _____

    e. Responds to antibiotic therapy _____

    _____

3. List the features that characterize gout. _____

_____

_____

_____

4. What neoplastic processes may involve bone? _____
_____
_____
_____

5. What disease or condition affecting the skeletal system is due primarily to endocrine gland dysfunction?
_____
_____
_____

6. What is a herniated intervertebral disk? How does it occur? How is it detected? _____
_____
_____
_____

7. What is osteoporosis? What is the cause? How can it be prevented? _____
_____
_____
_____

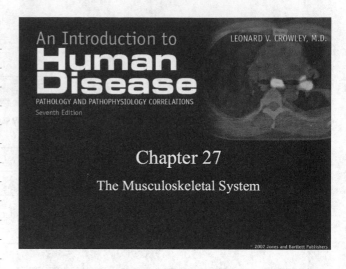

An Introduction to
LEONARD V. CROWLEY, M.D.

Human Disease

PATHOLOGY AND PATHOPHYSIOLOGY CORRELATIONS
Seventh Edition

Chapter 27

The Musculoskeletal System

© 2007 Jones and Bartlett Publishers

Skeletal System

- The *skeleton* is the *rigid supporting structure* of the body
- *All bones* have the *same basic structure*
- They are composed of an *outer layer* of compact bone, the *cortex*
- And an *inner spongy layer* in which the bone is arranged in a loose meshed lattice of thin strands called *bone trabeculae*
- The *spaces between* the *trabeculae contain* the *bone marrow*, which consists of fat and blood-forming tissue

© 2007 Jones and Bartlett Publishers

Skeletal System

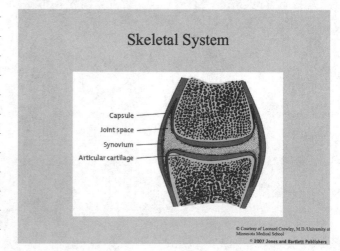

Capsule
Joint space
Synovium
Articular cartilage

© Courtesy of Leonard Crowley, M.D./University of Minnesota Medical School
© 2007 Jones and Bartlett Publishers

Skeletal System

- *Bone is* a specialized type of *connective* tissue
- Composed of a dense connective tissue framework impregnated with *calcium phosphate salts*
- Three different *types of cells* in *bone*
1. Osteoblasts
2. Osteocytes
3. Osteoclasts
- *Strength* and *thickness* of bones *depends* on *activity*
- *Bones* of skeleton are *connected* by *joints*
- There are three *types* of *joints*
  - Fibrous, Cartilaginous, Synovial

© 2007 Jones and Bartlett Publishers

Bone Formation

- Intramembranous
  - Mesoderm transformed into osteoblasts into bone
- Endochondral
  - Cartilage model converted into bone

© 2007 Jones and Bartlett Publishers

Congenital Malformations

- Achondroplasia
- Osteogenesis imperfecta
- Malformation of fingers and toes
- Congenital clubfoot (talipes)
- Congenital dislocation of the hip

© 2007 Jones and Bartlett Publishers

Notes

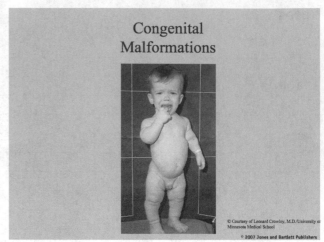

Congenital Malformations

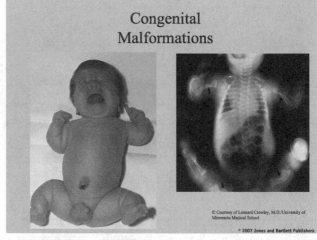

Congenital Malformations

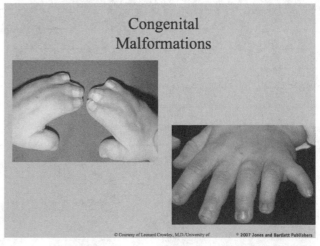

Congenital Malformations

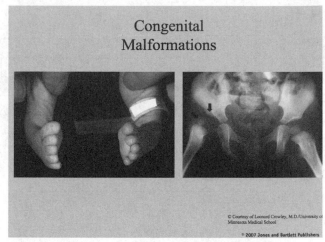

Congenital
Malformations

© Courtesy of Leonard Crowley, M.D./University of
Minnesota Medical School

© 2007 Jones and Bartlett Publishers

Rheumatoid Arthritis (RA)

- RA is a *systemic disease* affecting *connective* tissues throughout the body, specially in the *joints*
- Produces *chronic inflammation* and *thickening* of *synovial membrane*
- Classified as an *autoimmune* disease
- The blood and synovial tissues contain a substance, *rheumatoid factor*, an *autoantibody* produced by B lymphocytes directed against the individual's own gamma globulin
- Encountered *most frequently* in *young men* and *middle-aged women*
- Usually *affects small joints* of *hands and feet*

© 2007 Jones and Bartlett Publishers

Rheumatoid Arthritis (RA)

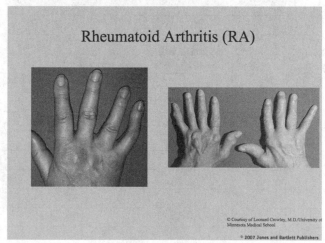

© Courtesy of Leonard Crowley, M.D./University of
Minnesota Medical School

© 2007 Jones and Bartlett Publishers

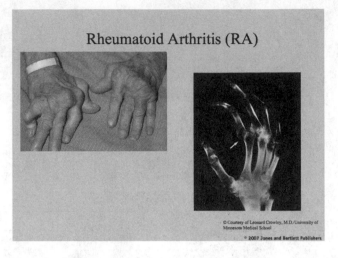

Rheumatoid Arthritis (RA)

© Courtesy of Leonard Crowley, M.D./University of
Minnesota Medical School

© 2007 Jones and Bartlett Publishers

Osteoarthritis

- Osteoarthritis is *not* a *systemic* disease
- It is a *"wear and tear" degeneration* of one or more *weight bearing joints*
- Causes *degeneration* of *articular cartilage*
- Seen in *older adults*, considered a *manifestation* of *normal aging process*

© 2007 Jones and Bartlett Publishers

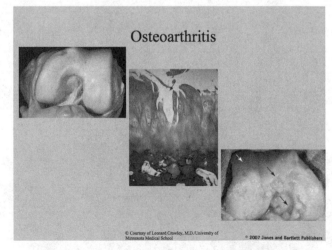

Osteoarthritis

© Courtesy of Leonard Crowley, M.D./University of
Minnesota Medical School

© 2007 Jones and Bartlett Publishers

Gout

- Disorder of *purine* metabolism
- *Breakdown* of *purines*, yields a relatively insoluble end-product called *uric acid*
- *Acute episodes* caused by precipitation of *uric acid crystals* in *joint fluid*
- *Uric acid stones* also may *form* within *kidney* and *lower urinary tract*
- Urate nephropathy (urate deposits plug tubules and damage kidneys)

© 2007 Jones and Bartlett Publishers

Gout

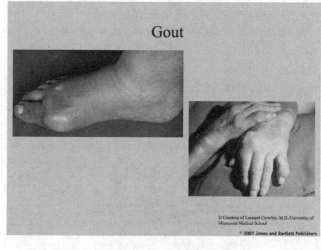

© Courtesy of Leonard Crowley, M.D./University of Minnesota Medical School

© 2007 Jones and Bartlett Publishers

Gout

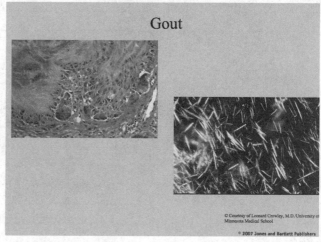

© Courtesy of Leonard Crowley, M.D./University of Minnesota Medical School

© 2007 Jones and Bartlett Publishers

Fractures

- Simple: bone broken into *only two pieces*
- Comminuted: bone is shattered into *many pieces*
- Compound: the *overlying skin* has been *broken*
- Pathologic: a fracture through a *diseased area in bone*
- Treatment
  - Closed reduction: plaster cast
  - Open reduction: internal fixation

© 2007 Jones and Bartlett Publishers

Osteomyelitis

- An *infection* of the *bone* and adjacent marrow cavity as a result of *bacteria*
- These organisms *gain access* to bone in two ways
1. Hematogenous
   - *Bacteria carried to the bone* from an infection in the body
2. As the result of direct implantation of bacteria
   - Due to conditions that expose the bone to *direct infection*

© 2007 Jones and Bartlett Publishers

Tumors of the Bone

- Metastatic tumors from prostate, breasts, and other organs
- Multiple myeloma: nodular deposits of neoplastic plasma cells are frequently present throughout the skeletal system
- Benign cysts and tumors: encountered occasionally
- Primary malignant bone tumors are unusual
- Chondrosarcoma: malignant tumor of cartilage
- Osteosarcoma: malignant tumor from bone-forming cells

© 2007 Jones and Bartlett Publishers

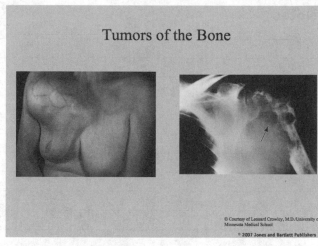

Tumors of the Bone

© Courtesy of Leonard Crowley, M.D./University of
Minnesota Medical School

© 2007 Jones and Bartlett Publishers

Osteoporosis

- *Generalized thinning* of the bone and *dimineralization* of the entire skeletal system, *"porous bones"*
  - Most *common* in *postmenopausal women*
    - Loss of estrogen accelerates rate of bone resorption
  - *Also* develops in *elderly men*
  - Remember that osteoporosis is *not* the same as osteoarthritis
  - *Osteoarthritis* is the *"wear and tear"* degeneration of one or more of the *weight-bearing joints*

© 2007 Jones and Bartlett Publishers

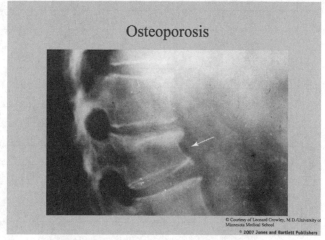

Osteoporosis

© Courtesy of Leonard Crowley, M.D./University of
Minnesota Medical School

© 2007 Jones and Bartlett Publishers

Notes

_____
_____
_____
_____
_____
_____
_____
_____
_____
_____
_____
_____
_____
_____
_____
_____
_____
_____
_____
_____
_____
_____
_____
_____
_____
_____
_____
_____
_____
_____
_____
_____

Avascular Necrosis

- There is *interference* of *blood supply* to the epiphysis of *bones*
- *Results* in *necrosis* and *degeneration* at *ends* of *bone*
- Disturbance in blood supply probably as a *result* of *injury*
- *Common sites*
  - Femoral head, tibial tubercle, articular surface of femoral condyle

© 2007 Jones and Bartlett Publishers

Avascular Necrosis

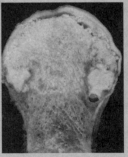

© Courtesy of Leonard Crowley, M.D./University of Minnesota Medical School

© 2007 Jones and Bartlett Publishers

The Spine

- The *vertebral column* forms the *central axis* of the *body*
- It consists of a series of *vertebrae joined* by *intervertebral disks* and *fibrous ligaments*
- Fibrocartilaginous cushions interposed between adjacent vertebral bodies
- Vertebral column made up of *four curves*
- The *cervical* and *lumbar curves arch forward*
- Those in the *thoracic* and *sacral regions bend* in the opposite direction

© 2007 Jones and Bartlett Publishers

_____
_____
_____
_____
_____
_____
_____
_____
_____
_____
_____
_____
_____
_____
_____
_____
_____
_____
_____
_____
_____
_____
_____
_____
_____
_____
_____
_____
_____
_____

Lumbar Spine

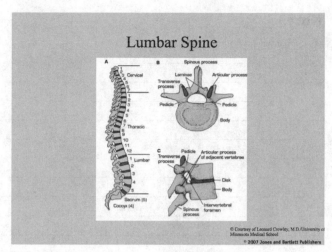

© Courtesy of Leonard Crowley, M.D./University of
Minnesota Medical School

© 2007 Jones and Bartlett Publishers

Scoliosis

- *Abnormal lateral curvature* of the *spine*
- Occurs in *4% of the population*
- Most cases are *idiopathic (cause is unknown)* in adolescent girls
- The spinal curvatures lead to an *asymmetry* of the *trunk*, so one shoulder is higher than the other, and the *pelvis* is *tilted*
- *Large curvatures cause pronounced disabilities*

© 2007 Jones and Bartlett Publishers

Scoliosis

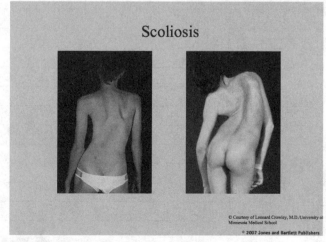

© Courtesy of Leonard Crowley, M.D./University of
Minnesota Medical School

© 2007 Jones and Bartlett Publishers

Intervertebral Disk Disease

- *With age*, the intervertebral disks undergo a *progressive wear-and-tear* degeneration of both the *nucleus* and *annulus*
- Nucleus pulposus may be *extruded* through tear in annulus fibrosis

© 2007 Jones and Bartlett Publishers

Intervertebral Disk Disease

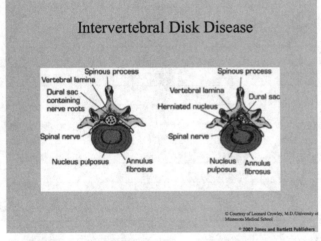

© Courtesy of Leonard Crowley, M.D./University of Minnesota Medical School

© 2007 Jones and Bartlett Publishers

Skeletal Muscle

- Contraction
  - *Myofilaments* slide together
  - *Communication between nerve* and *muscle* at *myoneural junction*
  - *Nerve stimulation* stimulates *acetylcholine*, which *interacts* with *receptors* on the *surface* of the *muscle fibers*
  - The *normal* structural and functional integrity of *skeletal muscle* depends on
  1. Intact nerve supply
  2. Normal transmission of impulses across the myoneural junction
  3. Normal metabolic processes within muscle cell

© 2007 Jones and Bartlett Publishers

Myositis

- Inflammation of muscle
- Localized
  - Follows *injury or* the result of *muscular overexertion*
- Generalized
  - *Widespread* degeneration and inflammation of skeletal muscle or *polymyositis*
  - Dermatomyositis: a type of *polymyositis* associated with *swelling* and *inflammation* of *skin*

© 2007 Jones and Bartlett Publishers

Hereditary Diseases
Skeletal Muscle

- A group of relatively rare diseases is characterized by *progressive atrophy or degeneration of skeletal muscle*
- These diseases are classified into two large categories
1. Progressive muscular atrophy
   - Secondary to motor nerve cell degeneration
2. Muscular dystrophy
   - Abnormality in muscle fibers that causes them to degenerate

© 2007 Jones and Bartlett Publishers

Myasthenia Gravis

- It is a chronic disease characterized by *abnormal fatigability of voluntary muscles* due to *abnormality* at the *myoneural junction*
- It appears to be an *autoimmune disease* where *autoantibodies* are formed *against acetylcholine receptors* at the *myoneural junction*

© 2007 Jones and Bartlett Publishers